MW00844290

# The Practical Beekeeper

## Volumes I, II & III
## Beekeeping Naturally

by Michael Bush

The Practical Beekeeper Volume I, II & III
Beekeeping Naturally



ISBN: 978-161476-064-1

X-Star Publishing Company
Nehawka, Nebraska, USA
xstarpublishing.com

670 pages

# Dedication

This book is dedicated to Ed and Dee Lusby who were the real pioneers of modern natural beekeeping methods that could succeed with the Varroa mites and all the other new issues. Thank you for sharing it with the rest of us.

# About the Book

This book is about how to keep bees in a natural and practical system where they do not require treatments for pests and diseases and only minimal interventions. It is also about simple practical beekeeping. It is about reducing your work. It is not a main-stream beekeeping book. Many of the concepts are contrary to "conventional" beekeeping. The techniques presented here are streamlined through decades of experimentation, adjustments and simplification. The content was written and then refined from responding to questions on bee forums over the years so it is tailored to the questions that beekeepers, new and experienced, have.

In place of an index there is a very detailed Table of Contents.

It is divided into three volumes and this edition contains all three: Beginning, Intermediate and Advanced.

# Acknowledgments

I'm sure I will forget to list many who have helped me along this path. For one thing many were often only known by the names they used on the many bee forums where they shared their experiences. But among those who are still helping, Dee, of course, Dean and Ramona, and all of the wonderful people of the Organic Beekeeping Group on Yahoo. Sam, you are always an inspiration. Toni, Christie thanks for your encouragement. All of you on the forums who asked the same questions over and over, because you showed me what needed to be in this book and motivated me to write down the answers. And of course all of you who insisted I put this in the form of a book.

# Foreword

I feel like G.M. Doolittle when he said he had already offered all of what he had to say for free in the bee journals and yet people kept asking for a book. I have virtually all of this on my website and have posted all of it many times on the bee forums. But many people have asked for a book. There is a little new here, and most of it is available for free already on my web site (www.bushfarms.com/bees.htm). But many of us understand the transient nature of the medium of the web and want a solid book on our shelf. I feel the same. So here is the book that you could already have read for free but you can hold it in your hands and put it on the shelf and know you have it.

I've done a lot of presentations and a few have been posted on the web. If you have an interest in hearing some of this presented by me try a web search for videos for "Michael Bush beekeeping" or other topics such as "queen rearing". The material here is also on www.bushfarms.com/bees.htm along with PowerPoint presentations from my speaking engagements.

# Table of Contents

# Volume I Beginning

# BLUF

***Learn from the bees***

> ***"Let the bees tell you"-Brother Adam***

BLUF stands for Bottom Line Up Front. That's what this chapter is. I am going to give you the shortcut to success in beekeeping right here and now. Not that the rest isn't worth reading, but the rest is merely elaboration and details. With apologies to C.S. Lewis (who said in *A Horse and His Boy*, *"no one teaches riding quite as well as a horse"*) I think you need to realize that ***"no one teaches beekeeping quite as well as bees."*** Listen to them and they will teach you.

***Trust the Bees***

> ***"There are a few rules of thumb that are useful guides. One is that when you are confronted with some problem in the apiary and you do not know what to do, then do nothing. Matters are seldom made worse by doing nothing and are often made much worse by inept intervention." —The How-To-Do-It book of Beekeeping, Richard Taylor***

If the question in your mind starts "how do I make the bees ..." then you are already thinking wrongly. If your question is "how can I help them with what they are trying to do..." you are on your way to becoming a beekeeper.

### ***Resources***

Here, then, is the short answer to every beekeeping issue. ***Give them the resources to resolve the problem and let them. If you can't give them the resources, then limit the need for the resources.***

For instance if they are being robbed, what they need is more bees to defend the hive, but if you can't give them that, then reduce the entrance to one bee wide and you will create the "pass at Thermopylae where numbers count for nothing". If they are having wax moth issues in the hive, what they need are more bees to guard the comb. If you can't give them that then reduce the area they need to guard by removing empty combs and empty space.

In other words, give them resources or reduce the need for the resources they don't have.

### ***Panacea***

Most bee problems come back to queen issues.

***There are few solutions as universal in their application and their success, than adding a frame of open brood from another hive every week for three weeks. It is a virtual panacea for any queen issues. It gives the bees the pheromones to suppress laying workers. It gives them more workers coming in during a period where there is no laying queen. It does not interfere if there is a virgin queen. It gives them the resources to rear a queen. It is virtually foolproof and does not require finding a queen or seeing eggs or accurately diagnosing the problem. If you have any issue with queenrightness, no brood, worried that there is no queen, this is the simple solution that re-***

***quires no worrying, no waiting, no hoping and no guessing. You just give them what they need to resolve the situation. If you have any doubts about the queenrightness of a hive, give them some open brood and sleep well. Repeat once a week for two more weeks if you still aren't sure. By then things will be well on their way to being fine.***

If you are afraid of transferring the queen from the queenright hive, because you are not good at finding queens, then shake or brush all the bees off before you give it to them.

If you are concerned about taking eggs from another new package or small colony, keep in mind that bees have little invested in eggs and the queen can lay far more eggs than a small colony can warm, feed and raise. Taking a frame of eggs from a small struggling new hive and swapping it for an empty comb or any drawn comb will have little impact on the donor colony and may save the recipient if they are indeed queenless. If the recipient didn't need a queen it will fill in the gap while the new queen gets mated and not interfere with things.

It saves a lot of worry and a lot of judging. Instead you can give them the resources and then observing what they do will probably give you a pretty good clue what really was going on. If they don't raise a queen, there is probably a virgin loose in there. If they do raise a queen, they obviously didn't have one or the one they had was not sufficient.

# Why this book?

I suppose you'd have to be living under a rock these days to have not heard that the honey bees and beekeepers are in trouble. The problems are complex, far reaching and mostly recent. They are certainly a threat to the survival of the beekeeping industry but, even more so, to the survival of many plants which we need or want for food and many other plants, that are a necessary part of the environment.

> ***"People who say it cannot be done should not interrupt those who are doing it."-George Bernard Shaw***

It seems like there is some controversy over whether it is even possible to keep bees without treatments. But there are many of us who are doing this and succeeding.

While most of us beekeepers spend a lot of effort fighting with the Varroa mites, I'm happy to say my biggest problems in beekeeping now are things like trying to get nucs through the winter here in Southeastern Nebraska and coming up with hives that won't hurt my back from lifting or simpler ways to feed the bees.

So my purpose is first of all to talk about how to deal with the current problems of beekeeping, and second of all how to work less and accomplish more at beekeeping.

Let's do a short overview of the problems in beekeeping and the solutions. The details are in the subsequent chapters and volumes.

***Unsustainable beekeeping system***

## Beekeeping Pests

So why are we having problem? We have a lot of recent pests and diseases that have made it to North America (and most other places in the world) in the last 30 years or so. (See the chapter *Enemies of the Bees*) As someone once said, "You can't keep bees like grandpa did cause grandpa's bees are dead." Most of us beekeepers have lost all of our bees one time or another in the last few decades and this seems to be getting worse. So part of the problem for beekeepers is the pests, but there are other issues.

## Shallow Gene Pool

We have a narrow gene pool to start with here in North America, and between pesticides, pests, and overzealous programs to control Africanized honey bees, many of the pockets of feral bees have been depleted leaving only the queens that people buy. When you consider that there are only a handful of queen breeders providing 99% of the queens, that's a pretty small gene pool. This deficiency used to be made up by feral bees and people rearing their own queens. But the recent trend is to encourage everyone to not rear their own queens and only buy them; especially in AHB (Africanized honey bee) areas.

## Contamination

The other side of the pest issue is that the standard answer offered by the experts has been to use pesticides in the hives by beekeepers to kill the mites and other pests. But these build up in the wax and cause sterile drones, which in turn causes failing queens. One estimate I heard from one of the experts on the subject put the average supersedure rate at three times a year. That means the queens are failing and being replaced three times a year. This is stunning to me since most of my queens are three years old.

## Wrong Gene Pool

The other side of helping bees with treatments of pesticides and antibiotics is that you keep propagating the bees that can't survive. This is the opposite of what we need. We beekeepers need to be propagating the ones that *can* survive. Also we keep propagating the pests that are strong enough to survive our treatments. So we keep breeding wimpy bees and super pests. Also for years we have bred bees to not rear drones, be larger, and use less propolis. Some of these make them reproductively challenged (less drones and larger bees hence larger slower drones) and some make them less able to handle viruses (less propolis).

## Upset Ecology of the Bee Colony

A bee colony is a whole system in itself of beneficial and benign fungi, bacteria, yeasts, mites, insects and other flora and fauna that depend on the bees for their livelihood and which the bees depend on to ferment the pollen and crowd out pathogens. All of the pest controls tend to kill the mites and insects. All of the antibiotics used by beekeepers tend to kill either the bacteria (Terramycin, Tylosin, essential oils, organic acids and thymol do this) or the fungi and yeasts (Fumidil, essential oils, organic acids and thymol do this). The whole balance of this precarious system has been upset by all the treatments in the hive. And recently beekeepers switched to a new antibiotic, Tylosin, which the beneficial bacteria has not had a chance to build up resistance to and which is longer lived; and they have switched to formic acid as a treatment which shifts the pH radically to the acidic and kills many of the microorganisms of the hive.

## Beekeeping House of Cards

So beekeepers, with the advice and assistance of the USDA and the universities, have built this precarious system of beekeeping that relies on chemicals, antibiotics and pesticides to keep it going. And beekeepers keep breeding the resistant pests that can survive the treatments, contaminating the entire wax supply with poisons (and we make our foundation out of that contaminated wax so it is a closed system) and breeding queens that can't survive without all of this treatment.

***How do we get a sustainable beekeeping system?***

## Stop Treating

The only way to have a sustainable system of beekeeping is to stop treating. Treating is a death spiral that is now collapsing. To leverage this, though, you really need to raise your own queens from local surviving bees. Only then can you get bees who genetically can survive and parasites that are in tune with their host and in tune with the local environment. As long as we treat we get weaker bees who can only survive if we treat, and stronger parasites who can only survive if they breed fast enough to keep up with our treatments. No stable relationship can develop until we stop treating.

The other problem, of course, is that if we just stop now with the system of beekeeping we have, the genetically and environmentally weakened bees will usually die. Even if they are genetically capable of surviving in a clean (uncontaminated) environment, we have to get to an environment they can survive in or they will still die. So what is that environment?

## Clean Wax

We need clean wax. Using foundation made from recycled, contaminated wax will not get that for us. The entire world wax supply is now contaminated with acaracides. Natural comb will provide clean wax.

## Natural Cell Size

Next we beekeepers need to control the pests in a natural way. We will elaborate more on this as we go, but Dee and Ed Lusby arrived at the conclusion that the solution to this was to get back to natural cell size. Foundation (a source of contamination in the hive from pesticide buildup in the world beeswax supply) is designed to guide the bees to build the size cells we want. Since workers are from one size and drones from another and since beekeepers for more than a century have viewed drones as the enemy of production, beekeepers use foundation to control the size cells the bees make. At first this was based on natural sizes of cells. Early foundation ran from about 4.4mm to 5.05mm. But then someone (François Huber was the first) observed that bees build a variety of cell sizes and that large bees emerged from large cells and small bees emerged from small cells. So Baudoux decided that if you enlarged the cells more you could get larger bees. The assumption was that larger bees could haul more nectar and therefore would be more productive. So now, today, we have a standard cell size of foundation that is 5.4mm. When you consider that at 4.9mm the comb is about 20mm thick and at 5.4mm the comb is 23mm thick this makes a difference in the volume. According to Baudoux the volume of a 5.555mm cell is 301cubic mm. The volume of a 4.7mm cell is 192 cubic mm. Natural cell size runs from about 4.4mm to 5.1mm with 4.9mm or smaller being the common size in the core of the brood nest.

So what we have is unnaturally large cells making unnaturally large bees. We will elaborate more on why and how in the chapter *Natural Cell Size* in Volume II. The short version is that with natural cell size we get control of the Varroa population and can finally keep our bees alive without all the treatments.

**Natural Food**

Honey and real pollen are the proper food of bees. Sugar syrup has a much higher pH (6.0) than honey (3.2 to 4.5) (sugar is more alkaline). Stating the same thing conversely, honey has a much lower pH than sugar syrup (honey is more acidic). This affects the reproductive capability of virtually every brood disease in bees plus Nosema. The brood diseases all reproduce more at the pH of sugar (6.0) than at the pH of honey (~4.5). And this is not to mention that honey and real pollen are more nutritious than pollen substitute and sugar syrup. Artificial pollen substitute makes for short lived, unhealthy bees.

# Learning

Newcomers in any field always seem to feel a bit overwhelmed, so before we get too far into this, let's talk about learning.

The most important thing you can learn in life is how to learn. I teach computer classes often and have always been a learner myself. I love to learn. I have discovered, though, that most people don't know how to learn. Here are some rules about learning that I don't think most people know.

**Rule 1: If you're not making mistakes, you're not learning anything.** I had a boss in construction who liked to say "If you're not making mistakes you're not doing anything." That may be true, but sometimes you are doing repetitious things and you can get to the point that you are not making mistakes, but if you are learning you will make mistakes! This is a fact. Making mistakes and learning are inseparable. If you're not making mistakes you're not pushing the limits of what you know, and if you're not pushing those limits, you're not learning.

My students in my computer classes often comment on how their children learn computers so quickly and easily and wish it was that easy for them. I tell them why it is easy for children. They are not afraid to make mistakes. Children are used to making mistakes. Adults are not. If you want to learn, get used to making mistakes. Learn from them.

I heard a story about a young man who was taking over as a bank president. The person who held the job before had been there for forty years and had made the company a lot of money. The young man asked him for advice before he left. The old man said that to make the bank money you make good decisions. The young man asked "how do you make good decisions?" The old man said, "you make bad decisions and learn from them." In the end, this is the really the *only* way to learn. Make mistakes and learn from them. I'm not saying you can't learn from other people's mistakes or from books, but in the end you have to make your own mistakes.

**Rule 2: If you're not confused, you're not learning anything.** If you are going to be a learner you will have to get used to being confused. Confusion is the feeling you get when you are trying to figure things out. Adults find this disconcerting, but there is no other way to learn. If you think back to the last card game you learned, you were told the rules, which you couldn't remember, but you started playing anyway. The first few hands were terrible, but then you started to understand the rules. But that was only the beginning. Then you played until you started to understand how to play strategically, but until you got good at it you were still confused. Gradually the whole picture of the rules and the strategies and how they fit together started to congeal in your mind and then it made sense. The only way from here to there, though, is that period of confusion.

The problem with learning and our world view is, we think things can be laid out linearly. You learn this fact, add this one and that one and then finally you know all the facts. But reality is not a set of linear facts; it is a set of relationships. It is those relationships and principles that understanding is made up of. It takes a lot of confusion to finally sort out all the relationships. There is no starting and ending point, because it is not a line, it is circles within circles. So you start somewhere and continue until you have the basic relationships.

**Rule 3: Real learning is not facts, it is relationships.** It's kind of like a jigsaw puzzle. You start somewhere, even though it doesn't look like anything yet. You sort things out by color and pattern and then you start fitting them together. Everything you learn in any subject is part of the whole puzzle and is related to everything else somehow.

The facts are just the pieces of the puzzle. You need them to figure out the relationships, but the pieces themselves don't make any sense until you have them connected. The connectedness of all things is one of the first things you need to learn in order to be able to learn.

A smart aleck news reporter once asked Albert Einstein how many feet were in a mile. Einstein said he had no idea. The news reporter then berated him, because he didn't know. Einstein said that's what he had books for, to look up things like that. He didn't want to clutter his mind with facts.

It is much more important to have a few facts and understand the relationships than lots of facts and no relationships. One little part of the puzzle put together is better than more pieces and none of them put together. Knowledge and understanding are not at all related. Don't go for knowledge; go for understanding, and knowledge takes care of itself.

**Rule 4: It's not so important what you know as it is that you know how to find out.** Tom Brown Jr. wrote a survival guide, *The Tracker*. I read survival guides all the time, but they usually frustrate me because they give recipes. Take this and that and do this with it and you have a shelter. The problem is, in real life you usually don't have one of the ingredients. Tom Brown, though, in his chapter on shelter, showed how he *learned* how to build a shelter. Telling you *how* to build a shelter and telling how to *learn* to build a shelter are as different as night and day. What you want to learn in life is not what the answers are, but how to find the answers. If you know that you can adjust to the materials and situations available.

The usual method is to look around and pay attention. Tom Brown learned to build a shelter by watching the squirrels, but he could have watched any animal that needed shelter and learned from them. Watching how other people and animals solve their problems and adapting those solutions is one way to learn.

# Bee Basics

In order to do beekeeping, you need a basic understanding of their life cycle and their yearly "colony" cycle. You have two levels of organisms—the individual bee (which can't exist as an organism for very long) and the colony superorganism.

### *Life cycle of a bee*

Bees are one of three main castes: queen, worker or drone. The queen is the one bee that reproduces, but even that she can't do by herself. She is the one bee that goes out and mates, during one period of her life, that lasts a few days, and then she lays eggs for the rest of her life. The workers, depending on their age, feed brood, make comb, store honey, clean house, guard the entrance or gather honey, pollen, water or propolis. The drones spend their days flying out to drone congregation areas (DCAs) in the early afternoon and flying home just before dark. They spend their lives in hopes of finding a queen to mate with. So let's follow each cast from egg to death:

### Queen

We will start with the queen since she is the most pivotal of any bee because there is generally only one of her. The reasons the bees raise a queen are: queenlessness (emergency), failing queen (supersedure), and swarming (colony reproduction).

*Circle of Attendants*

## Queenlessness

The cells for each appear slightly different or at least occur under different conditions that can be observed. A queenless hive will have no queen that can be found, little open brood and no unhatched eggs. The queen cells resemble a peanut hanging on the side or bottom of a comb. If the queen died or was killed the bees will take young larvae and feed it extensive amounts of Royal Jelly and build a large hanging cell for the larvae.

## Supersedure

In supersedure the bees are trying to replace a queen they perceive as failing. She is probably between 2 and 4 years old and not laying as many fertile eggs and not making as much Queen Mandibular Pheromone (QMP). These cells are usually on the face of the comb about $^{2}/_{3}$ of the way up the comb. There are, of course, exceptions. Jay Smith had a queen that was still laying well at 7 years named Alice, but three years seems to be the norm when the bees replace them.

## Swarming

Swarm cells are built to facilitate the reproduction of the superorganism. It's how the colony starts new colonies. The swarm cells are usually on the bottom of the frames making up the brood nest. They are usually easy to find by tipping up the brood chamber and examining the bottom of the frames.

The larvae that make a good queen are worker eggs that just hatched, which happens on day $3^{1}/_{2}$ from the day the egg was laid. On day 8 (for large cell) or day 7 (for natural sized cells) the cell will be capped. On day 16 (for large cell) or day 15 (for natural sized cells) the queen will usually emerge. On day 22, weather permitting, she may fly. On day 25, weather permitting, she may mate over the next several days. By day 28 we may see eggs from a new fertile queen. From that time on, she will lay eggs (weather and stores permitting) until she fails or swarms to a new location and starts laying there. The queen will live two or three years in the wild, but almost always fails by the third year and is replaced by the workers. In a swarm the old queen leaves with the first (primary) swarm. Virgin queens leave with the subsequent swarms, which are called afterswarms.

## Worker

*Worker Bee Gathering Propolis*

A worker egg starts out the same as a queen egg. It is a fertilized egg. Both are fed royal jelly at first, but the worker gets less and less as it matures. Both hatch on day $3^1/_2$ but the worker develops more slowly. From day $3\ ^1/_2$ until it is capped it is called "open brood". It is not capped until the 9th day (for large cells) or the 8th day (for natural sized cells). From the day it is capped until it emerges it is called "capped brood". It emerges on the 21st day (for large cells) or the 18th or 19th day (for natural sized cells). From when the bees start chewing through the caps until they emerge they are called "emerging brood". After emergence a worker starts its life as a nurse bee, feeding the young larvae (open brood). For those who say that a worker is an incomplete female while a queen is a fully functioning female, consider that only a worker can produce "milk" for the young. Only a worker can feed and care for the young. The queen does not have the right glands to produce food for young, nor the skills to care for them. Neither the worker nor the queen is a "complete mother"; it takes them both to rear the young. Workers and queens are anatomically different in many ways. Only a worker has the hypopharyngeal gland to feed the young. Only a worker has baskets for carrying pollen and propolis. Only a queen can lay fertile eggs. Only a queen can make sufficient pheromones to keep the hive working correctly.

For the first 2 days the newly emerged worker will clean cells and generate heat for the brood nest. The next 3 to 5 days it will feed older larvae. The next 6 to 10 days it will feed young larvae and queens (if there are any). During this period from 1 to 10 days old it is a Nurse Bee. From day 11 to 18 the worker will make honey, not gather but ripen nectar and take it from field bees bringing it back, and build comb. From days 19 to 21 the workers will be ventilation units and guard bees and janitors cleaning up the hive and taking out the trash. From day 11 to 21 they are House Bees. Day 22 to the end of their life they are foragers. Except during winter, workers usually live about six weeks or less, working themselves to death until their wings are too shredded to fly. If the queen fails a worker may develop ovaries and start to lay. Usually these are drone eggs and usually there are several to a cell and they are in worker cells.

## Drone

Drones are from unfertilized eggs. For those of you who studied any genetics, they are haploid, meaning they only have a single set of genes, where a worker and a queen are diploid, meaning they have pairs of genes (twice as many). Drones are larger than workers but proportionately wider, shorter than a queen, have a blunt back end, have huge eyes and no stinger. The egg hatches on day $3^1/_2$. The cell is capped on day 10 (for large cells) or as early as day 9 (for natural sized cells) and emerges on day 24 (for large cells) or between day 21 and 24 (for natural sized cells). The colony will raise drones whenever resources are plentiful so that there will be drones to mate with a queen if they are needed. It is unclear what other purposes they serve, but since a typical hive raises 10,000 or more of them in the course of year and only 1 or 2 ever get to mate, they may serve other purposes. If there is a shortage of resources the drones are driven out of the hive and die from cold or starvation. The first few days of their lives they beg food from the nurse bees. The next few days they eat right from the open cells in the brood nest (which is where they usually hang out). After a week or so they start flying and finding their way around. After about two weeks they are regularly flying to DCAs (Drone Congregation Areas) in the early afternoon and stay until evening. These are areas where drones congregate and where the queens go to mate. If a drone is "fortunate" enough to mate, his reward is to have the queen clamp down on his member and rip it out by the roots. He will die from the damage. The queen stores up the sperm in a special receptacle (spermatheca) and distributes it as she lays the eggs. When the queen runs out of stored sperm, she does not mate again, she fails and is replaced. I think drones have an undeserved reputation for being useless. In fact they are essential. Not only do they have a reputation for being useless but for being lazy. They are not lazy. They fly until they are exhausted every day that the weather permits, trying to ensure the continuation of the species.

***Yearly cycle of the colony***

By definition this is a cycle so we'll start when the year really begins, in the winter. I can speak to what happens in Nebraska. For your location I would consult local beekeepers.

## Winter

The colony tries to go into winter with sufficient stores, not only to survive the winter, but to build up enough by spring for the colony to reproduce. To do this the colony needs a good supply of honey and pollen. The bee colony appears to be dormant all winter. They usually don't fly unless the temperatures get up around 50° F (10° C). But actually the bees maintain heat in the cluster all winter and all winter the colony will rear little batches of brood to replenish the supply of young bees. These batches take a lot of energy and the cluster has to stay much warmer during them. The colony takes breaks between batches. As soon as there is any supply of fresh pollen coming in the colony will begin buildup in earnest. Usually the early pollen is the Maples and the Pussy Willows. In my location this is late February or early March. Of course if the weather isn't warm enough to fly, the bees won't have any way to get it. Beekeepers often put pollen patties on at this time so the weather won't be a deciding factor in the buildup.

## Spring

By spring the colony is now building up well. They should have raised at least one turnover of brood by now. They will really take off with the first bloom. This is usually dandelions or the early fruit trees. Here in Nebraska, that's the wild plums and chokecherries which will bloom about mid April. Between now and mid May the colony will be intent on swarm preparations. They will try to finish building up and then start back filling the brood nest with nectar so the queen can't lay. This sets off a chain reaction that leads to swarming. The more the queen doesn't lay the more she loses weight so she can fly. The less brood there is to care for, the more unemployed nurse bees there are (the ones who will swarm). Once critical mass of unemployed nurse bees is reached, they will build swarm cells, the queen will lay in them and the colony will swarm just before they are capped. All of this is assuming, of course, that there are abundant resources and that the beekeeper doesn't intervene. If they decide not to swarm then they go full throttle into nectar collection. If they decide *to* swarm then the old queen leaves with a large amount of the young bees and try to start a new home somewhere. Meanwhile the new queen emerges in a couple of weeks and starts laying in another couple of weeks and the remaining field bees haul in the crop to build up for the next winter.

## Summer

Our flow, here in Nebraska, is really mostly in the summer. This is usually followed by a summer lull. It seems to be driven, here in my location anyway, by a drop in rainfall. Sometimes if the rain is timed right there isn't really a lull at all, but usually there is. Our flow starts about mid June and ends when things dry up enough. Sometimes there's an actual dearth where there is no nectar at all and the queens stop laying. I'd say most of my nectar is soybeans, alfalfa, clover, and just plain weeds. This varies greatly by climate.

### Fall

We usually get a fall flow in Nebraska. It's mostly smartweed, goldenrod, aster and chicory with some sunflower and partridge pea and other weeds. Some years it's enough to make a crop. Some years it's not enough to get them through the winter and I have to feed them. Around mid October, usually, the queens stop laying and the bees start settling in for the winter.

## *Products of the hive*

The bees produce a variety of things. Most of these are gathered from the bees by people.

### Bees

Many producers raise bees and sell them. Package bees are available from the Southern United States usually in April.

### Larvae

Many people over the world eat bee larvae. It is not that popular here in the US. To raise larvae (which the bees have to do to get bees) the bees need nectar and pollen. Feeding syrup or honey and pollen or pollen substitute is a way to stimulate the bees in the spring to raise more brood and therefore more bees.

## Propolis

The bees make this from tree sap that is processed by enzymes the bees make and mix with it and sometimes they mix in beeswax. The substance most often gathered is from the buds of relatives of the poplar family, such as poplar, aspen, cottonwood, tulip poplar and others. It is used in the hive to coat everything. It is an antimicrobial substance and is used both for sterilizing the hive and for structural help. Everything in a hive is glued together with this. Openings that the bees think are too big are closed with this. Humans use it as a food supplement and as a topical anti microbial for cuts and for cold sores etc. It kills both bacteria and viruses. Propolis traps are available. A simple one is a screen over the top of the hive and you roll it up and put it in the freezer and then unroll it while it's frozen to break all the propolis off.

*Gathering propolis from old equipment*

## Wax

Anytime a worker bee has a stomach full of honey and nowhere to store it, it will begin to secrete wax on its abdomen. Most of the wax is then used to build comb. Some falls on the floor of the hive and is wasted. For humans, beeswax is edible, although it has no nutritional value. It is used in foundation, candles, furniture polish and cosmetics. The bees need it to store their honey in and raise their brood in. To get it from the bees, either crush comb and drain the honey, or use cappings from extracting and melt and filter them.

## Pollen

Pollen has a lot of nutritive value. It is high in protein and amino acids. It is popular as a food supplement and is believed by many to help with their allergies, especially if it is pollen collected locally. The bees need it to feed the young. Pollen traps are available commercially or you can find plans to build your own. The principle of a pollen trap is to force the bees through a small hole (the same as #5 hardware cloth) and in the process they lose their pollen which falls into a container through a screen large enough for pollen but too small for the bees (#7 hardware cloth). Some pollen traps must be bypassed about half the time so the hive doesn't lose its brood from lack of pollen to feed the brood. A week on and a week off seems to work. Other problems with pollen traps is drones not getting access in and out and if a new queen is raised, she has difficulty getting out and can't get back in. If you are allergic and trying to treat allergies with pollen take it in very small doses until you build a tolerance or until you have a reaction you don't want. If you have a reaction either take less or none at all depending on the severity.

*(Photo by Theresa Cassiday)*

**Pollination**

A "product" of having bees is that they pollinate flowers. Pollination is often a service that is sold. $50 to $150 (depending on the supply of bees) for $1^1/_2$ deep boxes is a typical charge for pollination. Pollination charges are usually based on having to move the hives in and out in a specific time frame so that the trees (or other plants) can be sprayed etc. It is less likely there will be charges for pollination if the bees can be left there year round and pesticides are not used. In this case it is usually a mutually beneficial situation for the beekeeper and the farmer and there usually is no charge or rent either way, although it's common for the beekeeper to give the farmer a gallon of honey from time to time.

## Honey

This is what is usually considered the product of the hive. Honey, in whatever form, is the major product of the hive. The bees store it for food for the winter and we beekeepers take it for "rent" on the hive. It is made from nectar, which is mostly watered down sucrose, which is converted to fructose by enzymes from the bees and dehydrated to make it thick.

Honey is usually sold as Extracted (liquid honey in a jar), Chunk comb (a chunk of comb honey in liquid in a jar), Comb honey (honey still in the comb. Comb honey is done in Ross Rounds, section boxes, Hogg Half combs, cut comb, and more recently Bee-O-Pac. It is also sold as creamed honey (where it is crystallized with small crystals).

Since the subject always comes up, all honey (except maybe Tupelo) eventually crystallizes. Some does this sooner and some later. Some will crystallize within a month; some will take a year or so. It is still edible and can be liquefied by heating it to about 100 degrees or so. Crystallized honey can be eaten as is also, or crushed to make creamed honey or feed to the bees for winter stores. It crystallized most quickly and therefore most smoothly, at 57° F. The closer it is stored to that temperature, the more quickly it will crystallize.

## Royal Jelly

The food fed to the developing queen larvae is often collected in countries where labor is cheap and sold as a food supplement.

# Four Simple Steps to Healthy Bees

I touched briefly on this in the chapter *Why this Book* but we will go into more depth here.

For the moment, let's look at just these four issues: comb; genetics; natural food; and no treatments. Let's gloss over the arguments and focus only on what we know to be facts and what we can do about them.

***Comb***

I find all the arguments over cell size and whether it does or does not help your Varroa issues and all the rest a bit tiresome. Varroa is no longer an issue in my beeyards and yet I find that the obsession of every bee meeting I go to seems to be Varroa and about half of what I end up talking about is Varroa. I went to natural cell and small cell at a time when no one believed it was possible to keep bees alive without treatments. After doing no treatments with repeatedly disastrous results before, I came to the same conclusion. But after going to small and natural cell size I was pleased to be back to keeping bees instead of managing mites. This anecdotal evidence is not enough for some, even as the same from others was not enough for me until I tried it, but unlike me they don't seem to be willing to try it. But let's consider your choices:

You can assume that cell size is irrelevant to everything, if you like. This seems like a doubtful assumption since we know for a fact it has everything to do with the size of bees. If scaling up the entire body of a bee to 150% of what it was naturally is not a significant change, then I don't know what you would consider significant. We've known this is a fact since Huber's observations and in addition we have reams of research by Baudoux, Pinchot, Gontarski and others as well as recent research by McMullan and Brown (The influence of small-cell brood combs on the morphometry of honeybees (Apis mellifera)—John B. McMullan and Mark J.F. Brown).

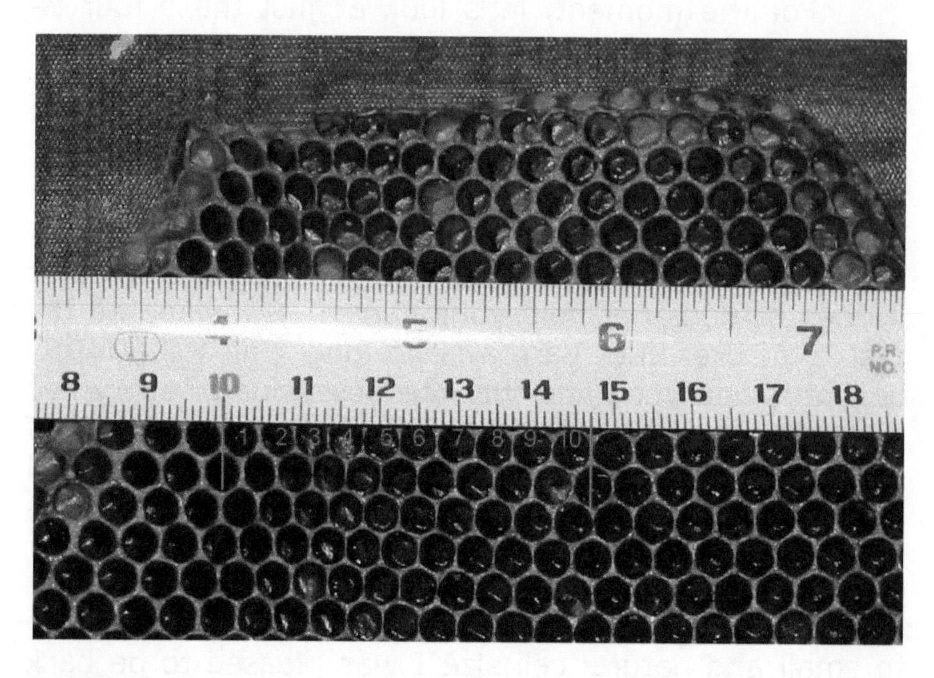


***Choices***

## Natural Cell Size

You can assume whatever you like about what size *is* natural. But in the end the only way to get natural cell size, and let the bees end the debate, is to stop giving the bees foundation and let them build what they want. Since that is what bees do if you let them and since that is actually less work for you than using foundation and less expense and since that's the only way to get uncontaminated combs (do an online search for the video of Maryann Frazier on contamination by acaracides in new foundation) it seems like a win-win-win to me. Even allowing the assumption that cell size is irrelevant, no one is saying that natural cell size is bad for the bees and no one I know of thinks that clean wax is bad for the bees and most are very convinced at this point that clean wax is essential for truly healthy bees.

## Why not let them build what they want?

Why wouldn't you let them build what they want? It seems there is a lot of fear that the bees will only build drones. I have heard this from many beekeepers. Obviously this is not true. If it were there would never have been any feral bees. If you want to know how much drone comb they will build and how many drones they will raise and how much influence you can have on it, read Clarence Collison's research on the subject (Levin, C.G. and C.H. Collison. 1991. The production and distribution of drone comb and brood in honey bee (Apis mellifera L.) colonies as affected by freedom in comb construction. BeeScience 1: 203-211.). The point is that in the end the amount of drones is controlled by the bees and leaving them that control in the first place will simplify life for them and you. The thing to do when the bees draw a frame full of drone comb in the middle of the brood nest, is set it to the outside edge of the box and give them another empty frame. Otherwise, if you take it out, their need for drone comb and drones unfulfilled, they will draw yet another frame of drone and contribute to the myth that if you let them, they will draw nothing but drone comb.

## Combs in frames?

Another fear seems to be that the bees will not draw the combs in the frames. They will mess up foundationless about the same rate as they mess up any other system of foundation. They will mess up plastic foundation a lot more than foundationless frames. But if they do, you just cut it loose and tie it into the frame, if it's brood, or harvest it, if it's honey.

**Draw comb without foundation?**

I've even heard old timers tell new beekeepers that without foundation the bees won't draw comb at all. This is so patently absurd that I don't see any need to respond to it.

**Wire?**

The last seems to be the myth that wire is necessary in order to extract. The wire was added to foundation to keep the foundation from sagging before it was drawn (see any older ABC XYZ of Bee Culture). It was not added to allow extraction. Extraction is done on unwired foundationless frames by many people, including me. But if wire is your hang-up, add some wire to the frames, level the hive and sleep well. I prefer to just use mediums and be able to lift the boxes and have had no need at all for the wires.

**How do you do foundationless?**

- With standard wedge frame, just break out the wedge and nail it sideways.
- With grooved top bars, put popsicle sticks in the groove or a half of a paint stick or a piece of a "one by" ripped
- With drawn wax, just cut the center of the comb out leaving a row of cells around the edges

- With an old frame with no comb, just put it between two drawn brood combs
- With a plastic foundation/frame, just cut the center of the foundation out leaving a row of cells around the edge
- When making your own, cut a bevel on the top bar so it slopes down to a point. You can also make them $1^1/_4$″ wide.

**Less work**

So how much work is foundationless? We talked about *how* to do it, but how much work is it? If you buy standard wedge frames and turn the wedge 90 degrees and glue and nail it back on you have a foundationless frame. That is pretty simple. You were going to break it out and nail it in anyway weren't you? The other methods above were less work than wiring wax foundation. The only slightly tricky thing would be plastic frames with built in foundation. Then you'd need to cut the center of the foundation out. That could be done with a number of tools, but I suppose a really hot knife would cut it out pretty quickly. A jig and a router would probably do ok as well and it would be simple to leave the corners and edges in for strength and for a guide. So how does this compare with putting in wire, crimping, foundation, embedding etc.? Or using plastic? You save as much as $1 a sheet if you wanted to get small cell or close to that if you wanted to get plastic.

**Downside?**

So, for less work and less money you can end up with clean wax, natural cell size and a natural brood nest as far as distribution of cell sizes and drones. What's the down side? If you don't wire the deeps you might end up with more collapsed comb if you have a migratory operation, because of bumpy roads combined with hot days and deep frames, but you could wire them and that would probably not be so much of a problem. You would also need to keep the boxes more level, which in a fixed operation isn't so hard; you just level the stands up, which you should have done anyway. But in a migratory operation it would take more work to level them than to just set the pallets down and not worry about them being level.

## Timeline

Worst case timeline is you retool at whatever pace you would have done by the other method anyway. You buy foundation and put it in all the time, right? Some rotate their comb out every five years or less. Some just replace comb as they need comb but either way if you stop using the large cell foundation and stop treating you'll eventually have natural clean comb by the only possible method to get clean comb unless someone finds a source of clean wax and makes their own foundation.

If you have a lot of large cell foundation around, you can sell it to someone local who was going to buy some anyway for the catalog price and save them the shipping. Or, if you're impatient, sell it cheap, if you're willing to take a small loss for healthier bees. You can make up the difference on all those strips that weren't working anyway that you won't have to buy.

## Worst case scenario

So let's look at worst case scenario. Let's assume that cell size isn't an issue one way or the other. It's unreasonable to assume that bees will be any *less* healthy on natural sized comb, so at worst they will be on a cell size no better. At worst the cost is less than rotating out your contaminated combs for contaminated wax foundation. There is hardly a down side to that. The *work* is less than wiring wax foundation. The *cost* is less than wiring wax foundation. The wax will be uncontaminated (at least unless or until *you* contaminate it) and we *know* that wax contamination is contributing to lack of longevity and fertility in queens and drones. So we know the bees will be healthier and the queens will do better.

## Best case scenario

This is the worst case scenario on all of the speculation on cell size and natural comb. The best case scenario is that it will solve your Varroa problems.

### *No Treatments*

I don't know what all the rest of you have experienced, but with no treatments (on large cell size) I lost all my bees whenever I wouldn't treat for a couple of years. But finally I lost them even after treating with Apistan. It was obvious that the mites had built resistance. I've heard of big outfits losing their entire operation *while* treating with Apistan or CheckMite. So we have reached the point where whether you treat or not, they all die anyway quite often. I think the problem here comes down to us not wanting to "do nothing". We want to attack the problem and so we do whatever the experts tell us because we are desperate. But what they are telling us is failing anyway. Once I lost them all *after* I treated them, I could no longer see any reason to treat them. Treating only perpetuates the problem. It breeds bees that can't survive whatever you are treating for, contaminates the comb and upsets the whole balance of the hive.

## Ecology of the hive

There is no way to maintain the complex ecology of a natural beehive while dumping in poisons and antibiotics. The beehive is a web of micro and macro life. There are more than 30 kinds of benign or beneficial mites, as many or more kinds of insects, 8,000 or more benign or beneficial microorganisms that have been identified so far, some of which we know the bees cannot live without and some of which we suspect keep other pathogens in balance. Every treatment we dump in a hive, from essential oils (which interfere with the bees' smell, which is how everything in the dark of the hive is communicated, and kill microorganisms, beneficial and otherwise); to organic acids (which kill microorganisms as well as many insects and benign mites) to acaracides (which are always just chemicals that kill arthropods which include insects and mites but kill mites at a slightly higher rate); to antibiotics (which kill the microflora most of which is either beneficial or benign but useful in maintaining the balance and crowding out pathogens); even to sugar syrup (which has a pH that is detrimental to the success of many of the beneficial organisms and advantageous to many of the pathogens: EHB, AFB, chalkbrood, Nosema etc. unlike the pH of honey that is much lower and detrimental to the pathogens and hospitable to many known beneficial organisms). I think we've reached the point that it's silly to act like we've been doing any good when the bees are collapsing in spite of, if not because of all of this.

## Downside of not treating

So what is the downside of not treating? Worst case is they die. They seem to be doing that regularly enough already aren't they? I don't see that I'm contributing to that by giving them the chance to reestablish a naturally sustainable system. I'm just not destroying that system arbitrarily to get rid of one thing with no regard to the balance of the system. Of the people I know who are not treating for anything, even on large cell; their losses are *less* than those who *are* treating. On small cell or natural cell they are even less. But even if you don't buy the cell size debate, not treating is working as well as treating is. I go to bee meetings all over the country and hear people who, like me, lost their bees when they were treating religiously and then decided to just stop. Their new bees are now doing better than when they were treating them. I feel bad when I see a dead hive, but I also say "good riddance" to the genetics that couldn't make it.

If you think you'll have too many losses (my guess is you already *do* have too many losses) and you can't take those losses, what would it take to make splits and overwinter enough nucs to make up those losses every spring with your own locally adapted stock? A bunch of walk away splits made in the middle of July, after cashing in on the main flow, will usually winter, at least around here, and not put a dent in your honey crop. You can also split the mediocre hives earlier since they weren't doing much anyway, requeen with cells from your best stock and not really affect your honey crop You can also do cut down splits on the strong hives right before the main flow and get good splits, well fed queens, more honey *and* more hives.

## Upside of not treating

What is the upside of not treating? You don't have to *buy* the treatments. You don't have to *drive* to the yard and put the treatments in and *drive* to the yard to take them out. You don't have to contaminate your wax. You don't upset the natural balance by killing off micro and macro organisms that you weren't targeting but who are killed by the treatments anyway. That would seem like upside enough, but you also give the ecosystem of the beehive a chance to find some natural balance again.

But the most obvious upside is that until you quit treating you can't breed for survival against whatever your issues are. As long as you treat you prop up weak genetics and you can't tell what weaknesses they have. As long as you treat you keep breeding weak bees and super mites. The sooner you stop, the sooner you start breeding mites adapted to their host and bees who can survive with them.

### *Breeding locally adapted queens*

Breeding locally adapted queens from the best survivors is another thing that I don't see a downside to. If you breed from your untreated survivors you'll get bees that are surviving where you are against what they face there. They will mate with the local ferals who are also surviving. The propaganda that you can't raise queens that are as good as or better than commercially available queens is just that—propaganda. The same is true with the need to requeen early in the spring. Early queens are often not well mated and often not well fed. Assuming you don't treat, you don't requeen regularly and you use your most successful survivors, your queens are more likely to be better because of the following:

- They are locally adapted.
- They are bred from survivors.
- You can raise them at optimum times to have plenty of nutrition and plenty of drones.
- They are probably never caged and go from laying in the mating nuc to the hive they are put in with no break. This develops better ovarioles and that makes

better pheromones. This results in them being more long lived, laying better patterns, swarming less and being accepted better.

- You save a lot of work. If you keep queens longer and mate from those that succeed at superseding at appropriate times you have bees that can requeen themselves. This will save you a lot of labor in finding queens and introducing queens as the bees will take care of this.
- Even on the hives you requeen, you can save labor by requeening with cells and not bothering to find the old queen. The new queen will typically be accepted and you didn't have to spend the day looking for the old one.
- You save a lot of money. Open mated production queens go for from $15 to $40 and breeders go for much more.
- You can easily keep spares in nucs and have queens whenever you need them.

**What about AHB?**

Those in AHB areas seem concerned about this approach. I'm not in such an area, but it seems to me that ancestry isn't my concern. Temperament is. Productivity is. Survival is. If you only keep the gentle ones and requeen the hot ones I think it will work fine. Those I know doing this in AHB areas have come to that conclusion. Another thing to consider is that F1 crosses are often hot. So if you keep bringing in outside stock you may be contributing to them being angry. You may be better off selecting for gentleness and requeening any hives that are hot with local stock that is gentle.

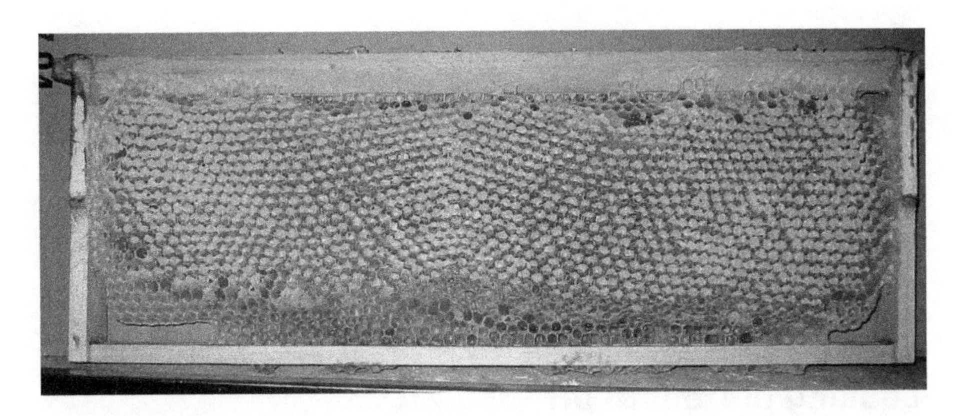

***Natural Food***

It's quite simply less work to use natural food. If I don't feed pollen substitute in the spring then I don't have to make patties etc. If I don't feed syrup, I don't have to buy sugar, I don't have to make syrup, I don't have to drive to the yards and I don't have to feed it. If I leave them honey to winter on, there is less honey for me to pull, haul home, extract, haul back empty to get cleaned up and then pull off to store, make syrup, drive to the yards to feed it etc. This is less work all the way around. Even if you don't believe that honey is more nutritious to bees (although I have to wonder why you want to produce honey if you think there is no difference between honey and sugar). It is definitely less work to leave it. Even if you believe that the difference in pH is irrelevant (which I seriously doubt), it's less work than making syrup and feeding syrup. Even if you are obsessed with the difference in price ($0.40 per pound for sugar vs. some variable price from say $0.90 to $2.00 pound for honey) by the time you extract the honey, buy the sugar, make the syrup, haul it to the yards, feed it, go back and pull the feeders etc. do you honestly think you came out that far ahead? It's not just a $0.60 a pound difference by the time you factor all of that in, unless your labor is of no value. So let's assume that the difference in the health of the bees is only marginal between honey and sugar and ignore that Nosema multiplies better at the pH of sugar than honey and so does chalkbrood and EFB and AFB. We'll ignore all of that and just assume it's marginal. If there is ANY difference it could tip the scale from a colony surviving and one dying and packages are up around $80 delivered here.

## Looking more into pH

Sugar syrup has a much higher pH (6.0) than Honey (3.2 to 4.5) (Sugar is more alkaline). Conversely, honey has a much lower pH than sugar syrup (Honey is more acidic). This affects the reproductive capability of virtually every brood disease in bees plus Nosema. They all reproduce better at pH 6.0 than at 4.5.

## Chalkbrood as example

> ***"Lower pH values (equivalent to those found in honey, pollen, and brood food) drastically reduced enlargement and germ-tube production. Ascosphaera apis appears to be a pathogen highly specialized for life in honeybee larvae." —Author. Dept. Biological Sci., Plymouth Polytechnic, Drake Circus, Plymouth PL4 8AA, Devon, UK. Library code: Bb. Language: En. Apicultural Abstracts from IBRA: 4101024***

Similar information is available concerning other bee diseases. Try an Internet search for pH and AFB or EFB or Nosema and you'll find similar results on their reproductive capability related to the pH.

Differences in pH affect other beneficial and benign organisms in the hive. The other more than 8,000 microorganisms in the hive are also affected by changes in pH Using sugar syrup also disrupts the ecological balance of the hive by disrupting the pH of the food in the hive and the food in the bees' gut.

## Pollen

If you don't use pollen substitute you can still leave pollen in the hives and if you really want you can set aside a hive or two or more (depending on the size of your operation) and trap a few pounds of pollen to put in an open feeder in the spring. Just freeze it in the meantime. I put it on a screened bottom board on top of a solid bottom board with an empty box on top with a lid. The screen keeps the bottom dry and the hive keeps it from getting rained on.

## Pollen trapping

The cost of trapping is mostly the trap. If you do it in a yard close to or on the way home it's easy enough to empty the traps every night. And now you don't have to buy pollen patties and you have superior nutrition.

If you doubt the difference, look for research on bee nutrition that compares substitutes to pollen. Bees raised on substitutes are short lived and weak.

### Synopsis

So what do you have to lose? You can get better genetics for your bees by breeding your own; cleaner comb by using foundationless and no treatments; longer lived bees from clean wax and feeding real pollen; and less work by leaving honey that you won't have to harvest and feed syrup back; and the worst case is that to get all this you'll work less and the best case is that it will all have a markedly positive effect on the health of your bees. Worst case, if you implement this a little at a time, you lose some bees, which you're already doing. Best case you lose less.

**Different Profit Formula**

Let's try a different profit formula. How much time, gas, work, and money do you spend on syrup, feeding, putting in patties, putting in treatments, taking out treatments, harvesting that last little bit of honey that you then have to make up with syrup, putting in foundation etc.? How much money and time would you save if you stopped doing all of that? How many more hives could you handle and how much more honey would they make?

# Choices

### ***Too Many Choices?***

I realize many people simply want someone to tell them to do "a" "b" and "c" and it will work for them. I also realize that in the context of a beginner this may be the best directions you can give, but on the other hand I have never appreciated that kind of "one size fits all" advice and have always preferred to know what my options were. Perhaps I overwhelm the newcomers with too many options, but on the other hand I don't feel I can say there is only one right answer when there really isn't. Perhaps I should leave out the things I've left behind, but I have an assortment of things I'm still using and it's difficult to say that one is better or worse than another when there are appealing things about them all.

### ***Beekeeping Philosophy***

Some of those options are related to your philosophy and your energy. In these examples I will assume you want to get to natural cell size or small cell size and no treatments. So, for instance, if you just can't handle the idea of plastic, then there is no point in considering Honey Super Cell or Mann Lake PF120s or PF100s or PermaComb or PermaPlus as options. You may as well just limit yourself to wax 4.9mm foundation or foundationless. But if plastic does not run contrary to your view of life, the PF120s will save a lot of labor over building foundationless frames, and a lot of cost over Honey Super Cell. So knowing you have that option might be helpful to you in making your choice.

### *Time and Energy*

More on the energy and time front, if you have the energy and time, I like to cut my frames down to $1^1/_4$" instead of the standard $1^3/_8$" but it takes time and energy and tools. So I have a lot of Mann Lake PF120s that are standard width and probably will never get time to cut them down.

## Feeding Bees

This also carries over to feeders and other things. For instance, having hive top feeders that hold five gallons is nice for feeding an outyard in early fall, but is also expensive. Feeding hives in my back yard can work fine with bottom board feeders (that cost me nothing) and more frequent trips. Having these options doesn't mean one is better than the other, but one may fit your situation better than the other. Buying feeders for 200 hives is not practical for me so I feed my outyards when necessary, with dry sugar in empty boxes. They tend to eat it but not store it. This saves me buying feeders, making syrup and save the bees having combs full of sugar syrup and me having to keep track of that so I don't harvest sugar syrup. Is that the best solution? It seems to work well for me, but may or may not work well for you.

### *Take your time*

My point is that options, in my opinion, are good, but they also sometimes create a lot of overwhelming decisions for a new beekeeper who has no frame of reference for those decisions. One good step is grow slowly in your beekeeping and don't invest too heavily in anything that is special equipment until you've had time to test it thoroughly. Most beekeepers have wasted a lot of money on equipment they eventually didn't use. Of course part of this may be to see what you can get by without, instead of trying out everything on the market. For example, feeding with an empty box and dry sugar is much cheaper and less investment than buying top feeders.

***Important Decisions***

One of the most important things to do is sort out the hard to change decisions from the less important, easy to change decisions.

If you pay attention to the rest of this you'll see that hardly anything I *would* buy is in a beginner beekeeper starter kit.

There are many things in beekeeping you can easily change as you go along. There is no point stressing out over these things. There are other things in beekeeping that are an investment and are difficult to change later.

## Easy Things to Change in Beekeeping:

You can always go to a top entrance. You only have to block the bottom one (with a $^{3}/_{4}$″ by $^{3}/_{4}$″ by $14^{3}/_{4}$″ entrance block on a ten frame standard bottom board) and propping up the top. It's not like everything you have is outdated if you decide that you want a top entrance.

You can always choose to put in or leave out a queen excluder. Odds are, sooner or later, you'll need one for something. They are handy for the bottom of an uncapping tank or as an includer when hiving a swarm etc. It's not that big of an investment to have one or two (or not). Nor is it that big of a problem to buy one later if you don't have one.

You can change the race of bees *very* easily. You'll probably requeen once in a while even if you *aren't* trying to change races, and all you have to do is buy a queen of whatever race you want and requeen. So it's not that critical what breed you pick. I doubt you'll be disappointed with an Italian or a Carni or a Caucasian. And if you decide you want something else, it's not hard to change.

**Difficult Things to Change in Beekeeping:**

The bigger issues are things that are an investment you have to live with or you have to go to a lot of trouble to modify or undo.

If you think you want small cell (or natural sized cell) you're one step ahead to use it from the start. Otherwise you'll have to either gradually phase out all of the large cell comb or do a shakedown and do it all at once. If you invested money in plastic foundation, this is disappointing (I have hundreds of sheets in my basement of large cell foundation I'll never use). But at least you won't have to cut down all your equipment.

If you buy a "typical" starter kit you'll get ten frame deeps for brood and shallows for honey. The ten frame deeps full of honey weigh 90 pounds. Some will argue that when they have brood in them they weigh less than that. That's true. But sooner or later you'll have one full of honey and you may not be able to lift it. If you go with all mediums you'll have to be able to lift 60 pound supers full of honey. If you go with eight frame mediums you'll only have to lift 48 pound boxes. I started off with the deep/shallow arrangement and had to cut down every box and frame to mediums. Then I cut all the ten frame boxes down to eight frames. It sure would have been easier to just buy eight frame mediums from the start. Interchangeability is also a wonderful thing.

Screened bottom boards are easy to just buy. It's harder to convert the old ones.

If you buy a lot of *anything*, you may decide you hate it later. Make changes slowly. Test things before you invest a lot in them. Just because one person likes it, doesn't mean you will like it.

---

***Choices I recommend***

So, if you want to minimize your choices and maximize your success I'll distill things down to what I would recommend with only a few choices:

## Frame depth

I'm going to recommend you use all the same size frames for everything, and since medium frames seem like the best compromise for everything, I'm going to recommend mediums for everything, mainly because of lighter boxes. That includes comb honey, extracted honey, brood etc. These are sometimes called Illinois supers. Or $^{3}/_{4}$ supers. They are $6^{5}/_{8}$" deep with $6^{1}/_{4}$" frames.

Reasons for all the same size: You can bait up supers with brood, or other frames from the brood chamber. You can pull honey from the supers for starting nucs etc. You can run an unlimited brood nest and if the queen lays in the supers, you just pull those frames of brood and swap them for some honey from the brood chamber. Different sizes are really a deterrent to good management of the hive.

Reasons for mediums instead of deeps: A 10 frame deep full of honey can weigh up to 90 pounds. A medium full of honey can weigh up to 60 pounds. 'Nuff said.

*Various frames from extra shallow to Dadant deep*

*Various depths of boxes from deep to extra shallow*

**Number of Frames**

Now that we have a frame size you need to pick a hive size. Standard is 10 frame. There is much to be said for being standard. On the other hand, there is much to be said for lighter (48 pounds vs. 60 pounds). The 8-frame equipment from Brushy Mountain or Miller Bee Supply or Walter T. Kelley or others, is very nice for making less work. You need to choose whether you want lighter boxes or standard sized ones. I converted to 8 frame. One of the other advantages of 8 frame equipment is that it is such a more versatile size. It is the same volume as a 5 frame nuc and can be used for a nuc. With a follower board it could even be used for a 2 frame mating nuc and then expanded, if need be, to eight frames eventually.

*Various widths of boxes from two frames to ten*

## Style of Frames and Cell Size of Foundation

Frames, foundation, cell size etc. You need to decide if you want plastic foundation, plastic frames, fully drawn plastic comb, etc. and what size you want the foundation. I would recommend just buying small cell or PermaComb or Honey Super Cell. If you want to use wax, buy small cell wax from Dadant or one of the other suppliers. The small cell plastic is no longer on the market from Dadant. But Mann Lake's PF120's are 4.95mm cell size and are one piece frame and foundation. If you want to not have to build frames, not have to wait for the bees to draw it and never have to worry about wax moths or small hive beetles then buy PermaComb or Honey Super Cell. I personally heat the

PermaComb to 200º F and dip it in 212º F beeswax and shake off all the excess wax. This results in 4.9mm cells and seems to handle all my mite problems. For now don't worry about regression or all that complex sounding stuff, but just stick with natural sized or small cell (aka 4.9mm) foundation. Or use foundationless (see that chapter for more information).

### Eight Frame Mediums

*Left to right, eight frame, ten frame, eight frame*

To minimize injuries from lifting and make life simple, buy all eight frame medium boxes. Pick a manufacturer who is reasonable in price and shipping to your location.

## Plastic Small Cell Frames

If you don't mind plastic, buy all Mann Lake PF120 frame/foundation so you don't have to learn to (and find time to) build frames, wire foundation etc. These have been the most successful at getting small cell comb right off the bat in my experience.

## If you don't like the idea of plastic

Then use foundationless. Certainly foundationless is the most appealing to me as you can't get any more natural than that. I would buy the wedge top bar frames and rotate the wedge 90 degrees so it makes a comb guide.

*Jay Smith style Bottom Feeder*

## Bottom Board Feeders

I would buy solid bottom boards and convert them into bottom board feeders. There is no reason to spend a lot of money on feeders if your management plan is to leave them honey instead of feeding and only feed in emergencies.

I would make those feeders in? the style with no entrance and a plug for a drain and build simple top covers with top entrances to eliminate skunk, mice, grass, snow and condensation issues.

***Essential Equipment***

**Here are some essentials for the beekeeper:**

**Large Smoker**

I would buy a good smoker. A large one. Large ones are easier to light and keep lit. Smaller ones are harder to light and keep lit. I would light the smoker anytime you are going to do more than just pop the top and I would light it most of the time even then if there is a dearth or any other reason to suspect they might be defensive. Don't oversmoke them. Make sure it's lit well and put a puff in the entrance and after you open up a puff across the top bars. Put the smoker down and leave it unless they start to get excited.

**Veil, jacket, or suit**

I would prefer, if I only have one protective suit, to have a jacket with a zip on veil. It's what I use the most, but it is nice to have a full coverall with a zip on veil. That way I can be pretty fearless of the bees. If you make them mad enough, long enough, they will still get in, but that would require quite a bit of time. If you have the money to spare, I'd buy both. I like the hood-ed ones, as opposed to the ones with a helmet. I was paranoid at first of the hood being in contact with my head, but I have three nylon outfits (one jacket and two coveralls), and two cotton, all with hoods, and have never been stung on the back of the head like I expected. My favorite jacket is the Ultra Breeze as it is mesh, sting proof and cool on a hot day. It's expensive and worth every penny.

**Gloves**

I would wear standard leather gloves and tuck them into the sleeves of the jacket. They will be easier to get on and off than the long ones and cheaper to buy.

**Some kind of hive tool**

Any little flat bar will work. One of my all time favorites is a very old light cleaver (the blade is about $1^1/_2$" wide and 6" long) that I sharpened on the end. I can pry a box apart or scrape things. It doesn't pull nails well and if the prying is really heavy I do worry about breaking it. If you're going to buy one, I really like the Italian Hive tool I got from Brushy Mountain It's got a lift hook on one end and is light and long has a lot of leverage. But I don't see it in their last catalog. My next favorite is the Thorne hive tool with a frame lifter and next is Maxant's Frame Lifter hive tool. But I do like the Italian one from Brushy Mountain better because the hook fits between the frames more easily.

**A bee brush**

You can buy one, or if you hunt or have birds you can use a large feather. It has to be a nice stiff quill to do any good. You will need to brush bees off from time to time. In order to harvest, in order to do other manipulations. Shaking can work sometimes, but sometimes you just need a brush. Like when the bees are all clustering on the edge of the hive you can brush them off before you set the next box on top.

**Nice to Have Beekeeping Equipment:**

These are nice, but not essential, you can do fine without them, but I don't think you will regret buying them.

**Tool box**

You can put your tools in a five gallon bucket, but if you want a really nice toolbox, Brushy Mountain has one that can double as a swarm box, has a place for a hive tool, a frame grip, a smoker, a frame perch and room inside for odds and ends. It makes a nice stool too. If you want to build your own, take a close look at the one Brushy Mt has and convert a nuc box.

**Queen Catcher**

The hair clip kinds are the nicest ones I've seen to pick up a queen without hurting her. You still have to be a little careful, but it is designed to not hurt her and to let the workers out. There are times you just need to know where she is while you rearrange things or do a split and then you can release her. This plus a marking tube and a paint pen and you can mark her too.

**Queen Muff**

I got one from Brushy Mountain You can catch the queen in the hair clip and put her in the muff and not worry about her flying off.

**A frame-nailing device**

This device (Walter T. Kelley has these) is very nice to put wooden frames together. It holds 10 frames in place for you to nail them. It is a little tricky to figure out at first, but it's a real time saver and frustration saver.

**A $^{1}/_{4}$" crown staple gun and compressor.**

Everyone who owns a car needs a compressor anyway. The staple gun is under a $100. Walter Kelley has one that is the right size. It will shoot from $1^{1}/_{2}$" to $^{5}/_{8}$" staples (which I buy at the local lumber or hardware store). The 1″ are perfect for frames. The $1^1/_2$″ are perfect to put boxes together. The $^5/_8$″ are nice for when you don't want it to go through a $^3/_4$″ board and the $1^1/_4$″ are nice when you don't want to go through two $^3/_4$″ boards (like when you put a cleat on for a handle on a homemade box). Then you don't have to pre drill all those holes in the frames. I was a carpenter for years and am pretty good at nailing, but when doing frames I bend as many nails as I don't bend. Half of them are bent and pulled out when nailing by hand. But maybe my problem is I used to "one lick" a 16p nail and I don't have the finesse.

### An Extractor

I would especially avoid buying a *new* extractor if you only have a few hives. If you find a good price on one, by all means pick it up, but buying a new one is a waste of money. Of course you can always keep your eye out for a bargain on a used one. I just crushed and strained and made cut comb for the first 26 years of my beekeeping. I finally bought a 9/18 radial when I started getting more hives. I'm glad I held out for a real extractor when I finally got one.

## Avoid Gadgets

I would avoid all the gadgets out there as they will be superfluous and expensive. I like the Italian hive tool from Brushy Mountain I would skip the frame holders and the frame grips and etc.

## Useful Gadgets

Of the gadgets out there, I have enjoyed. I like the "Ready Date" nuc calendars (betterbee.com) as a way to keep track of the status of a hive. If you have outyards and haul a smoker around the smoker box is a safety item worth having. You can put your smoker in it and not have to worry about catching your car on fire.

# Getting Started

Now that we've covered equipment decisions, let's get started beekeeping.

## Recommended Beginning Beekeeping Sequence

I've thought about this and I'm sure a lot of people will disagree but I'm going to give my advice on how I would start beekeeping if I were a beginner doing it over again. This is what I wish I had done the first time.

First you have to decide how to get some bees. It's very difficult to get them from a tree or a neighbor's house when you really don't know anything about them. This is really an advanced undertaking. That said, I admit that is exactly what I did. I took them out of houses and trees and bought some queens. But I really didn't do so well at it and I got stung a lot. So all in all I don't think it was that good for the bees, although it was educational for me.

If you have local beekeepers you may be able to get a nuc or some frames of brood etc. The downside to this is they are probably on Deep frames (9 $^{1}/_{4}$″ frames that go in a 9$^{5}/_{8}$″ box). I'm not going to recommend deeps. They are also probably on large cell comb, and I'm going to recommend natural or small cell comb.

You can order package bees. I used to get them through the mail, but lately that has gotten more and more expensive. Most locations you can find a bee supply place that brings in a truck load of package bees in the spring. If you find a local bee club or association they will probably be able to advise you on this. Two packages would be a good start.

## How Many Hives?

It is sound advice to get at least two hives. I think some beginning beekeepers don't get the *purpose* as they often want to experiment with two *different* kinds of hives, like a top bar hive and a Langstroth or a Langstroth eight frame medium and a Langstroth ten frame deep. But this defeats the purpose of having two hives. The main reason for having two hives is that the resource that is the hardest to come by and which is often needed to resolve issues of queenrightness, is frames of brood. But those frames of brood are not of much value if they are not interchangeable. If you really want a top bar hive and a Langstroth hive, then at least make them the same dimensions so the Langstroth frames are interchangeable with the top bars.

## Package or Nuc?

Another issue new beekeepers often misunderstand is a nuc vs. a package. It comes down to this: if you want bees on some kind of frame or comb other than what they are on, buy a package. In other words if the nuc is Langstroth deeps on large cell comb and you want a top bar hive or a small cell hive or a medium hive, then it's not practical to buy a large cell deep nuc and expect to put them in a medium box or a top bar hive.

On the other hand if you can get a nuc on the cell size, or frame you want, a good nuc will have a two week head start on a package and if you can get *local* bees in a nuc, especially local bees that have already wintered as a nuc, you will have a great advantage as they will be acclimatized to your climate, and an overwintered nuc always seem really to take off in the spring often surpassing even strong hives that have overwintered.

Don't get too sidetracked on this two week advantage though. It's great as I said, if they are on the cell size and frames you want, but if they are not, it is not only a lot of work to convert to another frame size, cell size, or hive type, but you will set them back at least that two weeks or more you would have gained with the nuc, in the process. So take that into account when deciding.

## Race of Bees

Assuming you are going to buy a package of bees, the next decision is what race. I hate to not have an opinion, but I really haven't seen a race of honey bees I didn't like. Well, I did have some really mean ones once, but they were the same breed I had been raising for decades. I will recommend you get something that is not a hybrid and can be open bred by you with good results. Caucasian, Italian, Cordovan (Italian), Russian and Carniolans are all fine. Take your pick. If you can get locally raised queens, that's better but for those of us in the North, there are seldom packages available with Northern queens. You can requeen with some later after you get them started.

### *More Sequence*

We covered choices in the previous chapter, now that we've made all these decisions, here's the order I'd get things in.

I know a lot of people will disagree with me, but I would buy an observation hive. They will say, correctly, that an observation hive takes more skill to run. But you will learn *so much* in just a few days of watching one, and so much in the first year of watching one, that I think they are invaluable. Even if they die or swarm, you should learn a lot. You used to be able to buy a nice four frame "Von Frisch" hive from Brushy Mountain I'm not sure if they still stock it as I haven't seen it in the catalog. It holds four medium frames (remember we want all the frames the same). You do have to make the hookup for the tube yourself but everything else is pretty much done for you. To hook up the tube I take a 1" long 1" diameter galvanized water pipe nipple and a $1^1/_8$" hole saw (that goes in a drill to make a $1^1/_8$" hole) and glue a piece of pine in the end of the Von Frisch hive and drill the 1 $^1/_8$" hole and use some channel locks or a pipe wrench to screw in the pipe nipple. Get some $1^1/_4$" tubing and attach it with a hose clamp. Cut a 1 x 4 to fit in under your window and another that fits under your storm window and drill a $1^3/_8$" hole in both of those so that with the windows closed they line up. Thread the $1^1/_4$" tubing (a sump pump kit works well) out through the window. I also added a screen molding behind the hinges and behind the door stop to increase the space between the glass by $^1/_4$". This works out perfectly. The $1^1/_2$" space that it comes with works if the bees are drawing their own comb in the hive. But if you ever swap drawn frames from a hive it's too close and PermaComb or Honey Super Cell is also too close.

### Observation Hive

If you get on the bee forums there are people who make observation hives, often to your specifications.

Also I would put a very small screw or a staple in back and on the door in the frame rest area to hold the frame out at the correct space. I seem to always be carrying the hive back in from outside and jostle the frames and they slide to one side and mess up the beespace.

Make some frames (or wax dip some PermaComb) and put the small cell foundation in it. Put these in the observation hive. Cut some Black cloth so that doubled up and folded over the hive it covers both sides to the floor. This is a privacy curtain.

### Nucleus Hive

When the bees outgrow the observation hive you will need somewhere to put them. If we are going with eight frame mediums we can just use one eight frame box for a nuc and all our equipment will be the same. If not, let's build or buy a medium nuc. Get a bottom and cover (or make them). This will make a good start for when they outgrow the observation hive. A nuc also gives you a place to keep a spare queen or make a small split and not leave them too much room. Put it together so it's ready before you get the bees. Now you wait for spring.

## Putting Bees in the Observation Hive

Come spring put the bees in the observation hive. I assume this is a package, so you need to make sure they are well fed. Spray the screen lightly with sugar syrup waiting periodically and spraying again until they lose interest in eating it off of the screen wire. Take the bees and the observation hive outside near the entrance to the observation hive. Cover the exit to the hive with a piece of cloth and a thick hair tie rubber band (they are easier to handle) Do the same with the outside entrance to the tube and the other end of the tube in the house. Lay the observation hive flat on its side on the ground and open the door. Put on your protective equipment. Pry open the lid to the box and carefully fish out the queen cage and set it aside. Now fish out the can and shake the bees off of it into the observation hive. Hit the box sharply on the ground to dislodge the cluster and then flip it upside down and pour the bees into the observation hive. Hit the box sharply on its side to knock the remaining bees to one end then dump them in. If there are still 20 bees or so in the box, don't worry about it. If there are hundreds of bees in the box, repeat the steps until there are only a few.

Spritz the queen lightly with some water so she won't be as likely to fly. Carefully pry the staple off of the queen cage, being careful not to open the screen and let out the queen. Put the queen cage over a cluster of the bees and holding the screen side down, open the screen and put the cage close to the bees watching for the queen to walk out. (Difficult, I know). If you didn't see her and you didn't see her fly off and you didn't see her go in, then we may have to keep an eye out for a while. Assuming she went in, use the smoker to drive the bees away from the door frame so they don't get squashed and close the door (squashing some stubborn and indecisive bees, but hopefully not too many.) Now brush all of the bees off of the outside of the hive and take it in the house. Holding the hose up to the pipe, pull off the cloth from both pieces and slide the hose on and clamp it (the clamp has to be on the hose before you do this.

You now have an observation hive. Fill a quart jar with 2:1 syrup (2 parts sugar to 1 part water) and feed them. Now go take the cloth off of the outside of the tube.

If you didn't see the queen go in, watch outside for any clusters of bees on the ground or bushes. If you see any, look carefully to see if there is a queen. If so, catch her with the hair clip catcher and put her at the tube entrance and see if she'll go in. If she doesn't, you may have to take the hive outside and do it all again, but probably you now have a queen in the hive.

If you bought two packages (recommended) then put the other in the nuc and buy your equipment for a hive and assemble it now.

Keep feeding them and watch them. Count the days until the queen starts to lay eggs. (usually at least three or four days but sometimes as long as two weeks) and how many days until they eggs hatch and how many days until you see capped brood and how many days until you see emergence. The hive will build slower at first but once bees start emerging the population will explode.

## Making a Split into the Nucleus Box

When they have pretty much filled the hive with honey, brood and pollen you need to move three frames and the queen to the eight frame hive. Feed them and keep feeding the observation hive. Try to be sure that the frame you leave in the observation hive has eggs. Now you get to watch them raise a queen. By the time the queen in the observation hive is laying, all of the brood will have emerged. The observation hive will be struggling again to get going, but the five frame nuc will quickly fill up and when four and one half frames of it are full, add the next box and order four medium boxes and enough frames for them and a screened bottom board and an inner and outer cover or a migratory cover. When the two eight frame boxes are full put the queen and all but two frames in the other hive. Make sure one of those frames has eggs and open brood and the other has pollen and honey. Put those two in one box with a top and bottom and let it raise a queen.

Now you have one hive, one nuc, and one observation hive (and if you bought a second package another hive). If you need a queen you can unite the nuc with the hive, or pull a frame of brood for the nuc to raise one or pull a frame of brood for the observation hive to raise one. You get to watch in detail what is going on with the bees in the observation hive. You can see pollen coming in, you can see nectar coming in, you can see when they are being robbed, you can see if they are having any problems. You can watch the queen lay. You can practice finding the queen without disturbing the hive.

## Managing Growth

As the observation hive gets too strong you can pull frames out and put them in your regular hive to boost them. As the nuc gets too strong you can pull frames and put them in the regular hive. You can replace them with undrawn foundation. If you only want one hive, you have one and some spare parts to fix it. If you want another hive, just let the nuc grow and put it in a regular hive too. Then start another nuc from some frames from the observation hive so you have two hives a nuc and an observation hive.

## Starting With More Hives

Of course if you wanted to start with more hives (a good idea actually), you could put a package in the observation hive and a package in the nuc or the hive at the same time. More redundancy lets you have resources to fall back on when they get into trouble. I wouldn't go with more than four hives to start off.

# Foundation and Frames

What kind of foundation and frames should you buy? Obviously if there was a "right" answer, there would only be one kind of foundation and one kind of frames. The reason there is not is that beekeepers have different preferences and different philosophies and different experiences.

Let's get a little terminology out of the way. With wax, about the only thicknesses I see available now are "Medium Brood", "Surplus" and "Thin Surplus". "Medium Brood" does *not* mean it goes in medium frames. It means it is of medium thickness. Surplus is thin and "Thin Surplus" is even thinner. Surplus is intended for comb honey.

***Brood foundation***

The thing the bees like to build from the most is no foundation. Foundationless frames are the best accepted, and the most natural. They have many advantages, from the Varroa control of smaller cells, to being able to cut out queen cells from a comb without worrying about hitting a wire or having plastic in the middle of the comb stop you.

The thing the bees like next is wax foundation. They can rework it to what they want. But the closer it is to what they want the better it will be accepted. I'd say, with unregressed ("normal") bees 5.1mm would be the best accepted, as that seems to be what they want to build. Dadant sells this. 4.9mm would be next and 5.4mm last. But I want the 4.9mm for the Varroa control aspect. So one aspect of foundation is the material (wax or plastic) and another is the size of the cell.

The other issue with wax foundation is reinforcement. DuraComb and DuraGilt have a smooth plastic core. This works well until the bees strip the wax off to use somewhere else or the wax moths eat down to the plastic. Then the bees won't rebuild on the plastic. Wires are often used in wax foundation. Some foundation comes with vertical wires in it and people use it as is. Some comes with none and some people wire it with horizontal wires. The wires slow down the process of the foundation sagging.

The material the bees seem to like the least and the beekeepers seem to like the most is plastic. The wax moths can't destroy the foundation (although they *can* destroy the comb). The bees can't rework the size very easily. Sizes of plastic vary from 5.4mm down to 4.95mm. It is available as sheets of plastic foundation or fully molded frames with foundation.

Fully "drawn" comb is also available in plastic. PermaComb (5.0mm equivalent cell size) is available in mediums and Honey Super Cell (4.9mm equivalent cell size) is available in deeps. Fully drawn, means the bees don't draw it out, it's already full thickness, and they just use it and cap it.

### *Foundation for supers*

The fully drawn comb is certainly an advantage here (once the bees have accepted and used it) as the bees have only to store the nectar and don't have to build any comb. The wax moths can't touch it nor can the small hive beetles.

The various plastic frames and plastic foundation for supers are the same as the ones available for brood, with the additional use by some of drone comb (easier to extract) and Honey Super Cell's 6.0mm cell size with a fake egg in the bottom of the cell. The fake egg supposedly fools the queen so she won't lay in it. The 6.0mm also discourages the queen as it's not quite a drone size (6.6mm) nor a worker size (4.4mm to 5.4mm) so she doesn't like to lay in it.

For comb honey, there is surplus and thin surplus. This is so the comb honey will be easy to chew and not have a thick core in the middle. It is available from most manufactures. Walter T. Kelley has it in 7/11 which, again, is a size the queen doesn't like to lay in so you can forgo the excluder and not get brood in the supers.

### ***Kinds of frames***

There are different kinds of frames and many of the foundations were planned to be used in one or the other of them. You can usually adapt either way, but you may want to take this into account when ordering frames and when ordering foundations.

*Top bars* come in grooved, wedge, and split (split is available from Walter T. Kelley). The grooved are usually used with plastic or with a wax tube fastener. I prefer them to the wedge. I can attach a lot more foundation a lot more reliably (so that it doesn't fall out) with a wax tube fastener than a wedge. The wedge type has a cleat that breaks off and is nailed into the frame to hold the foundation. The split is usually used for comb honey. The foundation is just dropped down into the split onto a solid bottom bar and put in the hive without nailing at all.

*Bottom bars* come in split, grooved and solid. I prefer solid, as the wax moths won't get into them. But your foundation may not fit with a solid bottom bar (depending on what you buy). The split ones are not very strong and always seem to break the first time I try to clean them up and put new foundation in them.

Grooved are usually used for plastic so that the plastic foundation snaps into the frame. The other issue is the exact size of the foundation you are using. Some is cut to go all the way to the bottom with split frames. Some is cut to fit in the groove. Walter T. Kelley seems to be the only supplier who carefully maps what fits in what in their catalog.

*Plastic one-piece frames*. These eliminate all the issues, other than acceptance and cutting out queen cells. No frames to build. The foundation obviously fits since it's already in there. If you buy Mann Lake PF120s (medium depth) or PF100s (deep depth) they are 4.95mm cell size so you get the advantage of small cell. They are cheap (in large lots they are a little over $1 each last I saw). There is no wiring to do and they are well accepted by the bees.

# Locating hives?

"Where should I put my hive?" The problem is there is neither a simple answer nor a perfect location. But in a list of decreasing importance I would pick these criteria with a willingness to sacrifice the less important ones altogether if they don't work out:

***Safety***

It's essential to have the hive where they are not a threat to animals who are chained or penned up and can't flee if they are attacked, or where they are likely to be a threat to passersby who don't know there are hives there. If the hive is going to be close to a path that people walk you need to have a fence or something to get the bees up over the people's heads. For the safety of the bees they should be where cattle won't rub on them and knock them over, horses won't knock them over and bears can't get to them.

***Convenient access***

It's essential to have the hive where the beekeeper can drive right up to it. Carrying full supers that could weigh from 90 pounds (deep) down to 48 pounds (eight frame medium) any distance is too much work. The same reason applies for bringing beekeeping equipment and feed to the hives. You may have to feed as much as 50 pounds or more of syrup to each hive and carrying it any distance is not practical. Also you will learn a lot more about bees with a hive in your backyard than a hive 20 miles away at a friend's house. Also a yard a mile or two from home will get much better care than one 60 miles from home.

***Good forage***

If you have a lot of options, then go for a place with lots of forage. Sweet clover, alfalfa being grown for seed, tulip poplars etc. can make the difference between bumper crops of 200 pounds or more of honey per hive and barely scraping a living. But keep in mind the bees will not only be foraging the space you own, they will be foraging the 8,000 acres around the hives.

***Not in your way***

I think it's important the hive does not interfere with anyone's life much. In other words, don't put it right next to a well used path where, in a dearth and in a bad mood, the bees may harass or sting someone or anywhere else where you are likely to wish they weren't there.

***Full sun***

I find hives in full sun have fewer problems with diseases and pests and make more honey. All things being equal, I'd go for full sun. The only advantage to putting them in the shade is that you get to work them in the shade, or it might help meet one of the other more important criteria.

If you live in a very hot climate, mid afternoon shade might be a nice to have, but I wouldn't lose sleep over it unless you have a top bar hive; then I would go for shade to prevent comb collapse.

***Not in a low-lying area***

I don't care if they are somewhere in the middle between low and high, but I'd rather not have them where the dew and the fog and the cold settle and I really don't want them where I have to move them if there's a threat of a flood.

***Out of the wind***

It's nice to have them where the cold winter wind doesn't blow on them so hard and the wind is less likely to blow them over or blow off the lids. This isn't my number one requirement, but if a place is available that has a windbreak it's nice. This usually precludes putting them at the very top of a hill.

***Water***

Bees need water. One of the issues is providing it. Another is to have it more attractive than the neighbor's hot tub. To accomplish this you need to understand that bees are attracted to water because of several things:

- Smell. They can recruit bees to a source that has odor. Chlorine has odor. So does sewage.
- Warmth. Warm water can be taken on even moderately chilly days. Cold water cannot because when the bees get chilled they can't fly home.
- Reliability. Bees prefer a reliable source.
- Accessibility. Bees need to be able to get to the water without falling in. A horse tank or bucket with no floats does not work well. A creek bank provides such access as they can land on the bank and walk up to the water. A barrel or bucket does not unless you provide ladders or floats or both. I use a bucket of water full of old sticks. The bees can land on the stick and climb down to the water.

***Conclusion***

In the end, bees are very adaptable, so make sure it's convenient for you, and if it's not too hard to provide, try to meet some of the other criteria. It's doubtful you'll have a place that meets all of the criteria listed above.

# Installing Packages

It occurs to me listening to all of the newbees on the bee forums and watching the U-Tube videos of inexperienced people doing their first installs and listening to the experts give advice at new beekeeper classes etc., that there is a lot of very bad advice out there. Sometimes it's just that a beginner doesn't know what a happy medium of something is, but all in all, I think it's just bad advice. So here's my take on a lot of that advice of what to do and not to do:

***Not to do:***

**Don't spray them with syrup**

Certainly if you insist on doing this, don't spray them much and don't use thick syrup. 2 parts water to 1 part sugar is plenty. Personally I would not and do not spray them at all. If you have to feed them because you can't get them installed, just spray a little on the screen and wait for them to clean it up. Repeat until they don't take it. But actually I think it's a better plan to refill the can with syrup. Pull it out (of course the bees can now get out so put a board or something over the hole). If you have the kind of can that has a round hole with a rubber grommet holding in a piece of cloth, pop this out and pour in the syrup. Replace the grommet and cloth and then replace the can. If there are just the small holes, then put a hole just big enough for the syrup to run in and fill it full of syrup. Then plug the hole with some softened beeswax. Check for leaks and put the can back.

Why? I've seen many drowned sticky bees from leaky cans or spraying of bees or worse, from overheated bees that regurgitate their honey stomachs as a reflex to cool them off. I don't want to see any more drowned bees. I watched a YouTube video the other day of someone knocking the bees to the bottom (which is fine if you're about to dump them into the hive) soaking them (literally) with syrup, turning the box around and soaking them some more from the other side, then after messing with the hive a bit, soaking them again. I doubt if half of them lived.

I've never seen bees die from *not* spraying them with syrup.

## Don't leave them in the shipping box

Don't put them in the hive in the shipping box in order to avoid dumping them out — especially if the box is on top of the top bars with an empty box on top. This is just asking for problems. Assuming you put the queen cage somewhere in the hive, the bees will cluster on the inner cover or cover and then draw combs in the empty box. Bees always prefer their own comb to drawing on foundation and will take every opportunity you give them to do so. Don't give them that opportunity. Bees are not hard to dump out of a box. Yes, this is one of those few things where gentleness and grace are not helpful, but that does not make it hard on the bees or upsetting to the bees. You may as well get used to the idea as someday you'll be shaking a swarm into a box instead of a swarm out of a box. If you really insist on letting them leave the box on their own, then put an empty deep (or medium or whatever) on the *bottom* and put the box in there and then put a box with frames on *top* of that. This takes advantage of the fact that the bees will try to cluster at the top and hang down from there. So hopefully that will be the inner cover and not the bottom bars. Make sure you remove the shipping box and the empty box *the next day*. Not four days later. Not five days later—t*he next day*. Otherwise you risk them building comb in the empty space.

**Don't hang the queen between the frames**

This almost always results in an extra comb between those two frames drawn on the queen cage. Release the queen and you won't have to worry about the messed up combs. This is even more important in a foundationless scenario such as a top bar hive or foundationless frames as one messed up between the frames comb will result in a repeat of the error the rest of the way across. Dump the bees in. Let them settle a bit. To keep the queen from flying, pull the cork from the non candy end (where she can get out now) and, while holding your thumb over the hole, lay the cage on the bottom and leave it. Put the frames back in and the lid on and walk away. Don't try to release her onto the top bars. Release her down on the bottom board.

One of the issues seems to be that people think that either they will abscond or they will kill the queen. In my experience leaving her caged does not seem to resolve these issues. If they want to leave they usually move to the hive next door anyway and abandon the queen. If you release the queen it also won't stop this from happening, but it also won't cause it. I've not had a problem with a package killing the queen. A bunch of confused bees have been shaken together from many hives and in the confusion they are just happy to find a queen. If they do kill the queen it is almost always because there is already one loose in the package that got shaken in. The bees prefer this queen because they have contact with her.

## Don't use an excluder as an includer too long

Don't use an excluder as an includer (to keep the queen *in*) after there is open brood in the hive. I wouldn't use it at all, but there is no point in it after there is open brood and it will keep the drones from being able to fly.

## Don't spray the queen with syrup

It will make a mess. Yes, it will probably keep her from flying, but it could also do her harm. I know some think it doesn't but they apparently have not seen a half dead sticky queen before. I've seen plenty. I don't spray her with anything, but if you insist, just use water or at most 2 parts water to 1 part sugar.

## Don't install bees without protective equipment

You have enough to worry about without worrying about them stinging you as well.

## Don't smoke a package

They are already in a docile mood and they need the pheromones to get organized, find the queen etc. There is no need to interfere with these pheromones as smoking will do little to nothing to calm a swarm or a package anyway.

## Don't postpone

Don't postpone installing them because it's a little drizzly or chilly. Unless it's like 10° F or less I would install them and consider it an advantage that they won't want to fly and they will settle in better anyway.

Just make sure you have food for them so they don't starve. Capped honey is best. Dry sugar that has been sprayed with enough water to get it damp will do.

### Don't feed in a way that makes excessive space

A package is a comb building team. They are looking to build comb everywhere they can. Don't give them space to build it places where they shouldn't. This includes putting empty boxes on top that they have access to, or a spacer for a baggie feeder etc. A frame feeder, a jar over the inner cover with duct tape covering any access or something similar is good. A bottom board feeder is good. Baggie feeders on the bottom board are good *if* you put the bees in first and the baggie feeders on after the bees are off of the bottom.

### Don't leave frames out

*Ever*. Not even for a few minutes. Often you intend to leave them out for a few minutes and forget to come back. When you close a hive up there should always be a full complement of frames in the box, or in the case of a top bar hive, a full complement of bars. Even if you use a follower to temporarily limit the space, fill the empty space with frames or bars. You never know when the bees will find their way over there.

### Don't dump bees on top of a baggie feeder

They will get covered in syrup as it all gets squished out by the weight of the bees falling on the baggie.

## Don't close up a newly hived package

Let them fly and breathe and get oriented.

## Don't leave empty queen cages around

The bees will cluster on them and act like a swarm thinking the cage is a queen because it still smells like one.

## Don't let messed up comb lead to more messed up comb

If you have foundationless or a top bar hive this is even more critical. With foundation you get a sort of clean slate every frame as there is another wall of foundation to start from. Still I would try to straighten out any messes quickly. Bees build parallel combs, so with foundationless one bad comb just leads to another. By the same token one good comb leads to another as well. The sooner you make sure the last comb from which the "next" is being built is straight and centered; the better off you will be because the next comb will be parallel to that one. If you have a top bar hive, make sure you have some frames built that you can tie combs into if they get crooked or fall off. That way you can always get at least the last one in the row straight again or, better yet, all of them straight. Especially with foundationless, I would check soon after installation and make sure they are off to the correct start, meaning the combs are in the frames and lined up correctly. The sooner you make sure, the better off you'll be.

If you're using foundation and the bees build fins off of the foundation or parallel combs where there is a gap you can't get to, scrape this off before it has open brood in it. The wax isn't nearly the investment that open brood is. Keep the hive clean of this messed up comb or it will haunt you for a long time to come. With plastic foundation you can just scrape it to the plastic. With wax foundation you'll need more finesse.

### Don't destroy supersedure cells

Packages often build supersedure cells and they often tear them back down after a few days, but you tearing them down will risk them ending up queenless. Sometimes there is something wrong with the queen that you don't know. Assuming that the bees are mistaken and you are correct about the quality of the queen is, in my experience, a bad bet.

### Don't panic if the queen in the cage is dead

Don't panic and assume they are queenless if the queen in the cage is dead when you get it. Odds are there is a queen loose in the package. Still I would contact the supplier just in case, but meantime install them and come back and check them before you install that new queen. You may just be sentencing her to her doom.

### Don't freak out if the queen doesn't lay right away

Some will lay as soon as there is comb $^{1}/_{4}$″ deep in the hive. Some take as long as two weeks to start to lay. If they aren't laying in two weeks they probably aren't going to and it's time to freak out.

**Don't freak out if one hive is doing better than the other**

There are many contributing factors. If they have eggs and brood they are probably doing fine.

**Don't get just one hive**

Get at least two. You'll have resources then to deal with issues that will come up.

**Don't feed constantly**

Don't just keep feeding figuring they will stop taking it when they don't need it. I've seen packages that swarmed when they hadn't even finished the first box because they backfilled it all with syrup. Feed until you see some capped stores. This is the sign that the bees have put some of it in "long term storage" meaning they consider it a surplus. If there is a nectar flow at that point, I would stop feeding.

**Don't mess with them everyday**

They may abscond if you mess with them too often.

**Don't leave them on their own for too long**

You'll miss the opportunity to learn and you may miss that things are not going correctly. I would check on them within three or four days for the first time and then wait at least that long between visits and try not to go through everything. Just get a general idea how things are going.

## Don't smoke them too much

Don't smoke them too much when working them after the install. The most common smoking mistakes:

- People have the smoker too hot and burn the bees with the flame thrower they are wielding
- People use far too much smoke causing a general panic instead of simply interfering with the alarm pheromone. One puff in the door is enough. Another on the top if they look excited is ok and after that having it lit and setting nearby is usually sufficient.
- People don't light the smoker because they think smoke upsets the bees, probably because of one of the above reasons.
- People blow the smoke in and immediately open the hive. If you wait a minute the reaction will be completely different. If you're doing something not too time consuming, like filling frame feeders or something, it's a good plan to smoke the next hive before you open this one. That way the minute will be up when you open that one.
- People don't smoke because they have the idea that it is either bad for the bees or somehow unnatural. Their exposure is only a puff or two once every week or two. People have been smoking bees for at least 8,000 years that we have documented for one very good reason. Nothing works better at calming them.

***Things to do:***

## Always install them in the minimum amount of space

It takes heat and humidity to raise brood and make wax. Always install them in the minimum amount of space that is large enough and is convenient for you to provide. In other words, if you have a five frame nuc box, that's excellent. If you don't, then use a single box. Yes a single five frame medium box is large enough if you don't have drawn comb in it. An eight frame medium box is large enough if it has drawn comb. While there is nothing wrong, per se, with putting them in more space, in a Northern climate, especially, it is a lot of work for them and they take off much better in a smaller space. While I probably wouldn't *buy* a five frame nuc just for this, I would use it if I had it.

## Have your equipment ready

Have your equipment ready before the bees arrive. Have the location picked and the equipment there. Have your protective equipment too.

## Wear your protective equipment

You have enough to worry about without thinking about getting stung.

### *How to install:*

When you have everything there, bees, equipment etc, then pull out four or five frames, pull out the can and the queen, slam the box on the ground to knock the bees loose and pour them out like thick oil, or like getting a pick out of a guitar. Tip the box back and forth as needed and when no more will pour slam it again to knock them loose and pour some more. When you are down to ten or twenty bees, set the package down. Pull the cork on a non candy end (if there is candy) of the queen cage and hold your finger over the hole and set it on the bottom board and let go. Gently set the frames in. Do not push them down on the bees on the bottom. Let the bees move and the frames will settle on their own.

If you release the queen (trickier to make sure she doesn't fly) then do *not* leave the cage. Shake all the bees off of it and put it in a pocket and take it in the house when you are done. Otherwise the bees will cluster on the cage and you'll end up with a queenless swarm on the cage.

## Frames tightly together

For some reason this seems to be ignored in the books and causes no end of problems for beekeepers. The frames should be tightly together in the center. A full complement of them (10 for a 10 frame box). If you leave excess space, the bees are likely to do something funky between, like an extra comb or one out from the face of the comb or fins off of the face of the comb. Your best prevention for this kind of "creative" construction is to push them tightly together. Better yet shave them down to $1^1/_4$" wide and put an extra frame in tightly together.

## Do feed them

A package will go through a lot of feed especially when they have no comb and no stores. Feed them until you start seeing capped honey or they start to backfill the brood nest. Do check on them to make sure things are going correctly. Better to catch things sooner than later, especially things like misdrawn comb.

# Enemies of the Bees

***Traditional Enemies of Bees***

Traditionally bees have had enemies; pests, predators and opportunists. Some are as large as a Bear and some are as small as a virus.

**Bears**

**Ursa.** Bears are not a problem for me. Some people live where there are bears and they are their biggest problem. All kinds of bears love to eat bee larvae and they don't mind honey too much either. Symptoms that you have a bear problem: Hives all tipped over and large chunks of the brood nest eaten. Sometimes vandals will tip over hives, but human ones don't usually eat the larvae. The only solutions I've heard of for bears are very strong electric fences with alternating ground wires on the fence (so they are sure to get grounded) and bait on the fence (bacon is popular) so that the bear gets its tender mouth parts on the fence. This seems to work most of the time. Some people put the hives up on a platform too high for the bears, but it is difficult to haul honey down from the platform and move boxes up. Of course sometimes the only way to stop a bear is to kill it and eat it. However this leaves a vacuum and another bear usually soon fills it. The legalities, difficulties and dangers of that method are best left to a hunting magazine.

**Bees Robbing**

BLUF: *if you have robbing you need to stop it immediately! Damage progresses quickly and can devastate a hive. Just make sure they are robbing and not orienting first, then if it's robbing, do something drastic. Close off the hive, cover it with wet cloth. Open all the strong hives to make the strong hives stay home and guard their own hives. But do something even if it's as simple as closing off the hive with screen wire completely. Then you can assess what you want to do to let them fly (small entrance, robber screen etc.). Bottom line, you cannot let robbing continue. You need to stop it now.*

Sometimes during a dearth the strong hives will rob the weak ones. Italians are particularly bad about this. Feeding seems to make this worse or sometimes set it off. Prevention is best. When you see that a dearth is setting in, reduce the entrances on all the hives. This will slow them all down some. But you need to have an eye on them to see that the dearth is over and open them back up during a flow.

I've noticed that queenless hives get robbed much more often than queenright hives. I had always thought it was because the robbers kill the queen, and they probably do, but when I make a nuc queenless in the fall just before I combine them with another nuc they seem to get robbed almost immediately.

One issue is being sure they are being robbed. Sometimes people mistake an afternoon orientation flight with robbing. Every warm, sunny afternoon during brood rearing you'll see young bees orienting. They will hover and fly around the hive. This is easily mistaken for robbers who also hover around a hive. But with practice you'll learn what young bees look like doing this. Young bees are fuzzy. Young bees are calm compared to robbers. Look at the entrance. Robbers are in a frenzy. Local bees might have a traffic jam at the entrance but they will still be orderly. Wrestling at the entrance is pretty much a give away, but lack of fighting at the entrance does not prove they are not being robbed; it just proves they have overcome the guard bees. One *sure* way to tell if they are being robbed is to wait for dark and close the entrance. Any bees in the morning who show up trying to get in are probably robbers — especially if there are a lot of them.

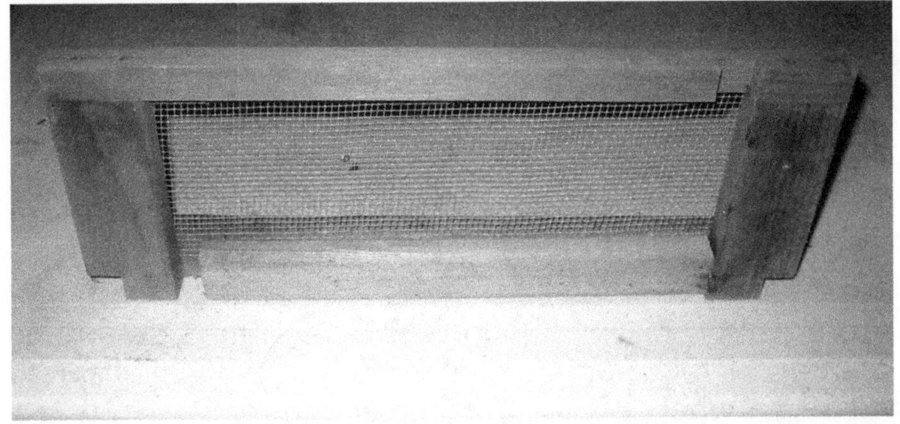

*Inside view of robber screen.*

*Outside of robber screen*

If you already have robbing occurring, here are some ways to stop it. A really weak hive can be closed up with some #8 hardware cloth for a day or two. The robbers can't get in and eventually get tired of trying. It helps if you can feed and water them. A little bit of pollen and a few drops of water will get a small nuc by. More will be required if there are more bees. After you open back up be sure to reduce the entrance. If you can feed, water and ventilate for 72 hours, you can close them up when they are full of robbers and force the robbers to join the hive. Another variety of confining them is to stop up the entrance with grass. The bees will eventually remove it, but hopefully the robbers will give up before then.

A "robber screen" can be built from scratch or you can use a screen door from Brushy Mountain (they seem to have modified theirs to work as a robber screen now). It is a screen that covers the area around the door and has an opening in the top (you will have to make the whole affair). This forces the robbers to turn a couple of corners to find their way in. Since they seem to go by smell this confuses them. It also stops skunks.

Vicks Vaporub around the entrance will also confuse the robbers because they can't smell the hive. It does not confuse the bees that live there because they remember how they got out.

A weak hive will sometimes get totally robbed out so there is not a drop of honey left. They will quickly starve. If you can't control the robbing it's better to combine some of the weak hives than let them get robbed out and starve. If you only have one strong and one weak, you can steal some emerging brood from the strong hive to boost the weak hive and shake off some nurse bees (the ones on the open brood) from the strong hive in the weak hive. Or you can just combine the weak with the strong. It's better than all the fighting and starving.

## Skunks

**Mephitis mephitis** and other varieties. Skunks are a common predator of bees all over North America. Symptoms are very angry hives, scratches on the front of the hives, little soggy piles of dead bees on the ground near the hives that have had the juice sucked out of them. Many solutions work fairly well. Putting the hives up higher or having a top entrance, carpet tack strips on the landing board, chicken wire on the landing board, robber screens, trapping, poisoning and shooting. I have really only done the shooting and screen doors, and ended up doing top entrances. But many swear by the other solutions. A raw egg in the shell with the end removed and three crushed aspirin in it with the other end of the egg buried in the ground in front of the hive(s) being harassed is one solution I've heard of that I would probably have tried if the top entrances had failed. Other poisons worry me because of my dog, chickens and horses.

## Opossums

**Didelphis marsupialis.** Pretty much same problems and solutions as the skunks.

## Mice

**Genus Mus.** Many species and varieties. Also shrews (Cryptotis parva). Mostly these are a problem during winter when the bees are clustered and the mice move in. Using #4 hardware cloth ($^{1}/_{4}$″ squares) over the entrances will let the bees in and out and not the mice. Or use only an upper entrance so the mice can't get in.

## Wax moths

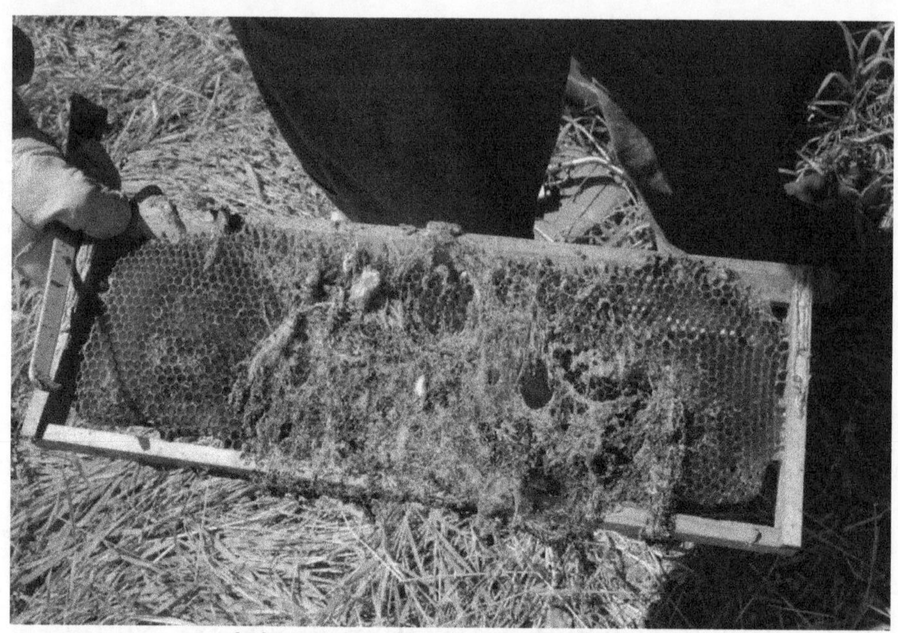

*(Photo by Theresa Cassiday)*

**Galleria mellonella (greater) and Achroia grisella (lesser)** wax moths are really opportunists. They take advantage of a weak hive and live on pollen, honey and burrow through the wax. They leave a trail of webs and feces. Sometimes they are hard to spot because they try to hide from the bees. They burrow down the mid rib (mostly in the brood chamber but sometimes in the supers) and they burrow in the grooves in the frames. This seems to preoccupy a lot of beekeepers and be the cause of a lot of chemical contamination in the hive, so let's address it here.

### Climate

First, understand that this is a very climate dependent issue. In a climate where you seldom if ever have a hard freeze the wax moths may live year round which will be an entirely different scenario than in a climate where you get hard freezes and a long winter. I will share what I do and how that works, but keep in mind you will need to adjust this to your climate and your situation and indeed, if you live where the wax moths never die from cold the method I use will not work at all and a different method will have to be used.

### Cause of Wax Moth Infestation

First, let's talk a bit about the moths. Galleria mellonella (greater wax moth) and Achroia grisella (lesser wax moth). Both will invade unguarded comb during the season when they are active. They prefer comb with pollen in it and as a second choice comb with cocoons in it, but they will even live on pure wax with nothing in it. Most of my wax moth issues are when a walk away split fails to raise a queen and the hive dies, or a mating nuc dwindles too much to guard the comb well enough. I really don't have any other wax moth issues, but in the past have when I have made some drastic mistakes.

### Beekeeping Mistakes

One year, based on someone else's shared experience, I left the boxes wet and put them in my basement. The wax moths not only destroyed all of those combs but so infested my house that I have never gotten rid of them. There have been wax moths flying around my house every since and that was in 2001. Never put supers, especially wet ones, in a warm place. Especially when you have the option to put them outside where they will freeze and the moths will die. That they have to have brood comb is a myth. They prefer brood comb, yes, but they do not require it.

### Wax Moth Control

My current method is this. I wait until late to harvest. The reasons for this are that I can better assess what I should leave for winter, thus saving feeding nearly as often, I save harvesting and then feeding, which is less work. I don't have to chase the bees out of the supers as I merely have to wait for a cold day when the bees are hunkered down and pull the supers which are empty of bees. After harvest I can put the wets on the hives and wait for some warm days for them to clean them up and after they are done, pull them off and stack them with no fear of wax moths as the weather is now cold and there are no moths around. If I want to harvest early, then I'd put the wet boxes back on and not pull them off until after a hard freeze.

The moths, in my part of the country, don't really get going until about late July or August and I try to have all of that drawn comb back on the hives by mid June at the latest, where the bees can guard them. So, I have no moths in the combs during the honey season (June through September), because they are guarded by the bees. I have no moths in the combs from October to May because we get freezing weather now and then which kills the moths and the moth eggs. I have none from May to June because they moths haven't built back up from winter yet.

### Infested Bee Colony

What to do with an infested colony. The reason a colony gets infested is that it is weak. Prevention is not to give them more territory than they can guard, in other words, don't leave a lot of drawn comb on a hive that is small and struggling. Once they are infested, the solution is to reduce them down to just the space the cluster of bees can cover. Remove all the rest of the comb. If you have a freezer, freeze it to kill the moths, or if it's too far gone, let the moths finish cleaning it up. If they get to go to the logical end they will turn all the comb into webs that just fall out of the frames or off of plastic foundation. If it's only got a tunnel or two in it, freezing is a way to save the comb. I usually only have problems with colonies that have died out because they have gone queenless or gotten robbed out. In my management style, I find another nice thing about foundationless frames is you can give them to a hive and it's just empty space for future expansion, not all that surface area to guard from the moths as you have with wax foundation. Also nice in bait hives because the bees will build in the frames but you don't have wax moths tearing up the foundation.

### Bt aka Bacillus thuringiensis

Some people use Bt (Bacillus thuringiensis) as either Certan or Xentari, on the combs. It will kill the moth larvae and seems to have no ill effects on the bees and studies have supported this view. It can be sprayed on infested combs even with the bees on them to clear up the infestation. It can be sprayed on foundation before putting it in the hive. It can be sprayed on combs before storing them. I simply haven't had the time to do this in recent years now, but, as I say, my management seems to keep them under control except in failing hives. But it would probably help in the failing hives if I had it on the combs ahead of time. Certan used to be approved for use on wax moths in the US but the certification ran out and there was no money in renewing it, so it's no longer labeled that way in the US, but is available labeled for that use from Canada and available labeled for use against moth larvae (but not wax moth per se) in the US as Xentari.

### Tropical Wax Moth Control

What I would do if I lived in a more tropical area where moths don't get killed by winter: I would put empty combs on top of strong hives so they can guard them. This isn't a good plan in a temperate climate.

### What not to do for Wax Moths

What I would not do, and is at the top of my list of things not to do, is use moth balls, particularly the Naphthalene ones. Slightly better, and on the FDA list as approved, is PDB (Para Dichlorobenzene). But both of these are carcinogens and I have no use for such things in my food supply, and beehives are part of my food supply.

### Hating Wax Moths

I have given up hating wax moths, which is an easy thing to do when you see them destroy the combs the bees have worked at building. The wax moths are just part of the ecosystem of the beehive. They do their work and it is probably useful work. They get rid of old comb that might have disease lurking in the cocoons. If you really do hate them and want to keep them even more under control, which I have given up on, you can make traps. Basically a two liter bottle with small holes in the sides and a mixture of vinegar, banana peel and syrup inside seems to work well. It also catches a lot of yellow jackets. The moths fly in the holes in the sides, drink, try to fly up and get trapped.

## Nosema

Caused by a fungus (used to be classified as a protozoan) called Nosema apis. Nosema is present all the times and is really an opportunistic disease. The common chemical solution (which I don't use) was

Fumidil which has been recently renamed Fumagilin-B. In my opinion the best prevention is to make sure your hive is healthy and not stressed and feed honey. Research has shown that feeding honey, especially dark honey, for winter feed decreases the incidence of Nosema. Also research done in Russia in the 70's has shown that natural spacing ($1^{1}/_{4}$" or 32mm instead of the standard $1^{3}/_{8}$" or 35mm) reduces the incidence of Nosema.

In my opinion moisture in the hive in winter, long confinement, any kind of stress and feeding sugar syrup increases the incidence. By all means, feed sugar syrup if you don't have honey and it means helping a struggling package or nuc or split. By all means, if you don't have honey, feed sugar syrup in the fall rather than let them starve, but, in my opinion if you can, try to leave honey on for their winter stores.

If you want a solution and don't want to use "chemicals" but want to use essential oils and such, thymol or lemongrass oil in syrup is an effective treatment. But keep in mind that these will kill many of the beneficial microbes in the hive as well.

Symptoms are a swollen white gut (if you disassemble a bee) and dysentery. Don't rely simply on dysentery. All confined bees get dysentery. Sometimes bees get into rotting fruit or other things that give them dysentery but it may not be Nosema. The only accurate diagnosis is to find the Nosema organism under a microscope.

If you want to get a grasp of how necessary (or not) it is to give preventative treatments for Nosema, I will point out a few things that may help clarify this for you. First, realize that many beekeepers have never treated for it, including me. Not only are there many beekeepers who don't want to put antibiotics in their hives, but in fact many beekeepers in the world are prohibited from using Fumidil by law. I am certainly not the only person who thinks it's a bad idea to put Fumidil in your hive. The European Union has banned its use in beekeeping. So we know they aren't using it legally anyway. Their reason? It is suspected of causing birth defects. Fumagilin can block blood vessel formation by binding to an enzyme called methionine aminopeptidase. Targeted gene disruption of methionine aminopeptidase 2 results in an embryonic gastrulation defect and endothelial cell growth arrest. What do they use for treatment in the EU? Thymol syrup.

**So why would you want to avoid Fumidil?**

Just how dangerous is Fumidil to your hive? It's hard to say exactly, but of all the chemicals people put in hives, it's probably one of the least dangerous. It does break down quickly. It doesn't appear to have a lot of downsides on the surface anyway. But if you're of the Organic kind of philosophy you're still thinking, why do I want to add antibiotics to my hive? I certainly don't want it in my honey and, in my view; anything that goes in the hive can end up in the honey. Bees move things all the time. Every book I've seen on comb honey talks about the bees moving honey from the brood chamber up to the comb honey supers during a cut-down split. Having an area of the hive that is the only part there when chemicals are applied is a nice idea, but it's a lot like a no-peeing section in a swimming pool.

**Microbial Balance**

What do antibiotics do to the natural balance of a natural system? Experience with antibiotics would say that they upset the natural flora of any system. They kill off a lot of things that perhaps should be there along with what shouldn't leaving a vacuum to be filled by whatever can flourish. Probiotics have become a big thing in people and horses and other animals now, mostly because we use antibiotics all the time and upset the normal flora of our digestive system. Are there beneficial microorganisms living in bees and beehives? Are they affected by Fumidil? Yes, it's unscientific of me to assume there are without some study to support it, but my experience says all natural systems are very complex all the way down to the microscopic level. I don't want to risk upsetting that balance.

Then there is the reason that it is outlawed in most of the world, which is that it causes a very specific birth defect in mammals.

### Propping up weak bees

Yes, those with the Scientific philosophy will find that statement offensive. But I know of no better way to say it. Creating a system of keeping bees that is held together by antibiotics and pesticides; that perpetuate bees that cannot live without constant intervention; is, in my organic view of beekeeping, counterproductive. We just continue to breed bees who can't live without us. Perhaps some people get some satisfaction of being needed by their bees. I don't know. But I would prefer to have bees who can and do take care of themselves.

What other non-organic practices may contribute to Nosema?

### Encouraging Nosema?

While the non-organic group tends to want to believe that feeding sugar instead of leaving honey will prevent Nosema, I have seen no evidence of this. Honey may have more solids and may cause more dysentery, but while dysentery is a symptom of Nosema, it is neither the cause nor is it evidence of Nosema. In other words, just because they have dysentery does not mean they have Nosema.

Many of the honey bee's enemies, such as Nosema, chalkbrood, EFB, and Varroa all thrive and reproduce better at the pH of sugar syrup and don't reproduce well at the pH of honey. This, however, seems to be universally ignored in the beekeeping world. The prevailing theory on how oxalic acid trickling works is that the bee's hemolymph becomes too acidic for the Varroa and they die, while the bees do not. So how is it helpful to feed the bees something that has a pH in the range that most of their enemies, including Nosema, thrive, rather than leave them honey that is in the pH range where most of their enemies fail?

### Bottom Line

The bottom line is this. You have to make up your mind what your risks are. What you are willing to put in your hives and therefore into your honey. How you want to keep bees. How much you trust a natural system or how much you want to strive for "better living through chemistry."

## Stonebrood

This is caused by a number of fungi including Aspergillus fumigatus and Aspergillus flavus. Extracts from this fungus are used to make Fumagilin used to treat Nosema. Larvae and pupae are susceptible. It causes mummification of the affected brood. Mummies are hard and solid, not sponge-like as with chalkbrood.

Infected brood become covered with a powdery green growth of fungal spores. The majority of spores are found near the head of the affected brood. The main cause is too much moisture in the hive. Add some ventilation. Prop open the inner cover or open up the SBB. Treatment is not recommended. It will clear up on its own.

## Chalkbrood

This is caused by a fungus, Ascosphaera apis. It arrived in the US in about 1968. The main causes are too much moisture in the hive, chilled brood and genetics. Add some (but not too much) ventilation. Prop open the inner cover or open up the SBB. If you find white pellets in front of the hive that kind of look like small corn kernels, you probably have chalkbrood. Putting the hive in full sun and adding more ventilation usually clears this up. Honey instead of syrup may contribute to clearing this up, since sugar syrup is much more alkaline (higher pH) than honey.

> ***"Lower pH values (equivalent to those found in honey, pollen, and brood food) drastically reduced enlargement and germ-tube production. Ascosphaera apis appears to be a pathogen highly specialized for life in honeybee larvae."—Author. Dept. Biological Sci., Plymouth Polytechnic, Drake Circus, Plymouth PL4 8AA, Devon, UK. Library code: Bb. Language: En. Apicultural Abstracts from IBRA: 4101024***

*Chalkbrood*

Hygienic queens will also contribute to clearing this up. Hygienic bees will remove larvae before they fungus has created spores. The upside of chalkbrood is it prevents EFB.

**European Foulbrood (EFB)**

Caused by a bacteria. It used to be called Streptococcus pluton but has now been renamed Melissococcus pluton. European foulbrood is a brood disease. With EFB the larvae turn brown and their trachea is even darker brown. Don't confuse this with larvae being fed dark honey. It's not just the food that is brown. Look for the trachea. When it's worse, the brood will be dead and maybe black and maybe sunk cappings, but usually the brood dies before they are capped. The cappings in the brood nest will be scattered, not solid, because they have been removing the dead larvae. To differentiate this from AFB use a stick and poke a diseased larvae and pull it out. The AFB will "string" two or three inches. This is stress related and removing the stress is best. You could also, as in any brood disease, break the brood cycle by caging the queen or even removing her altogether and let them raise a new one. By the time the new one has hatched, mated and started laying all of the old brood will have emerged or died. If you want to use chemicals, it can be treated with Terramycin. Streptomycin is actually more effective but is not approved by the FDA and the EPA.

### American Foulbrood (AFB)

Caused by a spore forming bacteria. It used to be called Bacillus larvae but has recently been renamed Paenibacillus larvae. With American foulbrood the larvae usually dies after it is capped, but it looks sick before. The brood pattern will be spotty. Cappings will be sunken and sometimes pierced. Recently dead larvae will string when poked with a matchstick. The smell is rotten and distinctive. Older dead larvae turn to a scale that the bees cannot remove.

**Holst milk test:**

*The Hive and The Honey Bee*. "Extensively Revised in 1975" edition. Page 623.

"The Holst milk test: The Holst milk test was designed to identify enzymes produced by B. larvae when speculating (Holst 1946). A scale or toothpick smear is swirled gently into a tube containing 3-4 milliliters of 1 per cent powdered skim milk and incubated at body temperature. If the spores of B. larvae are present, the cloudy suspension will clear in 10-20 minutes. Scales from EFB or sacbrood are negative in this test."

Test kits are available from several of the bee suppliers. Free testing is available at Beltsville Lab (http://www.ars.usda.gov/Services/docs.htm?docid=7473).

AFB is also a stress disease. In some states you are required to burn the hive and bees and all. In some states you are required to shake the bees off into new equipment and burn the old equipment. In some states they will make you remove all the combs and bees, and they will fumigate the equipment in a large tank. Some states just require you to use Terramycin to treat them. Some states if you are treating they will let you continue but if the bee inspector finds it they make you destroy the hives. Many beekeepers treat with Terramycin (sometimes abbreviated TM) for prevention. The problem with this is that it can mask the AFB. The spores of AFB will, for all practical purposes, live forever, so any contaminated equipment will remain so unless fumigated or scorched. Boiling will not kill it. Neither TM nor Tylosin will kill the spores, only the live bacteria. AFB spores are present in *all* beehives. When a hive is under stress is the most likely time for an outbreak. Prevention is best. Try not to let hives get robbed out or run out of stores. Steal stores and bees to shore up weak hives so they don't get stressed. What you are allowed to do if you get AFB varies by state, be sure to obey the laws in your state. Personally, I have never had AFB. I have not treated with TM since 1976. If I had an outbreak I would have to decide what I would do. It may depend on how many hives are affected what I might do, but if I had a small outbreak I would probably shake the bees out into new equipment and burn the old equipment. If I had a large outbreak, I might try breaking the brood cycle and swapping out infected combs. If we as beekeepers keep killing all bees with AFB we will not breed AFB resistant bees. If we as beekeepers keep using Terramycin as a preventative we will continue to spread TM resistant AFB.

> ***"It is well known that improper diet makes one susceptible to disease. Now is it not reasonable to believe that extensive feeding of sugar to bees makes them more susceptible to American Foul Brood and other bee disease? It is known that American Foul Brood is more prevalent in the north than in the south. Why? Is it not because more sugar is fed to bees in the north while here in the south the bees can gather nectar most of the year which makes feeding sugar syrup unnecessary?"—Better Queens, Jay Smith***

## Parafoulbrood

This is caused by Bacillus para-alvei and possibly combinations of other microorganisms and has symptoms similar to EFB. The easiest solution is a break in brood rearing. Cage the queen or remove her and wait for them to raise one. If you put the old queen in a nuc or the old queens in a queen bank, you can reintroduce them if they fail to raise a queen.

## Sacbrood

Caused by a virus usually called SBV (Sacbrood virus). Symptoms are the spotty brood patterns as other brood diseases but the larvae are in a sack with their heads raised. As in any brood disease, breaking the brood cycle may help. It usually goes away in late spring. Requeening sometimes helps also.

**Breaking the brood cycle to help with brood diseases**

For all of the brood diseases this is helpful. Even for Varroa as it will skip a generation of Varroa. To do this you simply have to put the hive in a position that there is no longer any brood. Especially no open brood. If you are planning to requeen anyway, just kill the old queen and wait a week and then destroy any queen cells. Don't go three or they will have raised a new queen. Wait another two weeks and then introduce a new queen (order the appropriate amount ahead of time). If you want to raise your own, just remove the old queen (put her in a cage or put her in a nuc somewhere in case they fail to raise a new one) and let them raise a queen. By the time the new queen is laying there will be no more brood. A hairclip catcher works for a cage. The attendant bees can get in and out and the queen cannot.

**Small Cell and Brood Diseases**

Small cell beekeepers have reported it helping with brood diseases. Especially once the size is down below 4.9mm. We know that once a cell falls below a certain level the bees chew it out and obviously this is many more cocoons in a large cell than a small cell. (See Grout's research on this). I don't know if it helps with brood diseases or not, but my speculation (and it is merely speculation) on this is that because small cells get chewed out before a lot of cocoons build up where 5.4mm cells get filled with generation after generation of cocoons until they are down around the 4.8mm or smaller size before they get chewed out. This leaves many more places for brood pathogens to accumulate.

## Neighbors

Frightened neighbors have been known to spray your hives with Raid, but usually they are too afraid to do that and just use pesticides on their flowers to get rid of bees. If they use Sevin many of your bees can die. "Courageous" neighborhood kids have been known to knock over hives in a show of bravery. Gifts of honey to neighbors and perhaps a good PR strategy help. If someone watches you open a hive with no veil it often belays their fears. But you could have the bad luck to open it on a grouchy day and get stung which only reinforces their fears. I'd wear a veil and no gloves and try not to react if you do get stung. That way they see it's not that big of a deal and the bees are not all trying to kill you.

### *Recent enemies*

Recently new enemies have turned up.

## Varroa Mites

Varroa destructor (previously called Varroa jacobsoni, which is a different variety of the mite that is in Malaysia and Indonesia) is a recent invader of beehives in North America. Varroa mites arrived in the USA in 1987. They are like ticks. They attach to the bees and suck the hemolymph from the adult bees and then get into cells before they are capped and reproduce there during the capped stage of the larvae development. The adult female enters the cell 1 or 2 days before it is capped, being attracted by pheromones given off by the larvae just before capping takes place. The female feeds on the larvae for a while and then starts laying an egg about every 30 hours. The first is a male (haploid) and the rest are females (diploid).

In an enlarged cell (see Chapter *Natural Cell Size* in Volume II) the female may lay up to 7 eggs and since any immature mites will not survive when the bee emerges, from one to two new female mites will probably survive. These will mate, before the bee emerges and emerge with the host bee.

*Varroa*

Varroa mites are large enough you can see them. They are like a freckle on a bee. They are purplish brown in color and oval shaped. If you look at one closely or with a magnifying glass you can usually see the short legs on it. To monitor Varroa infestations you need a screened bottom board (SBB) and a white piece of cardboard. If you don't have a SBB then you need a sticky board. You can buy these or make one with a piece of #8 hardware cloth on a piece of sticky paper. The kind you use to line drawers will work. Put the board under it and wait 24 hours and count the mites. It's better to do this over several days and average the numbers, but if you have a few mites (0 to 20) you aren't in too bad of shape if you have a lot (50 or more) in 24 hours you need to do something or accept the losses.

**Several chemical methods are available.**

I think that the goal should be no treatments. But these are the common ones.

Apistan (fluvalinate) and CheckMite (coumaphos) are the most commonly used acaracides to kill the mites. Both build up in the wax and both cause problems for the bees and contaminate the hive. I don't use them.

Softer chemicals used to control the mites are Thymol, oxalic acid, formic acid and acetic acid. The organic acids already naturally occur in the honey and so are not considered contaminates by some. Thymol is that smell in Listerine and although it occurs in Thyme honey, it doesn't occur otherwise in honey. I have used the oxalic acid and liked it for interim control while regressing to small cell. I used a simple evaporator made of brass pipe. My concerns about all of these are their impact on the beneficial microbes in the hive.

## Inert chemicals for Varroa mites

**FGMO** is a popular one of these. Dr. Pedro Rodriguez, DVM, has been a proponent and researcher on this. His original system was cotton cords with FGMO, beeswax and honey in an emulsion. The object was to keep the FGMO on the bees for a long period of time so the mites either get groomed or they suffocate on the oil. Later a propane insect fogger was used to supplement the cords in this control system. The other up side of the FGMO fog was it apparently kills the tracheal mites also. But this could also be interpreted as a down side because you are possibly perpetuating genetics of bees who can't handle tracheal mites.

**Inert dust.** The most common inert dust used is powdered sugar. The kind you buy in the grocery store. It is dusted on the bees to dislodge the mites. According to research by Nick Aliano, at the University of Nebraska, this method is more effective if you remove the bees from the hive and dust them and then return them. It is also very temperature sensitive. Too cold and the mites don't fall. Too hot and the bees die.

## Physical methods

Some methods are just hive parts or other things. Someone observed that there were less mites on hives with pollen traps and figured maybe the mites fell in the trap. The results were a screened bottom board (usually abbreviated SBB). This is a bottom board on the hive that has a hole covering most of the bottom covered with #7 or #8 hardware cloth. This allows the mites that get groomed off to fall down where they can't get back on the bees. Research shows that this eliminates 30% of the mites. I seriously doubt these numbers but

I do like screened bottom boards for monitoring mites and controlling ventilation and helping with any kind of control you actually do.

**What I do.** I use the small cell/natural cell and I use some screened bottom boards (SBB) and I used to monitor the mites with a white board under the SBB. My plan was as long as the mites stayed under control, and so far, since 2002 they have, that's all I would do. I never needed to do anything else and the mite levels dropped to where they were hard to detect. If the mites were to start going up while the supers are on I would probably remove the drone brood and maybe fog with FGMO or dust with powdered sugar. If they were still high after fall harvest, I might use oxalic acid vapor but I would also plan to requeen. So far I haven't needed any treatment since the bees were regressed. Just small cell has been effective for me for both kinds of mites and adequate under normal conditions.

## More about Varroa

Without getting into the issue of what methods are best, I think it's significant to the success and sometimes subsequent failure of many of the methods we, as beekeepers are trying to use. I used FGMO fog only for two years and when I killed all of the mites withoxalic acid at the end of that two years there was a total mite load of an average of about 200 mites per hive. This is a very low mite count. But some people have observed a sudden increase to thousands and thousands of mites in a short time. Part of this is, of course, all the brood emerging with more mites. But I believe the issue is also that the FGMO (and many other systems as well) manage to create a stable population of mites within the hive. In other words the mites emerging are balanced out by the mites dying. This is the object of many methods. SMR queens are queens that reduce the mites' ability to reproduce. But even if you get to a stable reproduction of mites, this does not preclude thousands of hitchhikers coming in. Using powdered sugar, small cell, FGMO or whatever that gives an edge to the bees by dislodging a proportion of the mites, or preventing the reproduction of mites and seems to work under some conditions. I believe these conditions are where there are not a significant number of mites coming into the hive from other sources.

All of these methods seem to fail sometimes when there is a sudden increase in mites in the fall.

Then there are other methods that are more brute force. In other words they kill virtually all the mites. Even these seem to fail sometimes. We have assumed it's because of resistance, and perhaps this is a contributing factor. But what if sometimes it's again because of this huge influx of mites from outside the hive? Granted having the poison in the hive over a period of time when this explosion of population occurs seems to be helpful, it still sometimes fails.

One explanation for this may be that bees robbing and drifting are causing it.

> ***"The percentage of foragers originating from different colonies within the apiary ranged from 32 to 63 percent"—Boylan-Pett & Hoopingarner,Acta Horticulturae 288, 6th Pollination Symposium, 1991 (see Bee Culture, 36, Jan 2010)***

I have not had this happen on small cell... yet. Nor have I had it happen on FGMO. I have seen it happen when I was using Apistan. But others have observed it with FGMO and I have to wonder how much this affects the success of many methods from Sucracide to SMR queens, from FGMO to Small Cell. It seems like there are at least two components to success. The first is to create a stable system so that the mite population is not increasing within the hive. The second is to find a way to monitor and recover from that occasional sudden influx of mites. Conditions that cause the mites to skyrocket seem to be in the fall when the hives rob out other hives crashing from mites and bring home a lot of hitchhikers while at the same time all the mites that had been in the cells are emerging with no brood to go back into.

### Tracheal Mites

Tracheal mites (Acarapis woodi) are too small to see with the naked eye. This was first called "Isle of Wight disease as this is where it was first observed and the cause, at the time, was not known. Then when they discovered it was a mite, it was called "Acarine disease" since it was the only known malignant mite on honey bees. Symptoms are crawling bees, bees that won't cluster in the winter and "K" wings where the two wings on each side have separated and make a shape like the letter "K". The tracheal mites have been in the US since 1984 that we know of. If you want to check for them you need a microscope. Not a really powerful one, but you still need one as they are too small to see with the naked eye. You're not looking to see the details of a cell, just a creature that is quite small.

Tracheal mites need to get into the trachea to feed and reproduce. The opening to the trachea on an insect is called a spiracle. Bees have several of these and they have a muscular system that allows the bees to totally close them if they want. Since the mites are much larger than the largest spiracle (the first Thoracic spiracle) they have to find young bees whose chitin is still soft so that they can chew out the first Thoracic spiracle enough to gain entry. Once inside, the much more spacious trachea provides the place they live and breed. Tracheal mites must do this while the bees are still 1 to 2 days old before their chitin hardens. A common control for them is a grease patty (sugar and cooking grease mixed to make a patty) because it masks the smell that the tracheal mites use to find a young bee. If they can't find young bees, they can't chew through the spiracle in old bees to get in and so they can't reproduce. Menthol is commonly used to kill the tracheal mites. FGMO and (by some reports) oxalic acid will also kill them. Breeding for resistance and small cell are also useful. The theory on the small cell helping is that the spiracles (the openings into the trachea) that the bees breathe through are smaller and the mites can't get in. But since they are already too small it is more likely that the smaller opening is less attractive to the mites who are looking for a hole they can enlarge enough to get in, or the chitin gets thicker the more you get from the edge and they can't chew it wide enough to gain entry. More research is needed on this subject. But basically, I'm just using small cell and they have not been a problem.

Tracheal mite resistance is not hard to breed for and may explain why small cell beekeepers aren't having any problems. If you never treat and you raise your own queens you'll end up with resistant bees. The mechanism of resistance to tracheal mites is not known. One theory is that they are more hygienic and groom off the tracheal mites before they can get in. Another is that they have either smaller spiracles or tougher spiracles that the mites can't get access through. Another could be similar to the grease patty treatment, in that the younger bees may not give off the odor that triggers the tracheal mites to seek them.

Acarapis dorsalis and A. externus are mites that live on honey bees that are indistinguishable from tracheal mites (A. woodi). They are classified differently simply based on the location where they are found. Leading to the obvious question, are they the same and they are just not able to get into the trachea?

## Small Hive Beetles

Another recent pest that has not been a problem where I am yet, is the small hive beetle (Aethina tumida Murray), or SHB. The larvae eat comb and honey, similar to wax moths, but are more mobile, more in groups and crawl out of the hive and into the ground to pupate. The adult beetles get the bees to feed them but the bees also like to corral them into tight corners. There is some controversy over whether these corners are bad because they give the beetles a place to hide, or good, because it gives the bees a place to corner them

The damage they do is similar to the wax moths but more extensive and they are harder to control. If you smell fermentation in the hive and find masses of crawling, spiky looking larvae in combs you may have SHB. The only chemical controls approved for use are traps made with CheckMite and ground drenches to kill the pupae, which pupate in the ground outside the hive.

While they have been identified in Nebraska, I have not had to deal with these, but I will probably go to more PermaComb in the brood nests if they become too much of a problem. Strong hives seem to be the best protection.

Some people use various traps (some homemade and some commercially available) and some people just ignore them. They seem to thrive on sandy soil and warm weather but can survive even in clay soil and nasty cold winters. How much of a problem they are, and how much effort needs to go into controlling them, seems related to those two main things: clay in the soil and cold in the winter.

## Are treatments necessary?

The standard books out there on beekeeping will come across as if treating is absolutely necessary and that bees would be extinct without human intervention. Just to give you an idea, here is my complete history of treating:

1974 used Terramycin because the books scared me into thinking they would die without.

1975-1999 no treatments whatsoever but lost them all in 1998 and 1999 to Varroa

2000-2001 used Apistan for Varroa. In 2001 they all died from Varroa anyway

2002-2003 used oxalic acid on some of them, FGMO on some, wintergreen oil on some and nothing on some of them also started regressed to small cell.

2004-present no treatments whatsoever

So the only 3 years *all* of my bees were treated for anything were 1974, 2000, 2001.

The only 5 years *any* of my bees were treated for *anything* would add years 2002, 2003

The 35 years (as of this printing) that *none* of my bees were treated for *anything* were: 1975,1976, 1977, 1978, 1979, 1980, 1981, 1982, 1983, 1984, 1985, 1986, 1987, 1988, 1989, 1990, 1991, 1992, 1993, 1994, 1995, 1996, 1997, 1998, 1999, 2004,

2005, 2006, 2007, 2008, 2009, 2010, 2011, 2012, 2013

I look for mites (as does the inspector every year) and I look hard at deadouts to see if they died from Varroa. I see no Varroa problems anymore. I occasionally find a Varroa.

I have never treated for Nosema or purposely treated for tracheal mites (although the wintergreen and the FGMO and the oxalic acid may have affected them)

I have bought some packages from time to time, but I was also expanding from about four hives to 200 and I was selling some small cell nucs at the same time and rearing queens.

# Queen Spotting

### *Do You Really Need to Find Her?*

I will preface this that you don't have to find the queen every time you look in the hive. In fact I have changed my methods to eliminate finding the queen as much as possible because it is so time consuming. If there is open brood then there was a queen at least a few days ago. But there are situations where you really need to find the queen. Requeening being the most likely. So here are a few tips.

### *Use Minimal Smoke*

First, don't smoke them very much, if at all, or the queen will run and there is no telling where she will be.

### *Look for the Most Bees*

The queen is usually on the frame of the brood chamber that has the most bees. This isn't always true, but if you start on that frame and work your way from there you will find her either on that frame or the next 90% of the time.

### *Calm Bees*

The bees are calmer near the queen.

### *Larger and Longer*

Of course the obvious thing is that the queen is larger, and especially that her abdomen is longer, but that isn't always easy to see when there are bees climbing all over her. Look for the larger "shoulders" The width of her back, that little bare patch on the thorax. These are all larger and often you get a peek at them under the other bees. Also the longer abdomen sticking out sometimes when you can't see the rest of her.

***Don't count on her being marked***

Don't count on your marked queen still being there and being marked. Remember they may have swarmed and you didn't catch it or they may have superseded and she may be gone.

***Bees around the queen act differently***

Look at how the bees act around the queen. Often there are several, not all, but several bees facing her. The bees around the queen act different. If you watch them every time you find a queen you'll start noticing how they act, and how they move different around her.

***The Queen Moves Differently***

Other bees are either moving quickly or just hanging and not moving. The workers move like they're listening to Aerosmith. The queen moves like she's listening to Schubert or Brahms. She moves slowly and gracefully. It's like she's waltzing and the workers are doing the bossanova. Next time you spot the queen notice how the bees in general move, how the bees around her move and how she moves.

### ***Different Coloring***

Usually the queen is slightly different color. I have not found this helpful because she's also usually close enough in color that she's still hard to spot by this.

### ***Believe there is a Queen***

Also, mental attitude makes a difference when trying to find anything from your car keys to hunting deer to finding a queen. As long as you are doing cursory looks thinking it won't be there you won't find it. You have to believe that the keys, or the deer or the queen *is* there. That you are looking right at it and you just have to see it. And then suddenly you do. You have to convince yourself that it is there and convince yourself that you will find it. I don't know how to explain it well enough, but you have to learn to think like that.

### ***Practice***

Of course the best solution to learning to find a queen is an observation hive. You can find one every morning when you get up, every evening when you get home, and every night before you go to bed and not disrupt them at all. It still doesn't give you the practice at finding the right frame on the first try or two, but does help you with spotting her. Having the queen marked in the observation hive is nice for showing the queen to visitors, but *not* having her marked works better for practicing finding the queen. Even if you buy all your queens marked you will often be finding an unmarked supersedure queen.

*Can you find her?*

*Here she is.*

*How about this one?*

*Does this help?*

# Fallacies

I'm sure some people believe these and will disagree, but here are some ideas that I consider myths of beekeeping:

***Myth: Drones are bad.***

Drones, of course are normal. A normal healthy hive will have a population in the spring of somewhere around 10-20% drones. The argument for almost a century or more (really just a selling point for foundation) was that drones eat honey, use energy and don't provide anything to the hive, therefore controlling the drone comb and therefore the number of drones will make a hive more productive. All the research I've heard of says the opposite is true. If you try to limit the number of drones your production will decrease. Bees have an instinctive need to make a certain number and fighting that is a waste of effort. Other research I've seen says that you will end up with the same number of drones no matter what you, the beekeeper do anyway.

***Myth: Drone comb is bad.***

This, of course, goes with the first one. The way a beekeeper attempts to control drones is by having less drone comb. But controlling drone comb is exactly the reason you end up with drone comb in your supers and then end up needing an excluder. The bees want a consolidated brood nest, but the lack of drone is more worrisome to them, so if you don't let them do it in the brood nest, they will raise a patch of drones anywhere they can get some drone comb. If you want the bees to stop building drone comb, stop taking it away from them. If you want the queen to not try to lay in the supers, let them have enough drone comb in the brood nest.

***Myth: Queen Cells are bad***

...and the beekeeper should destroy queen cells if they find them.

It seems like most of the books I've read convince beginning beekeepers that queen cells should always be destroyed. The bees are either going to swarm, and you want to stop them, or they are trying to replace that precious store-bought queen with a queen of unknown lineage mated with those awful feral drones. Most of the time when you destroy queen cells the bees swarm anyway, or they already swarmed before you destroyed them, and they not only swarm, but also end up queen-less. I see swarm cells as free queens of the highest quality. I put each frame that has queen cells on it, in its own nuc. Usually I try to leave one with the original hive and the old queen in a nuc. That way I've made a bunch of small splits and left the hive thinking it's swarmed already. With supersedure cells, I leave them because the bees apparently have found the queen wanting and I trust the bees. Destroying a supersedure cell is also likely to leave them queenless. The queen is probably about to fail, or she's already failed or died and you just removed their only hope of a queen.

***Myth: Home grown queens are bad***

...and beekeepers should buy queens because mating with the local bees is bad.

Of course this one goes with the above reasons given for why supersedures are bad. I think mating with the local bees is the preferred method. You get bees that are surviving in your area. I do know a lot of people who buy queens all the time because of this fallacy. The supersedure rate has grown over the years to the point that a typical introduced queen is almost instantly superseded. If that's true (and some of the experts tell me it is) then you'll have a home grown queen anyway, so why waste your money? There is a lot of research on how much better the quality of a queen is if you let her continue to lay from when she starts instead of banking her right after she starts laying. When you buy a commercial queen, you get one that was banked right after she started to lay. I have serious doubts that you can buy a better queen than you can raise yourself, especially if you have clean wax; and most especially if you've been collecting swarms from bees that live in your climate.

***Myth: Feral bees are bad***

...unproductive, swarmy and of bad disposition.

I've heard this often repeated—this or other disreputable things. Feral bees probably were at one time but lately have not been, bred for disposition. I've removed and caught many. Some are mean. Some are quite nice. Some are nervous, but not mean. Some are calm. These traits I have found easy to find in feral bees and easy to breed for. Just keep the good ones and requeen the bad ones. From my experience they are often more productive because they are more attuned to your climate and build up at the appropriate time to make a good crop. As far as "swarmy" I think all bees are swarmy. It's how they reproduce. I have not had any problems controlling swarming in any kind of bees.

***Myth: Feral swarms are disease ridden***

...and should either be left, killed or treated immediately by the beekeeper for every known disease.

I don't understand the concept. A healthy productive hive throws swarms. So the logical conclusion would be that they are healthy and productive.

***Myth: Feeding can't hurt anything***

I hear this one a lot. But I think feeding *can* hurt a lot. Feeding is one of the leading causes of problems. It attracts pests like ants, it sets off robbing, it often drowns a large number of bees, and worst, it often results in a nectar bound brood nest and swarming. If the hive is light in the fall, the beekeeper should feed. If the bees are starving, feed. If you're installing a new package or a swarm, feed until they get some capped stores. But once they have a little stored and there's a flow, let them do what bees do—gather nectar. A good rule of thumb is that they should have at least some capped comb and a flow before you stop feeding.

***Myth: Adding supers will prevent swarming.***

This is a common myth in beekeeping. It works after the reproductive swarm season is over, but the prime swarm season has little to do with supers. It has everything to do with the bees' plan to reproduce. If you want to head off a swarm the crux of the matter is you have to keep the brood nest open. Part of that plan is to put on supers before they backfill the brood nest but that alone cannot be relied on to stop them from swarming.

***Myth: Destroying queen cells will prevent swarming.***

In my experience this does not work. They will swarm anyway and end up queenless.

***Myth: Swarm cells are always on the bottom.***

The other part of this, I guess is that supersedure cells are always in the middle. This may be a good generality, but you need to look at the entire context of the situation. I would assume that queen cells on the bottom were swarm cells if the hive is building up quickly and is either very strong or very crowded. On the other hand if they are not strong or crowded and building, then I would assume they are not swarm cells. If the cells are more in the middle and conditions otherwise would cause me to expect swarm cells, then I would tend to view these as swarm cells. If the hive were not building and not crowded I would assume they are supersedure cells or emergency cells. Also swarm cells tend to be more numerous.

***Myth: Clipping the queen will prevent swarming.***

In my experience they will still swarm. It may buy you some time if you're paying attention (like the hives are in your back yard and you check every day for swarms). They will attempt to swarm and the clipped queen won't be able to fly. They will go back and then they will leave with the first virgin swarm queen to emerge. Counting on clipping to stop them from swarming will end in failure.

***Myth: 2 Feet or 2 miles***

...you have to move hives two feet or two miles or you will lose a lot of bees.

I hear this one a lot. Anytime you move bees there will be some chaos for at least one day, but I move bees all the time fifty, a hundred yards or more. The trick is to put a branch in front of the entrance to trigger reorientation. If you do this it works well. If you don't do this most of the field bees will go back to the old location. That and accept that there will be some confusion for a while, so don't move them if you don't have a reason.

***Myth: You have to extract***

...or that it's somehow cruel to the bees to not extract.

The beginner beekeepers all seem to think they have to buy an extractor. It's not their fault. It's what the books all say, right? You don't. I had bees for 26 years without one. You can make cut comb or crush and strain with little investment and no more work than extracting.

***Myth: 16 pounds of honey = 1 pound of wax.***

This is an old one that is still sold to beekeepers at various numbers. I know of no study to support it. And it's irrelevant. What is relevant is how productive a hive is with and without drawn comb. There is no doubt they will make more honey with drawn comb. But it would take a lot of hives before it would be worth buying an extractor. This concept is also used to sell foundation. In my experience the bees will draw comb faster without foundation than with it and the faster they have somewhere to store the nectar the more honey they make.

***Myth: You can't raise honey and bees***

...in other words, make splits and get production.

It's all in the timing. If you do the split right before the flow and let all the field bees drift back to the original hive you can actually get more honey and more bees.

***Myth: Two queens can't coexist in the same hive.***

People purposely set up two queen hives all the time. But if you look carefully you'll often find two queens naturally in a hive. Usually a mother daughter, where the supersedure queen is laying and the old queen is laying right beside her.

***Myth: Queens will never lay double eggs***

...in other words, all multiple eggs are a sign of a laying worker.

I've often seen double eggs from a queen. Rarely I've seen triples. I've seldom seen more than triples. Laying workers will lay from two to dozens in one cell. I look for more than two and eggs on the sides of the cells and not in the bottom. Also eggs on pollen. These I consider signs of laying workers.

***Myth: If there is no brood there is no queen.***

There are many reasons you might find a hive with no brood even though there is a queen. First, in my climate at least, from October to April there may or may not be brood because they stop in October and then raise little batches of brood with broodless periods in between. Second, some frugal bees will shut down brood rearing in a dearth. Third, a hive that has lost a queen and raised an emergency queen often is broodless because by the time the new queen has emerged, hardened, mated and started to lay 25 or more days have passed and *all* the brood has emerged. Fourth a hive can swarm and the new queen isn't laying yet. She won't be laying for probably at least three weeks after the hive swarmed. Many a beginner (or even a veteran) beekeeper has found a hive in this state, ordered a queen, introduced her and had her killed, ordered another queen, introduced her and had her killed and finally noticed there were eggs. Unmarked virgin queens are very hard to find even by the most experienced beekeeper. A frame of eggs and brood would have been a better insurance policy. That way *if* the hive is queenless they can raise one, and if they aren't it won't hurt anything and you'll know the answer to the question. See the section *Panacea* in the Chapter *BLUF.*

***Myth: Bees only like to work up***

...in other words they expand the hive and the brood only in an upward direction and not downwards.

If you install a package in a stack of five boxes, as I have done on occasion, you can easily disprove this. But then if you think about a swarm in a tree you already know this isn't true. The bees cluster at the top of whatever space there is and build comb down until they fill the void or reach a size they are satisfied with.

Bees start at the top of whatever space they have and work down. In a tree there is no other choice as there is no way to work up. Once a hive is established they move towards any space they can fill. So in the case of a tree if they have reached the bottom the brood nest will work its way into whatever space is available when it expands and then contract back when the season is over. In the case of a hive, however, beekeepers keep adding and removing boxes. We add them to the top because it's convenient to add them there and convenient to check on them there. The bees don't care. They work into where there is space available.

***Myth: A laying worker hive has one pseudo queen***

...and you are trying to get rid of her to fix the problem.

A laying worker hive has many laying workers. The only way to fix the problem is get them so disrupted they will accept a queen or give them enough pheromones from open worker brood to suppress the laying workers enough to get them to accept a queen. In other words, give them a frame of open brood every week until they start to rear a queen. Then you can either let them finish or introduce a queen.

***Myth: Shaking out a laying worker hive works***

...because the laying worker gets left behind because she doesn't know her way home.

I have not found this to be true and the research I've read says it's not true. There are many laying workers and they will have no trouble finding their way back. Shaking out a hive only works sometimes because you have disheartened them enough that in the chaos they will sometimes accept a queen.

***Myth: Bees need a landing board.***

Obviously they don't have one in most natural situations, so this is not a rational statement. I not only don't think they need one, I think they just help mice and skunks and do no favors to the bees.

***Myth: Bees need a lot of ventilation.***

Bees do need ventilation. But what they need is the right amount of ventilation. Of course in the winter, too much ventilation means too much heat loss. But even in the summer the bees are cooling the hive by evaporation, so on a hot day the inside of the hive may be cooler than the outside air. So too much ventilation could result in the bees being unable to maintain a cooler temperature inside. When wax heats up past the normal operating temperatures of a hive (> 93º F or 34º C) it gets very weak and combs can collapse.

***Myth: Bees need beekeepers.***

Actually bees need beekeepers like "fish need bicycles." Depending on your view of the world, bees have been surviving for millions of years on their own or at least since the creation. Its true beekeepers have spread them all over the world, but bees would have gotten there anyway eventually. How did African bees recently get to Florida? They were hitchhikers.

***Myth: You have to requeen yearly.***

I know many beekeepers who only requeen if they see a problem. Usually before you see a problem the bees have already superseded the problem queen. If they have, you have perpetuated genetics that know how to do this. If you have clean wax (no chemicals in the hive) your queens usually last about three years. If you don't have clean wax, your queens usually only last a few months. Either way, how does requeening yearly help? The most common claim is that a first year queen won't swarm, which is easily disproven by feeding a package incessantly, or that a second year queen is bound to swarm, which is easily disproven by the fact that most of my queens are three years old.

***Myth: A marginal colony should always be requeened.***

I've seen a lot of struggling colonies take off and make a good crop. They are often struggling because the population dwindled to the point that there weren't enough workers to forage and care for brood. Quite often a frame of emerging brood will snap them right out of this. On the other hand *some* colonies do just languish when they should have caught up. These I would requeen.

***Myth: You need to feed pollen substitute***

...to packages and to bees in the spring and fall.

I have never had luck getting bees to even take pollen once fresh pollen is available. I see no reason to feed a package pollen substitute when it is vastly inferior nutrition to real pollen that is readily available that time of year. Feeding real pollen early in the spring sometimes seems to be an effective way to stimulate buildup. Sometimes it seems to make no difference.

***Myth: You should feed syrup in the winter.***

I suppose your climate is directly related to this, but you can't get bees to take syrup in the winter here in Nebraska and if you could, I'm not sure it would be good for them to have all that humidity to deal with. Dry sugar they can take no matter how cold it is, but syrup they can only take if the syrup is above 50º F. Not a likely occurrence here even if the daytime temps got up to that, the syrup would have a time delay making it up to that temperature.

***Myth: You can't mix plastic and wax.***

This is not so much a myth as an over simplification. Putting undrawn plastic in with undrawn wax is like putting a piece of cherry pie and a bowl of broccoli in front of your kids at the same time. If you want them to eat the broccoli, you should wait to put out the cherry pie.

If you mix wax and plastic foundation, the bees will jump on the wax and ignore the plastic. If you put in all plastic they will use it when they need comb.

There is no great impending disaster if you mix them. They just have their preferences and if you want them to follow *your* preferences you should limit their choices.

Once it is drawn comb or comb that is being used, you can mix it freely with everything with no problems.

***Myth: Dead bees headfirst in cells have starved.***

This is a commonly held belief. All dead hives over winter will have many bees with their heads in cells. That's how they cluster tightly for warmth. I would read more into whether or not they are on contact with stores.

# Realistic Expectations

> ***"Blessed is the man who expects nothing, for he shall never be disappointed"—Alexander Pope***

I think it's important in every aspect of beekeeping to have realistic expectations. Not to say that those may not be exceeded at times, but also at times they will not be met as both failure and success are dependent on many related variables.

As examples, let's consider some of the variable outcomes.

### *Honey Crop*

Typically people tell beginner beekeepers not to expect a honey crop the first year. This is an attempt to set realistic expectations. However a good package with a good queen in a good year (appropriate amounts of well timed rainfall and flying weather) may far exceed this or may not even get well established. But generally it's a realistic expectation for the beekeeper that they should get established enough to get through the winter and maybe make a little honey.

### *Plastic Foundation*

People buy plastic foundation (and other plastic beekeeping equipment such as Honey Super Cell fully drawn comb) and sometimes are very disappointed. The bees typically will hesitate to draw the plastic (or use the Honey Super Cell) and this sets them back a bit. Sometimes the bees will draw a comb between two plastic foundations in order to avoid using it. Sometimes they will build "fins" out from the face of the foundation. None of these are unusual, but they also often draw it pretty well. How well they do depends on a combination of genetics and nectar flow. Many people seeing the hesitation decide never to use plastic again. But actually once the bees use it, comb on plastic foundation or even fully drawn plastic comb is used just like any other comb. The delay at first seems like a big setback, and for a package, perhaps it is, but once you get past it there is no problem getting it used after that.

### *Wax Foundation*

People use wax foundation and often it gets hot and buckles, or the bees chew it all up or the bees don't want to draw it and they drawn fins or combs between. They do this less with than with plastic, but still sometimes they do. The buckled foundation often gets comb built on it and the comb is a mess. Many people after an experience like this say they will never use wax foundation again. But really that's just how the circumstances went. If you put it in on a good flow the bees would not have chewed it and it would have been drawn before it buckled. My point is that people often have unrealistic expectations and when those are not realized, they are disappointed in the method when it was other circumstances that led to the problems.

### *Foundationless*

Some people use foundationless frames. Many have perfect luck with it but some will have bees that just don't get the concept and build some crossways comb. Since this happens just as often in plastic foundation, and wax foundation that has collapsed or fallen out etc. it would not seem that significant to me, but if the only experience you have is with the foundationless, you may assume that other methods don't have these problems. But they do. Again, genetics and timing of the flow have a lot to do with success or failure.

The most important concept to grasp with any natural comb hive is that because bees build parallel combs, one good comb leads to another in the same way that one bad comb leads to another. You cannot afford to not be paying attention to how they start off. The most common cause of a mess of comb is leaving the queen cage in as they always start the first comb from that and then the mess begins. I can't believe how many people want to "play it safe" and hang the queen cage. They obviously can't grasp that it is almost a guarantee of failure to get the first comb started right, which without intervention is guaranteed to mean every comb in the hive will be messed up. Once you have a mess the most important thing is to make sure the *last* comb is straight as this is always the guide for the *next* comb. You can't take a "hopeful" view that the bees will get back on track. They will not. You have to put them back on track.

This has nothing to do with wires or no wires. Nothing to do with frames or no frames. It has to do with the last comb being straight.

***Losses***

New beekeepers often assume that every hive should live forever and every hive should make it through the winter. Some winters, they do. But most winters kill off at least a few of the hives. Obviously the more hives you have the more this happens. I went years without losing a hive, but I only had a few and I always combined any that were borderline on strength and those were the days before tracheal mites, Varroa mites, Nosema ceranae, small hive beetle, and a host of viruses we now have. Now I have around two hundred hives and try to overwinter a lot of nucs, of marginal strength and there are those many new diseases and pests to stress them out. No winter losses are an unrealistic expectation. But high winter losses are a sign that you must be doing something wrong or the weather did something very quirky.

I always try to figure out the cause of winter losses. Often it is starvation from getting stuck on brood. Sometimes with nucs or small clusters it's a hard cold snap (-10 to -30 F) and the cluster just wasn't big enough to keep warm. I always look for dead Varroa Finding thousands of dead Varroa in the dead bees is a good indication that the Varroa were the primary cause of their death. A lack of such evidence is probably good evidence that it was something else.

Again, the point is that sometimes wintering exceeds or falls below even realistic expectations. But it's helpful to start with realistic expectations and work from there. Realistic expectations from healthy hives as far as losses are probably in the 10% range with some years worse and some years better.

### ***Splits***

One of the common questions I hear from new beekeepers is "how many splits can I make?" Of course the answer to this is probably the most variable of any except, perhaps, "how much honey will my hive make?" The difference between a good year and a bad year in beekeeping varies far more than 10 fold. I've had years where I got 200 pounds of honey from every hive and years where I harvested nothing and fed 60 pounds of sugar (between spring and fall) to every hive. Splits are similar. Some hives can't be split at all. Some can be split five times in a year. Most can only take one split and still make a decent crop of honey and be well stocked for winter.

The point of all of this is that results in beekeeping vary dramatically based on what is happening around the bees as well as things like the time of year, the way they are cared for and so on. It's very difficult to predict what the outcomes will actually be, so there is no point in having too high or low of expectations. Take things as they come and adjust. Be prepared for both exceptional success and failure and adjust as you go.

# Harvest

Beginners are often convinced they must have an extractor. There are many other options that make more sense. One would be comb honey.

***Comb Honey***

Normally I'm not shy about saying things my own way, but Richard Taylor said this so well, I will not even attempt to do better. For more of his wisdom check out his books including *The How-To-Do-It Book of Beekeeping*, *The Joy of Beekeeping* and *The Comb Honey Book*.

Richard Taylor on comb honey and extractors:

> ***"...time after time I have seen novice beekeepers, as soon as they had built their apiaries up to a half dozen or so hives, begin to look around for an extractor. It is as if one were to establish a small garden by the kitchen door, and then at once begin looking for a tractor to till it with. Unless then, you have, or plan eventually to have, perhaps fifty or more colonies of bees, you should try to resist looking in bee catalogs at the extractors and other enchanting and tempting tools that are offered and instead look with renewed fondness at your little pocket knife, so symbolic of the simplicity that is the mark of every truly good life."***

***Expense of making wax***

Richard Taylor on the expense of making wax:

> ***"The opinion of experts once was that the production of beeswax in a colony required great quantities of nectar which, since it was turned into wax, would never be turned into honey. Until quite recently it was thought that bees could store seven pounds of honey for every pound of beeswax that they needed to manufacture for the construction of their combs—a figure which seems never to have been given any scientific basis, and which is in any case quite certainly wrong."***

---

From *Beeswax Production, Harvesting, Processing and Products*, Coggshall and Morse pg 35

> ***"Their degree of efficiency in wax production, that is how many pounds of honey or sugar syrup are required to produce one pound of wax, is not clear. It is difficult to demonstrate this experimentally because so many variables exist. The experiment most frequently cited is that by Whitcomb (1946). He fed four colonies a thin, dark, strong honey that he called unmarketable. The only fault that might be found with the test was***

> ***that the bees had free flight, which was probably necessary so they could void fecal matter; it was stated that no honey flow was in progress. The production of a pound of beeswax required a mean of 8.4 pounds of honey (range 6.66 to 8.80). Whitcomb found a tendency for wax production to become more efficient as time progressed. This also emphasizes that a project intended to determine the ratio of sugar to wax, or one designed to produce wax from a cheap source of sugar, requires time for wax glands to develop and perhaps for bees to fall into the routine of both wax secretion and comb production."***

---

The problem with most of the estimates on what it takes to make a pound of wax is they don't take into account how much honey that pound of wax will support

From *Beeswax Production, Harvesting, Processing and Products*, Coggshall and Morse pg 41

> ***"A pound of beeswax, when made into comb, will hold 22 pounds of honey. In an unsupported comb the stress on the topmost cells is the greatest; a comb one foot (30 cm.) deep supports 1,320 times its own weight in honey."***

---

### *Crush and Strain*

I kept bees for 26 years without an extractor. I made cut comb honey and I did crush and strain to get liquid honey. When I finally did buy one I got a motorized radial 9/18 (holds 9 deeps or 18 mediums).

The method I arrived at to crush and strain is a double bucket strainer. I use these even when I'm extracting because they hold so much honey and it's the only way I can keep up with straining as I go.

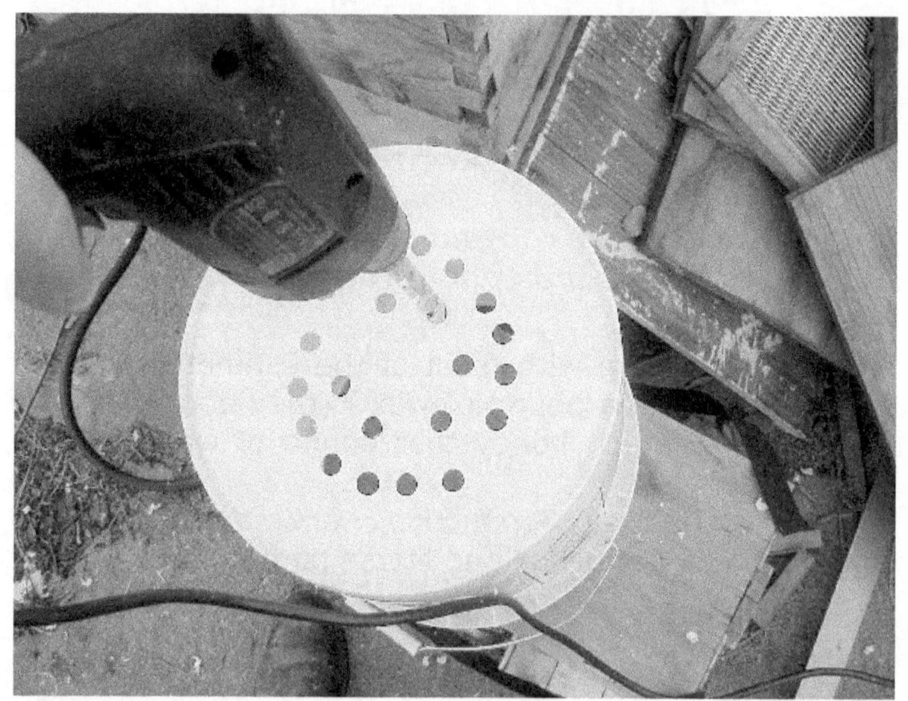

*Making the top bucket for the double bucket strainer. Drill the holes. If you make the holes small enough you can just use the bottom of the bucket for the strainer with no other strainer or screen. You can skim the wax off the top and leave whatever settles on the bottom. Cut the middle out of a lid (leaving an inch rim for the top bucket to rest on).*

*Using the double bucket strainer to strain honey.*

***Extracting***

Extracting is a process where the caps are cut off of the combs and they are spun in a centrifuge called an extractor.

*Cutting cappings off.*

*Cutting low spots.*

*Loading the extractor*

*Extracting.*

Removing bees for harvesting

This is always a topic rife with disagreement. A lot of this is due to personal experience. Timing of these methods changes the outcomes tremendously.

### Abandonment

C.C. Miller's favorite method is usually called "abandonment". This is where you pull each box off the hive and set it on its end so the top and bottom are exposed. This is best done at the end of the flow but not during a dearth and just after sunset but before dark. The bees tend to wander back to the hive and you can take the supers. If there is brood in them, they will not leave. If there is a dearth you will set off a robbing frenzy. If you do it in the middle of the afternoon this will be harder to deal with. This requires handling the boxes twice. Once to take them off and once to load them up. (I'm not counting the rest of the process)

### Brushing and/or shaking

Some people just pull each frame, shake or brush off the bees and put the frame in a different box with a cover. This puts many bees in the air and is a bit intimidating and is tedious. You move every box a frame at a time and then you load the boxes a box at a time.

### Bee Escapes

There are several kinds and the results may vary based on the kind. I never had any luck with the Porter escapes that go in the hole on the inner cover. But I have liked the triangular ones from Brushy Mountain Usually the supers are removed, the escape is put on (it's one way so be sure it's the right way, letting the bees out, but not in) and you wait a day or two for the bees to leave. Again, they will not leave if there is brood in the supers. I prefer to put one of these on a bottom board (with the escape down) and stack supers up about as high as I can reach them and then put one on top (with the escape up) and leave them overnight. If you live in SHB territory, I would not leave them longer. The biggest disadvantage is you have to handle every box three times if you put it on the hive (once to get them off, then put on the escape, then stack them back on the hive, then load them up) and twice if you put it on its own bottom board (once to stack them on the bottom board and once to load them up).

**Blowing**

The concept is to just blow all the bees off the combs. Some people use a leaf blower and some buy a bee blower. One argument against is that anything strong enough to blow the bees off will rip many of them in half. I've never used it so I can't say.

**Butyric**

I listed this separate from Bee Quick although they have some things in common, I don't consider them even in the same ballpark. Both are bee repellents that are used to drive the bees from the supers. Bee Go and Honey Robber are Butyric which is not a food safe chemical and smells like vomit. Honey robber smells like cherry flavored vomit. The chemical is put on a fume board, which is put on top of the hive. The bees are driven down and the supers are pulled off and loaded. They are only handled once. I have smelled it. I have never used it.

### Fischer Bee Quick

Jim Fischer doesn't want to give away his trade secrets so he won't say what's in this. But it smells like benzaldehyde to me. Benzaldehyde is the smell of Maraschino cherries or almond extract. After making benzaldehyde in my organic chemistry class, I've never been able to eat a Maraschino cherry again. It's also the main ingredient in artificial almond flavoring. But Jim Fischer assures us this is nothing but food grade essential oils. It certainly smells better and, by all accounts, is much safer than butyric. Otherwise it works on the same principle. You put it on a fume board on top and drive the bees down. The supers only have to be handled once to load them. I have smelled it and it smells fine, but I have never used it.

# Frequently Asked Questions

As a moderator and participant on various bee forums, I hear these questions often, so I thought I would address some of them here.

---

***Can queens sting?***

I've been handling queens off and on since 1974. Since I started rearing queens in 2004 I've been handling hundreds of them a year. I've never been stung by a queen. I have seen them go through the motions though.

Jay Smith, a beekeeper who reared thousands of queens a year for decades, said he was only stung by one once and he said she stung him right where he had squished a queen earlier and he thought she thought it was a queen.

Can they? Yes. Will they? Extremely doubtful. The few people who I've met who say they've been stung by a queen say it didn't hurt as bad as a worker.

***What if my queen flies off?***

This often comes with other questions like, she flew off what are the odds she came back. First let's look at what to do. If the queen flies, the first thing you do is stand still. She will orient on you and probably find her way back. The second thing to do is encourage the bees to guide her back with Nasonov pheromone. To do this, take a frame out that is covered in bees and shake them back into the hive. This will cause them to start fanning Nasonov. Third, if you don't see the queen fly back in (be watching and you may) then wait ten minutes with the cover of the hive off so she can smell the Nasonov. If you do these three things the odds are very good she will find her way back.

If you didn't do those things, there is probably a little better than 50/50 chance she will find her way back anyway.

How do you avoid her flying? Keep a close eye when you're popping the cork. Queens are fast. If you put the cage on top of the pile of bees you just dumped in the hive, she and that is down in the hive and you are bent over the top of the hive, then she is less likely to fly up.

***Dead bees in front of the hive?***

With the queen laying 1,000 to 3,000 eggs a day and bees living about six weeks, there are *always* some dead bees in front of the hive. Often you don't see them because they are in the weeds or grass. A *lot* of dead bees (piles of them) might be cause for concern because it may be a sign of pesticide poisoning or some other problem. But some are normal.

***Frame spacing in supers and brood nests?***

This question seems to come up a lot. The question is usually something like "should I put 9 or 10 frames in my supers?" or "should I put 9 or 10 frames in my brood boxes?"

My answer for the brood boxes is that I put 11 in. At least in a ten frame box. I shave the ends down in order to do this and I do it because it's the spacing the bees use if you let them. But 10 will do. They should be tightly together in the center, and not spaced out evenly. They are already further apart than the bees would prefer and spacing them any further usually results in burr comb or even an extra comb in between the frames. The theory of doing 9 in the brood box is that there will be more cluster space, less swarming and less rolling of bees. The reality, in my experience, is that it requires more bees to keep the brood warm, the surface of the combs is more irregular and this causes more rolling of the bees when removing frames. This irregularity is due to the fact that honey storage comb can vary in thickness but brood comb is always the same thickness. The results are that where they have honey and you have 9 frames, they have extra room to fill and they fill it with honey. If they have brood then they are not as fat as when they have honey in them. I tried 9 frames in the brood nest and was not impressed. I now have eight frame boxes and I have 9 frames in them (which requires shaving the end bars down). At 11 in a ten-frame box you get very flat consistent comb and you get smaller cell size more easily.

My answer for the supers is that *once they are drawn* you can put 9 or even 8 in the ten frame supers with good effect as the combs will just be thicker. But when it's bare foundation, the bees will often mess up the comb if you space it more than ten. Ten frames of bare foundation should always be tightly together in the middle of either a super or a brood box in order to prevent the bees from attempting to build a comb between the foundations instead of on them. With eight frame boxes you can do seven drawn combs or even six.

A related issue is messed up combs.

***Why do the bees mess up the combs?***

Some of this is genetics. Some bees build straight parallel combs no matter what you do. Some will burr things up every which way no matter what you do. But there are things you can do to stack the deck.

Some of it is giving them the freedom to mess it up. Push all the frames tightly together. Those spacers on the frames are there for a reason. Use them. Do not space the frames evenly in the box. When you have undrawn foundation, do *not* space less frames in a box. Bees, if they don't like your foundation (and they never do really) and if you give them the room (by spacing the combs more than $1^3/_8$" apart) will try to build a comb between two frames rather than build it on your foundation. So pushing it together makes the space between the foundations small enough to discourage this, as it's not enough room for a brood comb.

Some of it is that they don't like you deciding their cell sizes. They will build their own comb with much more enthusiasm than they will build foundation. So they try to avoid building on the foundation. One solution is to stop using foundation and go foundation-less. Another is to get foundation that is closer to what they wanted to build. 5.4mm standard foundation is much larger than typical natural worker brood comb. 4.9mm is closer.

They usually don't like plastic much. The solution to getting them to draw it is to give it to them when they need to draw comb. Don't give them wax foundation mixed with plastic foundation or they will ignore the plastic and draw the wax. Buy the wax coated plastic so they will accept it better. Spray some syrup on it or syrup with essential oils like Honey Bee Healthy, to cover the smell of the plastic. Once they've licked it clean they tend to accept it better.

Sometimes they will still mess it up.

***How do I clean up used equipment?***

Used equipment has been a controversial subject for more than a century. AFB (American foulbrood is still an issue but used to be an even bigger issue. The only real concern about used equipment is AFB. AFB spores live virtually forever (longer than us anyway) and infected equipment is probably one of the contributing factors to getting AFB. Many people with AFB just burn the equipment. Some scorch it. Some boil it in lye. Some "fry" it in paraffin and gum rosin.

So the issue usually is that you have at your disposal (either free or cheap) used equipment. Cleaning up from mice isn't too complicated. Just leave it out in the rain until it smells ok. Cleaning up from wax moths is just cutting out the webs (which are hard for the bees to remove) and scraping off the cocoons. If combs are dry and brittle, let the bees fix them, they will be fine. If they are dusty, the bees will clean them up. The real risk is AFB. If you have old brood comb, I would look for scale in the bottom of the cells which would indicate AFB. If there is scale, you'll have to take the threat of AFB pretty serious. Some would just burn at that point. So, assuming you find no scale then what do you do? I can't tell you what to do as it is always a risk and if you get AFB I don't want you blaming me. But I'll tell you what I do. I've always gotten mine from sources I believed to be honest, usually very cheap or free and just used the equipment with nothing done to it. I've never gotten AFB in my hives.

Now that I'm dipping my equipment, I would dip any used equipment, since I have the wherewithal.

***How do I prepare the hive for winter?***

More detail on this in Volume 2 *Wintering Bees* Chapter

The problem with answering this question is that it will depend on your location. There is a big difference in the issues faced by a beekeeper in South Georgia or Southern California, compared to one in Northern Minnesota or Anchorage Alaska.

So I can only give a generalization and call on my own experience in the middle of the country. I'm in Southeast Nebraska and used to be in Western Nebraska and the front range of the Rockies. So this advice is pretty useful in that range of climates.

Reduce the space. There is no reason to have extra empty space in a hive in the winter in the North. Any box that is empty combs or foundation I would pull off for the winter.

Block the mice. Mice can devastate a hive. Make sure if you have bottom entrances that you have mouse guards on. A piece of #4 hardware cloth works well for this.

Remove excluders. If you use excluders they need to be off before winter sets in. A queen can get stuck on the other side of the excluder and die in cold weather.

Make sure you have some kind of top entrance. I like all top entrances and no bottom entrances, but regardless you need at least a small one for release of moist air so you don't get condensation on the lid and so the bees can get out when the snow is deep or there are too many dead bees on the bottom board. Commonly people ask if the heat won't all escape. Heat is seldom the issue it's the condensation dripping on the bees that usually kills bees in winter.

Make sure they have enough stores. In my part of the country with Italian bees you need the hive to weigh about 150 pounds for good insurance for the winter. They probably will get by on 100 pounds, but they could also burn through that in the spring rearing brood and come up short. Any less than 100 pounds would worry me a lot. The time to feed is when the weather is still warm as they won't take syrup after it gets cold. Once you hit the target weight there is no need to feed anymore. Usually a 150 pound hive around here is two deep ten frame boxes, or three medium ten frame boxes or four medium eight frame boxes, mostly full of honey.

I have only wrapped once and was not favorably impressed, but if it's the norm for beekeepers where you live you might want to consider it. The normal wrap is 15# roofing felt as it provides some heat gain on sunny days. I found this sealed in too much moisture. Other wraps are wax impregnated cardboard and one style leaves an airspace around the hive. This seems like a wiser choice for the moisture issue. If I were trying again I'd either use the cardboard with an air-space or tack some one bys on the corners first and then use the felt with that airspace.

Avoid the temptation to think that heating a normal strong hive is helpful. It's really not. Thick insulation is not either. With insulation they won't get warm on a sunny day and do a cleansing flight. Don't move them indoors, they need to fly. Don't pile bales of straw around as it will just attract the mice. A wind break is nice if you can provide one. If you're using straw bales for this, build that wall a ways from the hives.

***How far do foragers fly?***

According to Brother Adam he had bees he knew flew five miles or more to gather heather nectar. According to Huber, he marked workers, took them different distances and released them and looked for them to turn back up at the hive. He said they always found their way back when they were $1^1/_2$ miles from the hive, but past that they didn't. He also says, and it makes sense, that it would depend on the foraging available. It also seems to vary by bee size. Brother Adam says his native Apis mellifera mellifera, which were smaller, flew the five miles to get the Heather, but the Italians he replaced them with, which were larger, would not. Dee Lusby says her small cell bees, after regression, came back with totally different pollens than before and that based on the blooms and the spread of flora that depend on pollination she's confident that the small cell bees forage much further than the large cell bees. This would be consistent with Brother Adam's observations.

***How far do drones fly to mate?***

I don't think anyone really knows. They fly to DCAs (Drone Congregation Areas) and there are certain topographical clues they look for as well as pheromone trails in order to find one. DCAs are usually at a place where a tree row meets a tree row. The research seems to show that drones fly to the nearest DCA. The location, being dependant on the terrain and the amount of other hives nearby, the distance is hard to predict. Most of the scientists, however, say they fly, on the average, a shorter distance than the queens.

***How far do queens fly to mate?***

As with many questions with bees, it's such a variable thing to start with; it's hard to say. According to Jay Smith, who tried an island for his mating yard, and he says the queens flew at least as far as two miles.

Some estimates I've seen are as much as four or five miles. But I've also heard beekeepers who say they've seen matings (as evidenced by drone comets and the queen returning to the mating nuc) that occurred right in the beeyard.

### *How many hives can I have on one acre?*

The problem with this question is it assumes the bees will stay on the 1 acre. They will forage the surrounding 8,000 acres.

### *How many hives can I have in one place?*

Another common question about beekeeping is "how many hives can I put in one place?" With awesome forage (like in the middle of 8,000 acres of sweet clover), and good weather, it may be close to impossible to put too many in one place. With poor forage and drought, it may be that only a few hives is too many. A typical number that is thrown about is 20. This is a nice round number that is applicable as a generality, but to be realistic it will depend on many things and many of those things vary from year to year.

### *How many hives to start with?*

The standard answer for a beginner is two. I'll say two to four. Less than two and you don't have resources to resolve typical beekeeping issues like queenlessness, suspected queenlessness, laying workers etc. More than four is a bit much for a beginning beekeeper to keep up with.

### ***Planting for bees***

Beekeepers always seem to want to know what to plant for their bees. Just make sure you understand that your bees will not just work the flowers on your land. They will be foraging a 2 mile radius which is 8,000 acres. It's difficult, unless you own that 8,000 acres, to plant enough to make a crop. But it's not hard to plant things that will fill out the year for the bees. The times of need in the hives are early (February to April), late (September to the killing frost) and during drought (which is usually midsummer around here and requires plants that will bloom when there is little rain). So I would focus on plants to fill those gaps. A variety of honey plants in general will tend to fill more gaps than focusing on only one or two plants. It certainly doesn't hurt to plant some sweet clover (both yellow and white as they bloom at different times) and some white Dutch clover and some birdsfoot trefoil and some borage and some anise hyssop and some tulip poplars and some black locust, but these don't tend to fill those early and late gaps, but do tend to make some honey and *may* fill a gap. Early plants that provide pollen are red maples, pussy willows, elms, crocuses, redbud, wild plums, choke cherries and other fruit trees. Dandelions are always good to have around. You can pick the dried heads from people whose lawns are full of them. Just pluck them and put them in a grocery sack and take them home and scatter them. Chicory and goldenrod often bloom in a drought and will bloom usually from about July until a killing frost. Asters are a good late blooming plant. The main thing to keep in mind, though, is that you're just trying to fill the gaps, not trying to create a crop.

***Queen excluders?***

The use of queen excluders has been controversial among beekeepers since the early days of their existence. I quit using them very early in my beekeeping. The bees did not want to go through them and they did not want to work the supers on the other side of them. They seemed very unnatural and constraining to me. I think they are handy to have around for things like queen rearing or a desperate attempt to find a queen, but I don't commonly use them.

**The reasoning for using them:**

The queen will be easier to find if I can narrow down the area I have to look. But I find the area I have to look is pretty narrow. I seldom find her other than where the highest concentration of bees is and that usually narrows it to a few frames. But this is a good reason if you need to find the queen often. In queen rearing this can be once a week or so and a queen excluder can save you some time.

Preventing brood in the supers. The only reasons I've seen a queen lay in the supers are, that she ran out of room in the brood nest, therefore she would have swarmed if she couldn't, or she wanted room to lay drones and there is no drone comb in the brood nest. Since brood comb is difficult to tear down because of cocoons, and supers usually have soft wax with no cocoons which is easily reworked the bees will build drone comb there if they don't have enough in the brood nest. If you don't want brood in the supers, give them some drone comb in the brood nest and you will have made great strides in this regard. Also, if you use all the same size box, you'll have no problem *if* she lays in the "supers" putting those frames back down in the brood nest, and if you use no chemicals, you can steal a frame of honey from there to fill out your super.

## If you want to use them

If you want to use an excluder, remember you have to get the bees going through it. Using all the same sized boxes, again, will help in this regard as you can put a couple of frames of open brood above the excluder (being careful not to get the queen of course) and get them going through the excluder. When they are working the super you can put those combs back down in the brood nest. Another option (especially if you don't have the same sized boxes) is to leave out the excluder until they are working the first super and then put it in (again making sure the queen is below it and the drones have a way out the top somewhere).

> ***"Beginning beekeepers should not attempt to use queen excluders to prevent brood in supers. However they probably should have one excluder on hand to use as an aide in either finding the queen or restricting her access to frames that the beekeeper must want to move elsewhere" -The How-To-Do-It book of Beekeeping, Richard Taylor***

### *Queenless bees?*

BLUF: Put a frame of open brood and eggs in the hive and you don't need to worry about this.

The question comes up all the time on beekeeping forums: "Are my bees queenless?" The symptoms leading to this question vary greatly and the time of year for the question varies greatly, but it is a very important question to get an answer to, or at least a resolution to and is sometimes remarkably more complex that it appears.

The most likely cause for the question is a lack of eggs and brood. Many beginning beekeepers couldn't find a queen if you marked her, clipped her and put her on one frame for them to find her, and even an experienced beekeeper in a well populated hive on a given day may have trouble finding one. So not seeing her doesn't prove anything. Not seeing eggs and brood is an important clue, but it doesn't mean that there is not a queen. It means there is not a laying queen and has not been one for a while, or you can’t spot eggs. But there very well may be a virgin queen that is not laying yet.

Let's do a bit of bee math. If you accidentally kill a queen today, how long before you'll see eggs from a replacement raised by the bees? About 26 days. How much open and capped brood will there be left by the time you see eggs from the new emergency queen? The answer is none. If bees lost a queen today, and started from four-day-old larvae (four days from the egg) to raise a queen, it would be another 12 days before she emerged. Another week for her to harden and orient. And another week to get mated and start to lay. That's approximately 26 days (give or take a week). In 26 days every egg has hatched, been capped and emerged. There is now no brood left in the hive, but, in this case, there is a queen.

The problem is if the new queen flew out to mate and didn't make it back, and the hive is truly queenless, the hive looks the same. No eggs, no brood, not even any capped brood. So how do you answer the question? You give them a frame of brood with eggs and see what they do. If you have a queen cell in a couple of days, then they are queenless. You can either get a queen for them or let them raise that one.

Another problem is when you find a few eggs and a few larvae and they are very scattered. This is sometimes due to laying workers but the bees have still kept up with removing the drone eggs from the worker cells, except for a few. But what if it's a new queen that is just starting to lay? Usually she will lay in a patch and not scattered all over. Laying workers require a lot more effort to deal with.

One way to get a clue as to whether a hive is queenless is listening to it. If you don't know what a queenless hive sounds like, try catching a queen and removing her from a hive and then wait a few minutes and listen. The hive will set up a roar. This is sometimes called a "queenless roar".

Another clue that there probably is a queen who is about to start laying, is to look for a patch of empty cells surrounded by nectar, in the cluster, where they have cleared a spot for her to lay.

A grouchy hive is often a sign they are queenless or a lethargic hive. But you still need to look for eggs and larvae.

The bottom line is that queenlessness is difficult to diagnose definitively. A combination of several of these symptoms (lack of eggs and brood, queenless roar, lethargy or anger) tends to convince me. But only one or two, I give them a frame of open brood with eggs and see what happens.

Of course this illustrates why you need more than one hive.

For more information see the section *Panacea* in the Chapter *BLUF*.

***Requeening***

There are several questions to do with this. One is "how often should I requeen?" Beekeepers have many opinions on this ranging from twice a year to never. I tend to let them requeen themselves, but then I have a handle on swarming and I do requeen if they are too defensive or are not doing well.

The second question is "how do I requeen?" This may involve several questions such as "what do I do if I can't find the old queen?" or "how do I know they will accept the new queen?"

I have not had good luck releasing a queen if they have a queen. About the only way to do this is if you raise your own queens and you introduce a cell or a virgin queen with a lot of smoke to cover her appearance in the hive. That way it is more likely to be perceived as a supersedure by the bees. Otherwise you need to remove the old queen in order to introduce a new laying queen. If you absolutely can't find the old queen and you absolutely think you need to introduce the new one, I'd use a push in cage. All in all it's the most reliable method anyway.

A standard candy release usually works fine if there aren't any complications (such as laying workers, angry hive, already rejected a queen, been queenless a long time, can't find the old queen etc.). This is where you uncork the candy end of the cage, (or in the case of the California cages, you add the plastic tube that has the candy in it or stuff a miniature marshmallow in the hole) and you put the cage in the hive and wait for the bees to eat the candy and release the queen. It is advantageous to acceptance to release the attendants in the queen cage, but if you are a beginner you may find that intimidating. A Queen Muff (from Brushy Mountain) will help much in this as you can do all of your manipulations in a situation where the queen can't fly off on you. If you catch the queen and put her head in the cage she will usually run back in.

Putting a queen cell in anywhere the bees are thick enough to keep it warm works well.

***Push In Cage***

This is the most reliable release for a laying queen. The concept of this is to give the queen some newly emerged attendants, who will accept her since they have never had any other queen, some food and a place to lay. Once she is a laying queen with attendants the hive will usually accept her without protest.

## Making a Push-In-Cage

Most people make these about 4 inches square (10 cm). I prefer to make them bigger. The larger they are the easier it is to get some honey (so she doesn't starve) some open cells (so she has a place to lay) and some emerging brood (so she has attendants). I like mine about 5 by 10 inches (12.5cm by 25cm). Cut some #8 hardware cloth (8 wires to an inch or $^{1}/_{8}$" wire cloth) $6^{1}/_{2}$" by $11^{1}/_{2}$" (about 16cm by 29cm). Pull off the first three wires all the way around leaving $^{3}/_{8}$" wires sticking out with no cross wires. This is to push into the comb so that the bees can't get under easily. Now come in $^{3}/_{4}$" from the corners (three more wires) and make a cut $^{3}/_{4}$" in (3 more wires) on all four corners. It really doesn't matter from which direction, but you're going to fold it around the corner. Fold the $^{3}/_{4}$" edge over. A board or the sharp edge of a table is helpful in doing this. Fold the $^{3}/_{4}$" corners over. You now have a box with no bottom that is $^{3}/_{4}$" tall and 5" by 10".

## Using a Push-in-Cage

Find a comb with emerging brood. This comb is bees who are fuzzy and struggling to get out of a cell they have just chewed open. A bee with its head sticking out of a cell is emerging brood. A bee with its behind sticking out of a cell is a nurse bee feeding a larvae or a house bee cleaning a cell. Shake (if the comb is strong enough) or brush all of the bees off of the comb. Release the queen on one side of the comb where there is emerging brood and some open honey. Put the cage over her so that it has both honey and emerging brood in it. Some open cells are nice too. Push the cage into the comb. It should stick up about $^3/_8$″ above the comb to make room for the queen to move around. Make room in the hive for this frame plus the $^3/_8$″. Some will have enough space and some will have to have a frame removed, but you need to have the frame with the push in cage and then $^3/_8$″ space between the cage and the comb on the next frame ($^3/_4$″ total) so that bees have access to the cage to meet the queen and feed them if they like. Come back in four days and release the queen by removing the cage.

***How do I keep queens for a few days?***

If you need to keep queens that come in cages with attendants and candy, you can minimize the stress by keeping them in a cool (like 60° to 70° F or 16° to 21° C) dark (like a closet) quiet (like a closet or the basement) place and give them a drop of water everyday so they can digest the candy and they will usually keep for a couple of weeks if they weren't too stressed to start with and the attendants are healthy. Give them a drop as soon as you receive them and one a day after that. If the candy looks like it will run out, you might have to give them a drop of honey and a drop of water every day. If all the attendants are dead they will need new attendants.

***What's an inner cover for?***

An inner cover was invented to create an air space to cut down on condensation on the cover. The original ones were made of cloth but over time the wooden ones took over. In the North the problem with winter is condensation and most of that is on the lid. The warm moist air from the cluster hits the cold lid, condenses and drips down on the cluster. An inner cover was designed to prevent this. Over the years, many other uses have been found for them. You can put an inverted jar over the hole to feed. You can put wet (just harvested and extracted) supers over them to get the bees to clean them up. You can put a Porter bee escape in the hole to get the bees out of a super (I've never had much luck with this). You can double screen the hole and use it between a nuc above and a hive below in the spring or fall to help the nuc stay warm. (This has not worked well for me in the winter due to condensation).

**Can I *not* use an inner cover?**

If you use migratory covers, you won't need one and probably don't want one. If you use a telescopic cover it will keep the cover from getting glued down with propolis. It's difficult to remove a telescopic cover that is propolized down to the box with no inner cover as there is nowhere to get your hive tool in to pry it apart. If you have a telescopic cover, I recommend you use the inner cover. If you live in the north and want to use migratory covers, make sure there is some kind of entrance (you can cut a notch in the cover to make one. See Brushy Mountain migratory covers for an example) and put some Styrofoam on top of the lid with a brick on top of the Styrofoam. The Styrofoam will keep the lid from being as cold and the vent at the top (through the notch) will allow the moist air out.

***What's that smell?***

Smells are always best investigated. They are very subjective and therefore it's best for you to see it for yourself to associate that smell with that occurrence. The most common smell that people get worried about is the smell of goldenrod honey ripening. This happens sometimes between summer and fall. To me, it smells like old gym socks. Some people say it smells like butterscotch. Most people think it smells sour.

If you smell the smell of rotting meat, I would investigate. Sometimes you have piles of dead bees from a pesticide kill or robbing. Sometimes you have a brood disease. It's worth investigating to see what the cause is.

***What's the best beekeeping book?***

All of them. Read every beekeeping book you can get your hands on. But my favorites are the old *ABC and XYZ of Bee Culture*, Langstroth's *The Hive and the Honey Bee*, everything by Richard Taylor and Brother Adam and the ones that I've posted on my classic bee books page. (http://www.bushfarms.com/beesoldbooks.htm) In addition if you're past all the beekeeping books and want to know even more, all of Eva Crane's books are fascinating.

For a beginner's book for natural beekeeping, *The Complete Idiot's Guide to Beekeeping* is awesome. For general beginning beekeeping, *Backyard Beekeeping* by Kim Flottum is very good and simple.

***What's the best breed of bees?***

There has been much speculation by beekeepers for many centuries on this. I suppose at the turn of the 19th to the 20th century there was probably the most agreement. Italians were pretty much what everyone wanted. Now there are just as many who want Carniolans or Caucasians or Buckfasts or Russians. I see more variation from hive to hive than race to race. I'd say the best breeds of bees are the ones that are surviving around you. That's what I'm raising.

But if you want to buy some queens, the issues are how well they do in your climate (for instance Italians are probably better adapted to the South and Carniolans are better adapted to the North), and health (hygienic behavior, tracheal mite resistance, Varroa mite resistance etc.).

***Why are there all these bees in the air?***

Another panicked posting on the bee forums several times a year will involve a lot of bees flying. This is usually interpreted by the new beekeeper as either a swarm or robbing. A swarm does put a lot of bees in the air, but they are going somewhere. In this case they are just hovering around the hive. If the bees seem happy and organized and not frantic and fighting on the landing board, and especially if it's short-lived and on a sunny afternoon; then it's probably just young bees orienting for the first time. Look for signs of wrestling or fighting on the landing board to rule out robbing. If there are no signs of robbing, this is the sign of a healthy hive. If the hovering bees seem to be leaving a trail of bees as they fly off, then it's probably a swarm gathering in one of your trees.

***Why are there bees on the outside of my hive?***

Typically beekeepers call this bearding because it often looks like the hive has a beard. Causes are heat, congestion and lack of ventilation. Make sure they have room and ventilation and don't worry about it.

Bees bearding is like people sweating. It's what bees do when they are hot.

It's good to cover the bases and then accept it. If you were sweating you'd take what steps were reasonable (turn on the fan, open the window, take off your sweater, drink lots of water) and then you'd accept that it's just hot.

With the bees, make sure they have top and bottom ventilation, (open the bottom entrance, remove the tray if you have a SBB, prop open the top box, slide a super back to make a gap) make sure they have enough room (put supers on as needed) and then don't worry about it. Bearding is not proof they are about to swarm. It is proof they are hot. I think lack of ventilation contributes to an "overcrowding swarm" but it's not the only cause and it's nothing to be concerned about if you've taken care of the bees having ventilation and room.

***Why are they dancing at the entrance in unison?***

A few times a year some new beekeeper wants to know what the bees are doing line dancing (rhythmically swaying) on the landing board. This is called "washboarding" and actually no one "knows why they do it, but they do. Personally I think it's a social dance. Perhaps even a thanksgiving dance.

***Why not use an electric fan for ventilation?***

The subject comes up a lot. I've never quite understood it, but I supposed it comes back to a desire to "help". Bees, however, have a very efficient and precise ventilation system and anything you do will probably interfere with it rather than help. The problem with an electric one is that the bees will find themselves fighting the ventilator. I think you're much better off to just give them some ventilation top and bottom and let them control it.

***Why did my bees die?***

With a death over winter, a post mortem would be to check:

- Are they not in contact with stores? It doesn't matter if they have honey if they can't get to it because they are stuck. If they are not in contact with stores they starved.
- If they are in contact with stores, are there thousands of dead Varroa on the bottom board or the tray under the SBB (I would have it in, of course)? If so, I think it's safe to say the primary cause was Varroa.
- Are there a lot of little clusters of bees in the hive instead of one large cluster? If so I would suspect Tracheal mites.
- Are the bees wet and moldy? If so I would suspect condensation got them wet and wet bees seldom survive.
- It is a commonly held belief that bees dead headfirst in the cells means they starved. All dead hives over winter will have many bees with their heads in cells. That's how they cluster tightly for warmth. I would

read more into whether or not they are on contact with stores.

- With a death during the active season, I'd look for piles of dead bees and if there are signs of robbing. Robbing can lead to piles of dead bees, but there are other symptoms like ragged comb and frantic bees. Pesticides usually have crawling dying bees and piles of them dead. A dwindling hive, you should probably check the brood on to make sure you don't have a brood disease.

***Why do bees make different colors of wax?***

Bees only produce one color of wax—white.

If they track a lot of pollen on the wax it turns yellow. If they raise brood in it, it turns brown from the cocoons. If they leave enough cocoons, it turns black.

As far as cappings, they produce two kinds. On honey it is made of wax which is air tight to keep the honey from absorbing moisture, so it starts white until they track pollen on it which may turn it yellow. On brood it is a mixture of wax and cocoons which can breathe so the pupae can get oxygen. Depending on how old and dark the cocoons are and how much are available, they vary from light yellow to dark brown.

***How often should I inspect?***

If you are a new beekeeper you should inspect often. Not because the bees need you to, but because you can't learn anything if you don't observe. As far as the bees are concerned you only need to check often enough to not let them run out of room. How often? Well I would try not to totally disrupt them every day. If you have an observation hive you can learn a lot there. If you have a window on the hive or a Plexiglas inner cover you can observe more. But with a typical hive I would figure on opening the hive once a week or so until you are comfortable guessing what is going on inside by assessing the outside. Eventually, if you think about what you expect to see and open it and see if you're right, you'll get good at assessing without opening.

### *Should I drill a hole?*

Usually the idea is either for a top entrance or for ventilation. I don't like holes in my equipment. Here are times I regretted drilling holes:

- Times I wanted to close up a hive and forgot the hole. (moving and using a bee escape come to mind)
- Times I accidentally put my hand either over, under or in the hole when lifting the super.
- Times in winter when I wanted to close it up more.
- Times that a hive gets weak and forgets to guard both entrances and they get robbed and I have to find a way to close it off.
- Times that I need a box without a hole and the only one handy has a hole in it.

There is nothing you accomplish by putting a hole in the box that you can't do by sliding the box back $^3/_4$" or putting in a couple of shingle shims or using a Imirie shim.

If you have holes in your equipment you can plug them with a tin can lid tacked over the hole. In the beeyard in a pinch you can plug them temporarily with a wad of beeswax.

### *How do you brush bees?*

There are two primary ways to get bees off combs. Brushing and shaking. Practice a few different techniques to see what works for you shaking them. It will depend on many things. New soft comb (on foundation or not, wired or not) that is heavy with honey will break if you shake it too hard. When hot it is even softer. Foundationless that is not attached all the way around will be even more fragile. These should be brushed. Old black brood comb will not break no matter how hard you slam it. Older comb that is not so soft you can shake well enough without breaking it, but there is a limit and you need to learn that limit based on all of the variables (new, soft, old full of cocoons, heavy with honey, light with brood etc.). Also don't shake a frame with queen cells or you'll damage the queen. Use a brush. Doing a double shake (one shake immediately followed by a second as fast as you can) works if you do it just right. Practice it until you get it to work. You can "pound" bees as C.C. Miller called it. You grab the end of the top bar firmly and hit your other fist on that fist. The jar will knock them off.

It's one of those things that is more art than science but there are principles, and the primary one is surprise. The secondary one is that it's hard, not soft. It seems contrary because normally in beekeeping you are trying to be slow and graceful and not do anything suddenly. And to get bees off you have to be sudden and hard. There is no graceful and soft way to do it.

### *How many cells on a frame?*

Deep frame of 5.4mm foundation: 7000
Deep frame of 4.9mm foundation: 8400
Medium frame of 5.4mm foundation: 4620

Medium frame of 4.9mm foundation: 5544

***Burr comb?***

The main cause of burr between boxes is thin top bars. Plastic frames all have these. I just accept it.

> ***"...that very practical Canadian bee-keeper, J.B. Hall, showed me his thick top-bars, and told me that they prevented the building up of so much burr-comb between the top-bars and the sections...and I am very glad that at the present day it can be dispensed with by having top-bars 1-$^1/_8$ inch wide and $^7/_8$ inch thick, with a space of $^1/_4$ inch between top-bar and section. Not that there is an entire absence of burr-combs, but near enough to it so that one can get along much more comfortably than with the slat honey-board. At any rate there is no longer the killing of bees that there was every day the dauby honey-board was replaced."--C.C. Miller, Fifty Years Among the Bees.***

> ***"Q. Do you believe that a half-inch thick brood-frame top-bar will tend to prevent the bees building burr-comb on such frames, as well as the three-quarter inch top-bar? Which kind do you use?***

***A. I do not believe that the one-half inch will prevent burr-combs quite as well as the three-quarter. Mine are seven-eighths."--C.C. Miller, A Thousand Answers to Beekeeping Questions***

---

# Appendix to Volume I: Glossary

Note: many of these terms are Latin and the plural of the ones with an "a" ending will be "ae". The plural of the "us" endings will be "i". Also meanings are given in the context of beekeeping.

**7/11 or Seven/Eleven** = Foundation with a cell size that is 700 cells per square decimeter with 11 cells left over. Hence 7/11. Actually 5.6mm cell size. Used because it is a size the queen dislikes laying in because it's too big for worker brood and too small for drone brood. If the queen does lay in it, it will usually be drones. It's only currently available from Walter T. Kelley.

***A***

**Acute Paralysis Virus aka APV** = A viral disease of adult bees which affects their ability to use legs or wings normally. It can kill adults and brood.

**Abdomen** = The posterior or third region of the body of the bee that encloses the honey stomach, stomach, intestines, sting and the reproductive organs.

**Abscond** = When the entire colony of bees abandons the hive because of pests, disease or other adverse conditions.

**Acarapis woodi** = Tracheal Mite, which infests the bees' trachea; sometimes called Acarine Disease or Isle of Wight disease.

**Acarapis dorsalis** = Mite that lives on honey bees that is indistinguishable from Tracheal mites (Acarapis woodi). It is classified differently simply based on the location where it is found, on the back.

**Acarapis externus** = Mite that lives on honey bees that is indistinguishable from Tracheal mites (Acarapis woodi). It is classified differently simply based on the location where it is found, on the neck.

**Accelerated queen rearing** = A system of mating nucs where there are usually two queens in the mating nuc a week apart, one in a nursery cage and one loose and mating. Every week the one that is now mated is removed the one in the cage is released and the new cell is put in with a hair curler cage on it.

**Africanized Honey Bees** = I have heard these called Apis mellifera scutelata But Scutelata are actually African bees from the Cape. They used to be called Adansonii, at least that's what Dr. Kerr, who bred them, thought they were. AHB are a mixture of African (Scutelata) and Italian bees. They were created in an attempt to increase production of bees. The USDA bred these at Baton Rouge from stock obtained from Dr. Kerr in Brazil. The USDA shipped these queens to the continental US over the course of many years. The Brazilians also were experimenting with them and the migration of those bees has been followed in the news for some time. They are extremely productive bees that are extremely defensive. If you have a hive hot enough that you think they are AHB you need to requeen them. Having angry bees where they might hurt people is irresponsible. You should try to requeen them (see the chapter *Requeening a Hot Hive* in Volume 3) so no one (including you) gets hurt.

**Afterswarm** = A swarm after the primary swarm. These are headed by a virgin queen.

**Alarm pheromone** = A chemical (iso-pentyl acetate) substance which smells similar to artificial banana flavoring, released near the worker bee's sting, which alerts the hive to an attack.

**Alcohol wash** = Putting a cupful of bees in a jar with alcohol to kill the bees and mites so you can count the Varroa mites. A sugar roll is a non-lethal method of doing the same.

**Allergic reaction** = A systemic reaction to something, such as bee venom, characterized by hives, breathing difficulty, or loss of consciousness. This should be distinguished from a normal reaction to bee venom, which is itching and burning in the general vicinity of the sting.

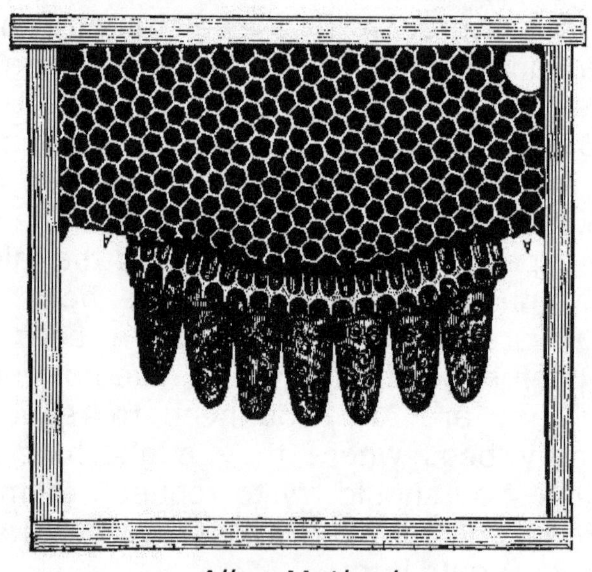

*Alley Method*

**Alley Method** = A graftless method of queen rearing system where bees are put in a "swarm box" to convince them of their queenlessness and a strip of old brood comb is cut and put on a bar for the bees to build into queen cells.

**American Foulbrood** = For more detail see the chapter on *Enemies of the Bees.* Caused by a spore forming bacteria. It used to be called Bacillus larvae but has recently been renamed Paenibacillus larvae. With American foulbrood the larvae usually dies after it is capped, but it looks sick before. The brood pattern will be spotty. Cappings will be sunken and sometimes pierced. Recently dead larvae will string when poked with a matchstick. The smell is rotten and distinctive. Older dead larvae turn to a scale that the bees cannot remove.

**Anaphylactic shock** = Constriction of the smooth muscle including the bronchial tubes and blood vessels of a human, caused, in the context of beekeeping, by hypersensitivity to venom possibly resulting in sudden death unless immediate medical attention is received.

**Antenna** = One of two sensory organs located on the head of the bee, which enable bees to smell and taste.

**Attendants** = Worker bees that are attending the queen. When used in the context of queens in cages, the workers that are added to the cage to care for the queen.

**Apiary** = A bee yard.

**Apiarist** = A beekeeper.

**Apiculture** = The science and art of raising honey bees.

**Apis mellifera mellifera** = These are the bees native to England or Germany. They have some of the characteristics of the other dark bees. They tend toward being runny (excitable on the combs) and a bit swarmy, but also seem to be well adapted to damp Northern climates.

**Apis mellifera** = Includes the honey bees originating in Africa and Europe.

***B***

**Bacillus larvae** = The outdated name for Paenibacillus Larvae, the bacteria that causes American foulbrood.

**Bacillus thuringiensis** = A naturally occurring bacteria that is sprayed on empty comb to kill wax moths. Also sold to control larvae of other specific insects.

**Backfilling** = A term coined by Walt Wright to describe the process of the bees creating a honey bound brood nest. The process where the bees put honey in the brood nest to prevent the queen from laying to prepare for swarming.

**Baggie feeder** = These are just gallon Ziploc baggies that are filled with three quarts of syrup, laid on the top bars and slit on top with a razor blade with two or three small slits. The bees suck down the syrup until the bag is empty. A box of some kind is required to make room. An upside down Miller feeder or a one by three shim or just any empty super will work. Advantages are the cost (just the cost of the bags) and the bees will work it in cooler weather as the cluster keeps it warm. Disadvantages are you have to disrupt the bees to put new bags on and the old bags are ruined.

**Bait hive aka Decoy hive aka Swarm trap** = A hive placed to attract stray swarms. Optimum bait hive: At least 20 liters of volume. 9 feet off the ground. Small entrance. Old comb. Lemongrass oil. Queen substance.

**Balling** = Worker bees surrounding a queen either to confine her because they reject her or to confine her to protect her.

**Banking queens** = Putting multiple caged queens in one nuc or hive.

**Bearding** = When bees congregate on the front of the hive.

**Bee blower** = A gas or electrically driven blower used to blow bees from supers when harvesting.

**Bee bread** = Fermented pollen stored in the hive to use to feed brood.

**Bee brush** = Soft brush or whisk or large feather or handful of grass used to remove bees from combs.

**Bee escape** = A device constructed to permit bees to pass one way, but prevent their return; used to clear bees from supers or other uses. The most common one seems to be the Porter escape which is made to go in the hole in the inner cover. The most effective one seems to be the triangular one which is its own board.

**Bee Go** = Butyric which is used to drive bees from supers. This smells a lot like vomit.

**Bee gum** = A piece of a hollow tree used for a hive.

**Bee haver** = A term coined by George Imirie. One who has bees but has not learned enough technique to be a beekeeper.

**Bee jacket** = A white jacket, usually with a zip on veil and elastic at the sleeves and waist, worn as protection when working bees.

**Bee Parasitic Mite Syndrome aka Parasitic Mite Syndrome** = A set of symptoms that are caused by a major infestation of Varroa mites. Symptoms include the presence of Varroa mites, the presence of various brood diseases with symptoms similar to that of foulbroods and sacbrood but with no predominant pathogen, AFB-like symptoms, spotty brood pattern, increased supersedure of queens, bees crawling on the ground, and a low adult bee population.

**Bee Quick** = A chemical, that smells like benzaldehyde that is used to drive bees from supers.

**Bee space** = A space between $^1/_4$ and $^3/_8$ inch which permits free passage for a bee but too small to encourage comb building, and too large to induce propolizing.

**Bee suit** = A pair of white coveralls made for beekeepers to protect them from stings and keep their clothes clean. Most come with zip-on veils.

**Bee tree** = A hollow tree occupied by a colony of bees.

**Bee vac aka Bee vacuum** = A vacuum used to suck up bees when doing a cutout or removal. Usually converted from a shop vac. It needs careful adjustment to not kill the bees.

**Bee veil** = Netting or screen for protecting the beekeeper's head and neck from stings.

**Bee venom** = The poison secreted by special glands attached to the stinger of the bee which is injected into the victim of a sting.

**Beehive** = A box usually with movable frames, used for housing a colony of bees.

**Beelining** = Finding feral bees by establishing the line which the bees fly back to their home. This can also include marking and timing the bees to get the distance and triangulating the location by releasing the bees from various places.

**Beek** = Beekeeper

**Beekeeper** = One who keeps bees. An Apiarist.

**Beeswax** = A substance that is secreted by bees by special glands on the underside of the abdomen, deposited as thin scales, and used after mastication and mixture with the secretion of the salivary glands for constructing the honeycomb. The melting point of beeswax is 144 to 147 °F.

**Better Queens method** = A graftless queen rearing method similar to Isaac Hopkins' actual queen rearing method (as opposed to the "Hopkins Method"). Sort of the Alley Method but with new comb instead of old.

**Betterbee** = A beekeeping supply company out of New York. They have many things no one else does. They also have eight frame equipment.

**Benzaldehyde** = A colorless nontoxic liquid aldehyde C6H5CHO that has an odor like that of bitter almond oil, that occurs in many essential oils and is sometimes used to drive bees out of honey supers. Also the flavor added to Maraschino cherries. What Bee Quick smells like.

**Black scale** = Refers to dried pupa, which died of American foulbrood.

**Boardman feeder** = These come in all the beginners' kits. They go in the entrance and hold an inverted quart mason jar. I'd keep the jar lid and throw away the feeder. They are notorious for causing robbing. They are easy to check but you have to shake off the bees and open the jar to refill them.

**Bottling tank** = A food grade tank holding 5 or more gallons of honey and equipped with a honey gate to fill honey jars.

**Bottom bar** = The horizontal piece of the frame that is on the bottom of the frame.

**Bottom board** = The floor of a bee hive.

**Bottom board feeder** = This is picture of the bottom board feeder that Jay Smith came up with. It's simply a dam made with a 3/4″ by 3/4″ block of wood put an inch or so back from the where the front of the hive would be (18″ or so forward of the very back). The box is slid forward enough to make a gap at the back. The syrup is poured in the back. A small board can be used to block the opening in the back. The bees can still get out the front by simply coming down forward of the dam. The picture is from the perspective of standing behind the hive looking toward the front. The edges of the dam have been enhanced and labels put on to try to make more sense. This version doesn't work on a weak hive as the syrup is too close to the entrance. It drowns as many bees as the frame feeders.

**Bottom supering** = The act of placing honey supers under all the existing supers, directly on top of the brood box. The theory is the bees will work it better when it's directly above the brood chamber; as opposed to *top* supering which would be just putting the supers on top of the existing supers.

**Box Jig** = Jig for nailing boxes. (for more pictures see chapter by that name in Volume 3)

**Brace comb** = A bit of comb built between two combs to fasten them together, between a comb and adjacent wood, or between two wooden parts such as top bars.

**Braula coeca** = A wingless fly commonly known as the bee louse.

**Breeder hive** = The hive from which eggs or larvae are taken for queen rearing. In other words the donor hive.

**Bricks** = Used to keep the lids from blowing off in the wind and often used in particular configurations as visual clues as to the state of a hive.

**Brood** = Immature bees not yet emerged from their cells; in other words, egg, larvae or pupae.

**Brood chamber** = The part of the hive in which the brood is reared; may include one or more hive bodies and the combs within. Sometimes used to refer to a deep box as these are commonly used for brood.

**Brood nest** = The part of the hive interior in which brood is reared; usually the two bottom boxes.

**Brushy Mountain** = A beekeeping supply company out of North Carolina (http://www.brushymountainbeefarm.com/). A big proponent of all mediums and eight frame boxes. They have many items no one else has.

**Bt** = Bacillus thuringiensis. A naturally occurring bacteria that is sprayed on empty comb to kill wax moths. Also sold to control larvae of other specific insects.

**Buckfast** = A strain of bees developed by Brother Adam at Buckfast Abbey in England, bred for disease resistance, disinclination to swarm, hardiness, comb building and good temper.

**Burr comb** = Small pieces of comb outside of the normal space in the frame where comb usually is. Brace comb would fall into this category.

***C***

**Candy plug** = A fondant type candy placed in one end of a queen cage to delay her release.

**Capped brood** = Immature bees whose cells have been sealed over with papery caps.

**Capping melter** = Melter used to liquefy the wax from cappings as they are removed from honeycombs.

**Cappings** = The thin wax covering over honey; once cut off of extracting frames.

**Capping scratcher** = A fork-like device used to remove wax cappings covering honey, so it can be extracted. Usually used on low areas that get missed by the uncapping knife.

**Carniolan bees** = Apis mellifera carnica. These are darker brown to black. They fly in slightly cooler weather and in theory are better in northern climates. They are reputed by some to be less productive than Italians, but I have not had that experience. The ones I have had were very productive and very frugal for the winter. They winter in small clusters and shut down brood rearing when there are dearths.

**Castes** = The three types of bees that comprise the adult population of a honey bee colony: workers, drones, and queen

**Carts** = Used for wheeling boxes or hives around.

**Caucasian bees** = Apis mellifera caucasica. They are silver gray to dark brown. They do propolis excessively. It is a sticky propolis rather than a hard propolis. They often coat everything with this sticky kind of proplolis, like fly paper. They build up a little slower in the spring than the Italians. They are reputed to be more gentle than the Italians. Less prone to robbing. In theory they are less productive than Italians. I think on the average they are about the same productivity as the Italians, but since they rob less you get less of the really booming hives that have robbed out all their neighbors.

**Cell** = The hexagonal compartment of a honey-comb.

**Cell bar** = A wooden strip on which queen cups are suspended for rearing queen bees.

**Cell cup** = Base of an artificial queen cell, made of beeswax or plastic and used for rearing queen bees or an empty beginning of a queen cell that the bees often build for no reason.

**Cell finisher** = A hive used to finish queen cells i.e. take them from capped to just before emergence. Sometimes queenright, sometimes queenless.

**Cell starter** = A hive used to start queen cells i.e. take them from just grafted to capped. Sometimes a "swarm box" or sometimes just a queenless hive.

**Chalkbrood** = This is caused by a fungus Asco-sphaera apis. It arrived in the US in 1968. If you find white pellets in front of the hive that kind of look like small corn kernels, you probably have chalkbrood. Putting the hive in full sun and adding more ventilation usually clears this up. Honey instead of syrup may contribute to clearing this up, since sugar syrup is much more alkaline (higher pH) than honey.

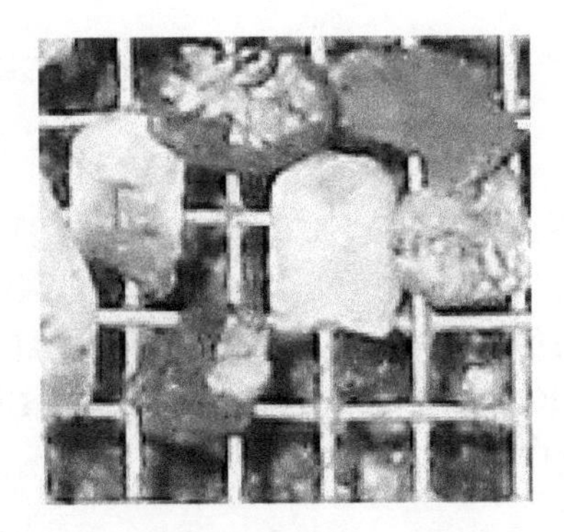

**Checkerboarding** (aka Nectar Management) = A method of swarm control and hive management pioneered by Walt Wright, that involves putting alternating frames of capped honey and empty drawn comb above the brood nest in late winter.

**Chest hive** = a hive that is laid out horizontally instead of vertically.

**Chilled brood** = Immature bees that have died from exposure to cold; commonly caused by mismanagement or sudden cold spells.

**Chimney** = When the bees fill only the center frames of honey supers.

**Chinese grafting tool** = Grafting tool made of plastic, horn and bamboo that has a retractable "tongue" that slides under the larvae and, when released, pushes it off of the "tongue". Popular because it is easier to operate than most grafting needles and it lifts up more royal jelly in the process. Quality varies and most recommend buying several and picking the ones you like out of those.

**Chitin** = Material which the exoskeleton of an insect is made of.

**Chronic Paralysis Virus aka CPV** = Symptoms: bees trembling, unable to fly, with K-wings and distended abdomens. One variety called the hairless black syndrome, is recognized by hairless, black shiny bees crawling at the hive entrance.

**Chunk honey** = Cut comb honey packed into jars then filled with liquid honey.

**Clarifying** = Removing visible foreign material from honey or wax to increase its purity.

**Clipping** = The practice of taking part of one or both wings off of a queen both for discouraging or slowing swarming and for identification of the queen.

**Cloake Board AKA FWOF (Floor without a floor)** = A device to divide a colony into a queenless cell starter and reunite it as a queenright cell finisher without having to open the hive.

*Cloake board*

**Cluster** = The thickest part of the bees on a warm day, usually the core of the brood nest. On a day below 50° F the only location where the bees are. It is used to refer both to the location and to the bees in that location.

**Cocoon** = A thin silk covering secreted by larval honey bees in their cells in preparation for pupation.

**Coffin hive** = a hive that is laid out horizontally instead of vertically.

**Colony** = The superorganism made up of worker bees, drones, queen, and developing brood living together as a family unit.

**Colony Collapse Disorder** = A recently named problem where most of the bees in most of the hives in an apiary disappear leaving a queen, healthy brood and only a few bees in the hive with plenty of stores.

**Comb** = The wax structures in a colony in which eggs are laid, and honey and pollen are stored. Shaped like hexagons.

**Comb foundation** = A commercially made structure consisting of thin sheets of beeswax with the cell bases of a particular cell size embossed on both sides to induce the bees to build a that size of cell.

**Comb Honey** = Honey in the wax combs, either cut from larger combs or produced and sold as a separate unit, such as a wooden section $4^1/_2$" square, or a plastic round ring.

**Conical escape** = A cone-shaped bee escape, which permits bees, a one-way exit; used in a special escape board to free honey supers of bees.

**Cordovan bees** = A subset of the Italians. In theory you could have a Cordovan in any breed, since it's technically just a color, but the ones for sale in North American that I've seen are all Italians. They are slightly more gentle, slightly more likely to rob and quite striking to look at. They have no black on them and look very yellow at first sight. Looking closely you see that where the Italians normally have black legs and head, they have a purplish brown legs and head.

**Creamed honey** = Honey that has undergone controlled granulation to produce a finely textured candied or crystallized honey which spreads easily at room temperature. This usually involves adding fine "seed" crystals and keeping at 57º F (14º C).

**Crimp-wired foundation** = Comb foundation into which crimp wire is embedded vertically during foundation manufacture.

**Crimper** = A device used to put a ripple in the frame wire to both make it tight and to distribute stress better and give more surface to bind it to the wax.

**Cupralarva** = A particular brand of graftless queen rearing system.

**Cut-comb Honey** = Comb honey cut into various sizes, the edges drained, and the pieces wrapped or packed individually

**Cut-out** = Removing a colony of bees from somewhere that they don't have movable comb by cutting out the combs and tying them into frames.

***D***

**Dadant** = A beekeeping supply company out of Illinois. Founded by C.P. Dadant who was a pioneer in the modern beekeeping era and invented, among other things, the Jumbo and the square Dadant box. ($19^7/_8$" by $19^7/_8$" by $11^5/_8$"), published and wrote for the American Bee Journal and translated *Huber's Observations on Bees* from French to English and published many books including but not limited to the later versions of *The Hive and the Honey Bee*.

**Dadant deep** = A box designed by C.P. Dadant that is 11 $^5/_8$" deep and the frame is $11^1/_4$" deep. Sometimes called Jumbo or Extra Deep.

**Dearth** = A period of time when there is no available forage for bees, due to weather conditions (rain, drought) or time of year.

**Decoy hive aka Bait hive aka Swarm trap** = A hive placed to attract stray swarms.

**Deep** = In Langstroth terms, a box that is $9^5/_8$" deep and the frame is $9^1/_4$" deep. Sometimes called a Langstroth Deep.

**Deformed Wing Virus** = A virus spread by the Varroa mite that causes crumpled looking wings on fuzzy newly emerged bees.

**Demaree** = The method of swarm control that separates the queen from most of the brood within the same hive and causes them to raise another queen with the goal of a two queen hive, increased production and reduced swarming.

**Depth** = The vertical measurement of a box or frame.

**Dequeen** = To remove a queen from a colony. Usually done before requeening, or as a help for brood diseases or pests.

**Detritus** = Wax scales and debris that sometimes build up at the bottom of a natural colony.

**Dextrose** = Also known as glucose, it is a simple sugar (or monosaccharide) and is one of the two main sugars found in honey; forms most of the solid phase in granulated honey.

**Diastase** = A starch digesting enzyme in honey adversely affected by heat; used in some countries to test quality and heating history of stored honey.

**Diploid** = Possessing pairs of genes, as workers and queens do, as opposed to haploid, possessing single genes as drones do.

**Disease resistance** = The ability of an organism to avoid a particular disease; primarily due to genetic immunity or avoidance behavior.

**Dividing** = Separating a colony to form two or more colonies. AKA a split

**Division** = Separating a colony to form two or more colonies.

**Division board** = A wooden or plastic piece like a frame but tight all the way around used to divide one box into more compartments for nucs.

**Division board feeder or Frame feeder** = A wooden or plastic compartment which is hung in a hive like a frame and contains sugar syrup to feed bees. The original designation (Division) was because it was *used* to make a division between two halves of a box to divide it into nucs, usually for queen rearing or making increase (splits). Most of them have a beespace around them now and cannot be used to make a division.

**Domestic** = Bees that live in a manmade hive. Since all bees are pretty much wild this is a relative term.

**Doolittle method** = A method of queen rearing that involves grafting young larvae into queen cups. First discovered by Nichel Jacob in 1568, then written about by Schirach in 1767 and then Huber in 1794 and finally popularized by G.M. Doolittle in his book *Scientific Queen Rearing* in 1846.

**Double screen** = A wooden frame, $^1/_2$ to $^3/_4$" thick, with two layers of wire screen to separate two colonies within the same hive, one above the other. Often an entrance is cut on the upper side and placed to the rear of the hive for the upper colony and sometimes other openings are incorporated which would then be a Snelgrove board.

**Double story or Double deeps** = Referring to a beehive wintering in two deep boxes.

**Double wide** = A box that is twice as wide as a ten frame box. $32^1/_2$" wide.

**Drawn combs** = Full depth comb ready for brood or nectar with the cell walls drawn out by the bees, completing the comb as opposed to foundation that has not been worked by the bees and has no cell walls yet.

**Drifting** = The movement of bees that have lost their location and enter hives other than their own home. This happens often when hives are placed in long straight rows where returning foragers from the center hives tend to drift to the row ends or when making splits and the field bees drift back to the original hive.

> ***"The percentage of foragers originating from different colonies within the apiary ranged from 32 to 63 percent"—from a paper, published in 1991 by Walter Boylan-Pett and Roger Hoopingarner in Acta Horticulturae 288, 6th Pollination Symposium (see Jan 2010 edition of Bee Culture, 36)***

**Drone** = The male honey bee which comes from an unfertilized egg (and is therefore haploid) laid by a queen or less commonly, a laying worker.

**Drone comb** = Comb that is made up of cells larger than worker brood, usually in the range of 5.9 to

7.0mm in which drones are reared and honey and pollen are stored.

**Drone brood** = Brood, which matures into drones, reared in cells larger than worker brood. It is noticeably larger than worker brood and the cappings are distinctly dome shaped.

**Drone Congregation Area** = A place that drones from many surrounding hives congregate and wait for a queen to come. In other words a mating area. Drones find them by following both pheromone trails and topographical features of the landscape such as tree rows.

**Drone layers** = A drone laying queen (one with no sperm left to fertilize eggs) or laying workers.

**Drone laying queen** = A queen that can lay only unfertilized eggs, due to age, improper or late mating, disease or injury.

**Drone mother hive** = The hive which is encouraged to raise a lot of drones to improve the drone side of mating queens. Based on the myth that you can make bees raise more drones. Taking drone comb from the ones you want to perpetuate and giving them to other colonies is the only real way to succeed at this as the mother colony will then raise more drones while the colonies receiving the drone comb will raise less of their own because they will be raising the ones from the drone mother.

**Drumming** = Tapping or thumping on the sides of a hive to make the bees ascend into another hive placed over it or to drive them out of a tree or house.

This will not get all of them out, but will move a significant number.

**Dorsal-Ventral Abdominal Vibrations dance** = A dance used to recruit forages. Also used on queen cells about to emerge and possibly other times.

**Dwindling** = Any rapid decline in the population of the hive. The rapid dying off of old bees in the spring; sometimes called spring dwindling or disappearing disease.

**Dysentery** = A condition of adult bees characterized by severe diarrhea (as evidenced by brown or yellow streaks on the front of the hive) and usually caused by long confinement (from either cold or beekeeper manipulation), starvation, low-quality food, or Nosema infection.

***E***

**Eight frame** = Boxes that were made to take eight frames. Usually between $13^1/_2$" and 14" wide depending on the manufacturer. Typically $13^3/_4$" wide.

**Eggs** = The first phase in the bee life cycle, usually laid by the queen, is the cylindrical egg $^1/_{16}$" (1.6 mm) long; it is enclosed with a flexible shell or chorion. It resembles a small grain of rice.

**Eke** = The term originated with skeps and it was "an enlargement" which is the equivalent of today's super. In current usage it usually refers to a shim that is either added to the top for feeding things like pollen patties or added under a shallow to make it into a deep. The term is used more frequently in Britain.

**Electric embedder** = A device that heats the foundation wire by running current through it for embedding of wires in foundation.

**End bar** = The piece of a frame that is on the ends of the frame i.e. the vertical pieces of the frame.

**Entrance reducer** = A wooden strip used to regulate the size of the entrance.

**Escape board** = A board having one or more bee escapes in it used to remove bees from supers.

**European Foulbrood** = Caused by a bacteria. It used to be called Streptococcus pluton but has now been renamed Melissococcus pluton. European Foul Brood is a brood disease. With EFB the larvae turn brown and their trachea is even darker brown. Don't confuse this with larvae being fed dark honey. It's not just the food that is brown. Look for the trachea. When it's worse, the brood will be dead and maybe black and maybe sunk cappings, but usually the brood dies before they are capped. The cappings in the brood nest will be scattered, not solid, because they have been removing the dead larvae. To differentiate this from AFB use a stick and poke a diseased larvae and pull it out. The AFB will "string" two or three inches.

**Ether wash** = Putting a cupful of bees in a jar with a spray of starter fluid to kill the bees and mites so you can count the Varroa mites. A sugar roll is a non-lethal and much less flammable method of doing the same.

**European Honey Bees** = Bees from Europe as opposed to bees originating in Africa or other parts of the world or bees crossbred with those from Africa.

**Eyelets** = Optional small metal piece fitting into the wire-holes of a frame's end bar; used to keep the reinforcing wires from cutting into the wood. Many people use a staple across where it would split the wood instead.

**Extra shallow** = A box that is $4^{11}/_{16}$ or $4^{3}/_{4}$" deep. Usually used for cut comb. Sometimes modified for sections.

**Extracted honey** = Honey removed from combs usually by means of a centrifugal force (an extractor) in order to leave the combs intact but with hobbyists often from crushing the comb and straining it (see Crush and Strain).

**Ezi Queen** = A particular brand of graftless queen rearing system.

***F***

**Frame feeder or division board feeder** = A wooden or plastic compartment which is hung in a hive like a frame and contains sugar syrup to feed bees. The original designation (Division) was because it was *used* to make a division between two halves of a box to divide it into nucs, usually for queen rearing or making increase (splits). Most of them have a beespace around them now and cannot be used to make a division.

**Feeders** = Any device used to feed bees.

**Fermenting honey** = Honey which contains too much water (greater than 20%) in which yeast has grown and caused some of it to turn into carbon dioxide, water and alcohol.

**Feral (queen or bees)** = Since all North American bees are considered to have come from domestic stock, what most people call "wild" bees are really "feral" bees. Some use the term for survivor bees that were captured and used to raise queens meaning they *were* feral as opposed to *are* feral.

**Fertile queen** = An inseminated queen.

**Fertilized** = Usually refers to eggs laid by a queen bee, they are fertilized with sperm stored in the queen's spermatheca, in the process of being laid. These develop into workers or queens.

**Festooning** = The activity of young bees, engorged with honey, hanging on to each other usually to secrete beeswax but also in bearding and swarming..

**Field bees** = Worker bees which are usually 21 or more days old and work outside to collect nectar, pollen, water and propolis; also called foragers.

**Flash heater** = A device for heating honey very rapidly to prevent it from being damaged by sustained periods of high temperature

**Flight path** = Usually refers to the direction bees fly leaving their colony; if obstructed, may cause bees to accidentally collide with the person obstructing and eventually become aggravated.

**Floor Without a Floor AKA FWOF AKA Cloake Board** = A device to divide a colony into a queenless cell starter and reunite it as a queenright cell finisher without having to open the hive.

**Follower board** = A thin board used in place of a frame usually when there are fewer than the normal number of frames in a hive. This is usually referring to one that has a beespace around it and is used to make the frames easier to remove without rolling and to cut down on condensation on the walls. Sometimes it's used to refer to a board that is bee tight and used to divide a box into two colonies. When designed and used in this manner it should be called a division board.

**Food chamber** = A hive body filled with honey for winter stores. Typically a third deep used in unlimited brood nest management.

**Forage** = Natural food source of bees (nectar and pollen) from wild and cultivated flowers. Or the act of gathering that food.

**Foragers** = Worker bees which are usually 21 or more days old and work outside to collect nectar, pollen, water and propolis; also called field bees.

**Foundation** = Thin sheets of beeswax embossed or stamped with the base of a worker (or rarely drone) cells on which bees will construct a complete comb (called drawn comb); also referred to as comb foundation, it comes wired or unwired and also in plastic as well as one piece foundations and frames as well as different thicknesses (thin surplus, surplus, medium) and different cell sizes (brood =5.4mm, small cell = 4.9mm, drone=6.6mm).

**Foundationless** = A frame with some kind of comb guide that is used without foundation.

**Frame** = A rectangular structure of wood designed to hold honeycomb, consisting of a top bar, two end bars, and a bottom bar; usually spaced a bee-space apart in the super.

**Frame feeder** = Sometimes called a "division board feeder". It takes the place of one or more frames. Less bees drown if you put floats in.

**Fructose** = Fruit sugar, also called levulose (left handed sugar), a monosaccharide commonly found in honey that is slow to granulate

**Fumagilin-B** = Bicyclohexyl-ammonium fumagillin, whose trade name was Fumidil-B (Abbot Labs) but now seems to be called Fumagilin-B, is a whitish soluble antibiotic powder discovered in 1952; some beekeepers mix this with sugar syrup and feed it to bees to control Nosema disease. Fumagilin is more soluble than Fumidil. Its use in beekeeping is outlawed in the European Union because it is a suspected teratogen (causes birth defects). Fumagilin can block blood vessel formation by binding to an enzyme called methionine aminopeptidase. Targeted gene disruption of methionine aminopeptidase 2 results in an embryonic gastrulation defect and endothelial cell growth arrest. It is made from the fungus that causes stonebrood, Aspergillus fumigatus. Formula: (2E,4E,6E,8E)–10-{[(3S,4S,5S, 6R)-5–methoxy-4-[2–methyl–3-(3–methylbut–2-enyl) oxiran–2-yl]-1-oxaspiro[2.5]octan-6-yl]oxy}-10-oxo-deca-2,4,6,8-tetraenoic acid

**Fumidil-B** = The old trade name for Fumagilin, see above entry.

**Fume board** = A device used to hold a set amount of a volatile chemical (A bee repellent like Bee Go or Honey Robber or Bee Quick) to drive bees from supers.

***G***

**Gloves** = Leather, cloth or rubber gloves worn while inspecting bees.

**Glucose** = Also known as dextrose, it is a simple sugar (or monosaccharide) and is one of the two main sugars found in honey; forms most of the solid phase in granulated honey.

**Grafting** = Removing a worker larva from its cell and placing it in an artificial queen cup in order to have it reared into a queen.

**Grafting tool** = A needle or probe used for transferring larvae in grafting of queen cells.

**Granulate** = The process by which honey, a super-saturated solution (more solids than liquid) will become solid or crystallize; speed of granulation depends of the kinds of sugars in the honey, the crystal seeds (such as pollen or sugar crystals) and the temperature. Optimum temperature for granulation is 57° F (14° C ).

**Guard bees** = Worker bees about three weeks old, which have their maximum amount of alarm pheromone and venom; they challenge all incoming bees and other intruders.

**Gum** = A hollow log beehive, sometimes called a log-gum, made by cutting out that portion of a tree containing bees and moving it to the apiary, or by cutting a hollow portion of a log, putting a board on for a lid and hiving a swarm in it. Since it contains no moveble combs, and since each individual state in the US has laws that require movable combs, it is therefore illegal in the US.

***H***

**Hair clip queen catcher** = A device used to catch a queen that resembles a hair clip. Available from most beekeeping supply houses.

**Haploid** = Possessing a single set of genes, as drones do, as opposed to pairs of genes as workers and queens have.

**Hemolymph** = The scientific name for insect "blood."

**Hive** = A home for a colony of bees.

**Hive body** = A wooden box containing frames. Usually referring to the size of box being used for brood.

**Hive stand** = A structure serving as a base support for a beehive; it helps in extending the life of the bottom board by keeping it off damp ground. Hive stands may be built from treated lumber, cedar, bricks, concrete blocks etc.

**Hive staples** = Large C-shaped metal nails, hammered into the wooden hive parts to secure bottom to supers, and supers to super before moving a colony.

**Hive tool** = A flat metal device used to pry boxes and frames apart, typically with a curved scraping surface or a lifting hook at one end and a flat blade at the other.

**Hoffman frame** = Frames that have the end bars wider than the top bars to provide the proper spacing when frames are placed in the hive. In other words, self-spacing frames. In other words, standard frames.

**Honey** = A sweet viscous material produced by bees from the nectar of flowers, composed largely of a mixture of dextrose and levulose dissolved in about 19 to 17 percent water; contains small amounts of sucrose, mineral matter, vitamins, proteins, and enzymes.

**Honey bound** = A condition where the brood nest of a hive is being backfilled with honey. This is a normal condition that is used by the workers to shut down the queen's brood production. It usually happens just before swarming and in the fall to prepare for winter.

**Honeydew** = An excreted material from insects in the order Homoptera (aphids) which feed on plant sap; since it contains almost 90% sugar, it is collected by bees and stored as honeydew honey.

**Honey bee** = The common name for Apis mellifera.

**Honey Bee Healthy** = A mixture of essential oils (lemon grass and peppermint) sold to boost the immune system of the bees.

**Honey crop** = The honey that was harvested.

**Honey crop also called honey stomach or honey sac** = An enlargement at the posterior of a bees' esophagus but lying in the front part of the abdomen, capable of expanding when full of liquid such as nectar or water. Used for transportation purposes for water, nectar and honey.

**Honey extractor** = A machine which removes honey from the cells of comb by centrifugal force. The two main types are tangential where the frames lie flat and are flipped to extract the other side, and radial where the frames are like spokes in a wheel and both sides are emptied at the same time.

**Honey flow** = A time when enough nectar-bearing plants are blooming such that bees can store a surplus of honey.

**Honey gate** = A faucet used for removing honey from tanks and other storage receptacles.

**Honey house** = A building used for activities such as honey extraction, packaging and storage.

**Honey plants** = Plants whose flower (or other parts) yields enough nectar to produce a surplus of honey; examples are asters, basswood, citrus, eucalyptus, goldenrod and tupelo.

**Honey Super Cell** = Fully drawn plastic comb in deep depth and 4.9mm cell size

**Honey supers** = Refers to boxes of frames used for honey production. From the Latin "super" for above as a designation for any box above the brood nest.

**Hopkins method** = A graftless method of queen rearing that involves putting a frame of young larvae horizontally above a brood nest.

**Hopkins shim** = A shim used to turn a frame flatways for queen rearing without grafting.

**Horizontal hive** = a hive that is laid out horizontally instead of vertically in order to eliminate lifting boxes.

**Hornets and Yellow Jackets** = Social insects belonging to the family Vespidae. Nest in paper or foliage material, with only an overwintering queen. Fairly aggressive, and carnivorous, but generally beneficial, they can be a nuisance to man. Hornets and Yellow Jackets are often confused with Wasps and honey bees. Wasps are related to hornets and yellow jackets, the most common of which are the paper wasps which nest in small exposed paper combs, suspended by a single support. Hornets, yellow jackets and wasps are easy to distinguish by their shiny hairless body, and aggressiveness. Yellow jackets, unfortunately, look like the bees in the cartoons and advertisements, bright yellow and black and shiny. Honey bees are generally fuzzy black, brown or tan, never bright yellow, and basically docile in nature.

**Hot (temperament)** = Bees that are overly defensive or outright aggressive.

**Housel positioning theory** = A theory proposed by Michael Housel that natural brood nests have a predictable orientation of the "Y" in the bottom of the cells. Basically that when looking at one side an upside down "Y" will appear in the bottom and from the other side a right side up "Y" will appear and the center comb will have a sideways "Y" that is the same from both sides. Basically if we assume a third bar in my notation to make these "Y"s and assume a nine frame hive and each pair is what the comb looks like from that side: ^v ^v ^v ^v >> v^ v^ v^ v^

**Hydroxymethyl furfural** = A naturally occurring compound in honey that rises over time and rises when honey is heated.

**Hypopharyngeal gland** = A gland located in the head of a worker bee that secretes "royal jelly". This rich blend of proteins and vitamins is fed to all bee larvae for the first three days of their lives and queens during their entire development.

***I***

**Israeli Acute Paralysis Virus aka IAPV** = The virus currently being blamed for CCD. First discovered in Israel where it was quite devastating to colonies.

**Illinois** = A box that is $6^5/_8$" in depth and the frames are $6^1/_4$" in depth. AKA Medium AKA Western AKA $^3/_4$ depth.

**Imirie shim** = A device credited to the late George Imirie that is a $^3/_4$" shim with an entrance built in. It allows you to add an entrance between any two pieces of equipment on the hive.

**Increase** = To add to the number of colonies, usually by dividing those on hand. See Split.

**Infertile** = Incapable of producing a fertilized egg, as a laying worker or drone laying queen. Unfertilized eggs develop into drones.

**Inhibine** = Antibacterial effect of honey caused by enzymes and an accumulation of hydrogen peroxide, a result of the chemistry of honey.

**Inner cover** = An insulating cover fitting on top of the top super but underneath the outer cover, typically with an oblong hole in the center. Used to be called a "quilt board". In the old days these were often made of cloth.

**Instar** = Stages of larval development. A honey bee goes through five instars. The best queens are grafted in the 1st (preferably) or 2nd instar and not later than that.

**Instrumental insemination aka II or AI** = The introduction of drone spermatozoa into the spermatheca of a virgin queen by means of special instruments

**Invertase** = An enzyme in honey, which splits the sucrose molecule (a disaccharide) into its two components dextrose and levulose (monosaccharides). This is produced by the bees and put into the nectar to convert it in the process of making honey.

**Isomerase** = A bacterial enzyme used to convert glucose in corn syrup into fructose, which is a sweeter sugar; called isomerose, is now used as a bee feed.

**Italian bees** = A common race of bees, Apis mellifera ligustica, with brown and yellow bands, from Italy; usually gentle and productive, but tend to rob and brood incessantly.

***J***

**Jenter** = A particular brand of graftless queen rearing system.

***K***

**Kashmir Bee Virus** = A widespread disease of bees, spread more quickly by Varroa, found everywhere there are bees.

**Kenya Top Bar Hive** = A top bar hive with sloped sides. The theory is that they will have less attachments on the sides because of the slope.

**Kidneys** = Bees don't actually have kidneys. They have malpighian tubules which are thin filamentous projects from the junction of the mid and hind gut of the bee that cleanse the hemolymph (blood) of nitrogenous cell wastes and deposit them as non-toxic uric acid crystals into the undigestible food wastes for elimination. They serve the same purpose in bees as kidneys do in higher animals.

***L***

**Landing board** = An extraneous construction that makes small platform at the entrance of the hive for the bees to land on before entering the hive. Usually just a longer bottom board. Sometimes a sloped approach is added. Bees in nature have none. I call it a "mouse ramp" as the only actual purpose I see it provide is a place for mice to get into the hive more conveniently.

**Lang** = Short for Langstroth hive.

**Langstroth, Rev. L.L.** = A Philadelphia native and minister (1810-95), he lived for a time in Ohio where he continued his studies and writing of bees; recognized the importance of the bee space, resulting in the development of the most commonly used movable-frame hive.

**Langstroth hive** = The basic hive design of L.L. Langstroth. In modern terms any hive that takes frames that have a 19" top bar and fit into a box $19^{7}/_{8}$" long. Widths vary from five frame nucs to eight frame boxes to ten frame boxes and from Dadant deeps, Langstroth deeps, Mediums, Shallows and Extra Shallow. But all would still be Langstroths. This would distinguish them from WBC, Smith, National DE etc.

**Large Cell** = Standard foundation size = 5.4mm cell size

**Larva, open** = The second developmental stage of a bee, starting the 4th day from when the egg is laid until it's capped on about the 9th or 10th day.

**Larva, capped** = The second developmental stage of a bee, ready to pupate or spin its cocoon (about the 10th day from the egg).

**Laying workers** = Worker bees which lay eggs in a colony caused by them being a few weeks without the pheromones from open brood; such eggs are infertile, since the workers cannot mate, and therefore become drones.

**Leg baskets** = Also called pollen baskets, a flattened depression surrounded by curved spines located on the outside of the tibiae of the bees' hind legs and adapted for carrying flower pollen and propolis.

**Lemon Grass essential oil** = Essential oil used for swarm lure which contains many of the constituents of Nasonov pheromone.

**Levulose** = Also called fructose (fruit sugar), a monosaccharide commonly found in honey that is slow to granulate.

**Long hive** = a hive that is laid out horizontally instead of vertically.

***M***

**Malpighian tubules** = Thin filamentous projects from the junction of the mid and hind gut of the bee that cleanse the hemolymph of nitrogenous cell wastes and deposit them as non-toxic uric acid crystals into the undigestible food wastes for elimination. They serve the same purpose as kidneys in higher animals.

**Mandibles** = The jaws of an insect; used by bees to form the honeycomb and scrape pollen, in fighting and picking up hive debris.

**Marking** = Painting a small dot of enamel on the back of the thorax of a queen to make her easier to identify and so you can tell her age and if she has been superseded.

**Marking pen** = An enamel pen used to mark queens. Available at local hardware stores as enamel pens. Also from beekeeping supply houses as Queen marking pens.

**Marking Tube** = A plastic tube commonly available from beekeeping supply houses that is used to safely confine a queen while you mark her.

**Mating flight** = The flight taken by a virgin queen while she mates in the air with several drones.

**Mating nuc** = A small nuc for the purpose of getting queens mated used in queen rearing. These vary from two frames of the standard size used by that beekeeper for brood, to the mini-mating nucs sold for that purpose with smaller than normal frames. The concept of all mating nucs is to use less resources to get queens mated

**Maxant** = A beekeeping equipment manufacturer that makes uncappers, extractors, hive tools etc.

**Medium** = A box that is $6^5/_8$″ in depth and the frames are $6^1/_4$″ in depth. AKA Illinois AKA Western AKA $^3/_4$ depth.

**Medium brood (foundation)** = When used to refer to foundation, medium refers to the thickness of the wax *not* the depth of the frame. In this case it's medium thick and of worker sized cells.

**Melissococcus pluton** = New name given by taxonomists for the bacterium that causes European foulbrood. The old name was Streptococcus pluton.

**Midnite** = An F1 hybrid cross of two specific lines of Caucasians and Carniolans. Originated by Dadant and Sons and sold for years by York. Originally they were two lines of Caucasians, but eventually became a cross between Caucasians and Carniolans.

**Migratory beekeeping** = The moving of colonies of bees from one locality to another during a single season to take advantage of two or more honey flows or for pollination.

**Migratory cover** = An outer cover used without an inner cover that does not telescope over the sides of the hive; used by commercial beekeepers who frequently move hives. This allows hives to be packed tightly against one another because the cover does not protrude over the sides.

**Miller Bee Supply** = A beekeeping supply company out of North Carolina *(www.millerbeesupply.com/)*. Among other things, they have eight frame equipment.

**Miller feeder** = Top feeder popularized by C.C. Miller.

**Miller Method** = A graftless method of queen rearing that involves a ragged edge on some brood comb for the bees to build queen cells on.

**Moisture content** = In honey, the percentage of water should be no more than 18.6; any percentage higher than that will allow honey to ferment.

**Mouse guard** = A device to reduce the entrance to a hive so that mice cannot enter. Commonly #4 hardware cloth.

**Movable combs** = Combs that are built in a hive that allows them to be manipulated and inspected individually. Top bar hives have movable combs but not frames. Langstroth hives have movable combs *in* frames.

**Movable frames** = A frame constructed in such a way to preserve the bee space, so they can be easily removed; when in place, it remains unattached to its surroundings.

***N***

**Nadiring** = Adding boxes below the brood nest. This is a common practice with foundationless including Warre' hives.

**Nasonov** = A pheromone given off by a gland under the tip of the abdomen of workers that serves primarily as an orientation pheromone. It is essential to swarming behavior and nasonoving is set off by disturbance of the colony. It is a mixture of seven terpenoids, the majority of which is Geranial and Neral, which are a pair of isomers usually mixed and called citral. Lemongrass (Cymbopogon) essential oil is mostly these scents and is useful in bait hives and to get newly hived bees or swarms to stay in a hive.

**Nasonoving** = Bees who have their abdomens extended and are fanning the Nasonov pheromone. The smell is lemony

**Natural cell** = Cell size that bees have built on their own without foundation.

**Natural comb** = Comb that bees have built on their own without foundation.

**Nectar** = A liquid rich in sugars, manufactured by plants and secreted by nectary glands in or near flowers; the raw material for honey.

**Nectar flow** = A period of time when nectar is available.

**Nectar Management aka Checkerboarding** = a method of swarm control originated by Walt Wright where the stores above the brood chamber are alternated with drawn comb late in the winter. Reports from those using it are of massive harvests and no swarming.

**New World Carniolans** = A breeding program originated by Sue Cobey to find and breed bees from the US with Carniolan traits and other commercially useful traits.

**Newspaper method** = A technique to join together two colonies by providing a temporary newspaper barrier. Usually one sheet with a small slit. Usually you make sure both colonies can still fly and ventilate.

**Nicot** = A particular brand of graftless queen rearing system.

**Nosema** = Disease caused by a fungus (used to be classified as a protozoan) called Nosema apis. The common chemical solution (which I don't use) was Fumidil which has been recently renamed Fumagilin-B. Feeding honey or syrup is an effective remedy. Symptoms are a white distended gut, dysentery and especially seeing Nosema under a microscope from the gut of a field stripped bee.

**Nuc, nuclei, nucleus** = A small colony of bees often used in queen rearing or the box in which the small colony of bees resides. The term refers to the fact that the essentials, bees, brood, food, a queen or the means to make one, are there for it to grow into a colony, but it is not a full sized colony.

**Nurse bees** = Young bees, usually three to ten days old, which feed and take care of developing brood.

***O***

**Observation Hive** = A hive made largely of glass or clear plastic to permit observation of bees at work

**Open-air Nest** = A colony that has built its nest in the open limbs of a tree rather than in the hollow of a tree or a hive.

**Open Mesh Floor** = A bottom board with screen (usually #8 hardware cloth) for the bottom to allow ventilation and to allow Varroa mites to fall through. In the US this is typically called a screened bottom board.

**Outer cover** = The last cover that fits over a hive to protect it from rain; the two most common kinds are telescoping and migratory covers.

**Outyard** = Also called out apiary, it is an apiary kept at some distance from the home or main apiary of a beekeeper.

**Ovary** = The egg producing part of a plant or animal.

**Ovule** = An immature female germ cell, which develops into a seed.

**Ovariole** = Any of several tubules that compose an insect ovary.

**Oxytetracycline aka Oxytet** = An antibiotic sold under the trade name Terramycin; used to control American and European foulbrood diseases.

***P***

**Package bees** = A quantity of adult bees (2 to 5 pounds), with or without a queen, contained in a screened shipping cage.

**Parasitic Mite Syndrome aka Bee Parasitic Mite Syndrome** = A set of symptoms that are caused by a major infestation of Varroa mites. Symptoms include the presence of Varroa mites, the presence of various brood diseases with symptoms similar to that of foulbroods and sacbrood but with no predominant pathogen, AFB-like symptoms, spotty brood pattern, increased supersedure of queens, bees crawling on the ground, and a low adult bee population.

**Parasitic Mites** = Varroa and tracheal mites are the mites with economic issues for bees. There are several others that are not known to cause any problems.

**Paralysis aka APV aka Acute Paralysis Virus** = A viral disease of adult bees which affects their ability to use legs or wings normally.

**Parthenogenesis** = The development of young from unfertilized eggs laid by virgin females (queen or worker); in bees, such eggs develop into drones.

**Para Dichloro Benzene (aka PDB aka Paramoth)** = Wax moth treatment for stored combs. A known carcinogen.

**PermaComb** = Fully drawn plastic comb in medium depth and about 5.0mm equivalent cell size after allowing for cell wall thickness and taper of the cell..

**PF100 (deep) and PF120 (medium)** = A small cell one piece plastic frame available from Mann Lake. Measures 4.95mm cell size. Users report excellent acceptance and perfectly drawn cells.

**Phoretic** = In the context of Varroa mites it refers to the state where they are on the adult bees instead of in the cell either developing or reproducing.

**Piping** = A series of sounds made by a queen, frequently before she emerges from her cell. When the queen is still in the cell it sounds sort of like a quack quack quack. When the queen has emerged it sounds more like zoot zoot zoot.

**Play flights aka orientation flights** = Short flights taken in front and in the vicinity of the hive by young bees to acquaint them with hive location; sometimes mistaken for robbing or swarming preparations.

**Pollen** = The dust-like male reproductive cells (gametophytes) of flowers, formed in the anthers, and important as a protein source for bees; fermented pollen (bee bread) is essential for bees to rear brood.

**Pollen basket** = An anatomical structure on the bees legs where pollen and propolis is carried.

**Pollen bound** = A condition where the brood nest of a hive is being filled with pollen so that there is nowhere for the queen to lay.

**Pollen box** = A box of brood moved to the bottom of the hive during the honey flow to induce the bees to store pollen there, or a box of pollen frames that was put on the bottom purposefully. This provides pollen stores for the fall and winter. The term was coined by Walt Wright.

**Pollen pellets or cakes** = The pollen packed in the pollen baskets of bees and transported back to the colony made by rolling in the pollen, brushing it off and mixing it with nectar and packing it into the pollen baskets.

**Pollen substitute** = A food material which is used to substitute wholly for pollen in the bees' diet; usually contains all or part of soy flour, brewers' yeast, wheast, powdered sugar, or other ingredients. Research has shown that bees raised on substitute are shorter lived than bees raised on real pollen.

**Pollen supplement** = A mixture of pollen and pollen substitutes used to stimulate brood rearing in periods of pollen shortage

**Pollen trap** = A device for collecting the pollen pellets from the hind legs of worker bees; usually forces the bees to squeeze through a screen mesh, usually #5 hardware cloth, which scrapes off the pellets which fall through #7 hardware cloth into a drawer with a screened bottom so the pollen won't mold.

**Porter bee escape** = Introduced in 1891, the escape is a device that allows the bees a one-way exit between two thin and pliable metal bars that yield to the bees' push; used to free honey supers of bees but may clog since drone bees often get stuck.

**Prime swarm** = The first swarm to leave the parent colony, usually with the old queen.

**Proboscis** = The mouthparts of the bee that form the sucking tube or tongue

**Propolis** = Plant resins collected, mixed with enzymes from bee saliva and used to fill in small spaces inside the hive and to coat and sterilize everything in the hive. It has antimicrobial properties. It is typically made from the waxy substance from the buds of the poplar family but in a pinch may be anything from tree sap to road tar.

**Propolize** = To fill with propolis, or bee glue.

**Pupa** = The third stage in the development of the bee during which it is inactive and sealed in its cocoon.

**Push In Cage** = Cage made of #8 hardware cloth used to introduce or confine queens to a small section of comb. Usually used over some emerging brood.

***Q***

**Queen** = A fully developed female bee responsible for all the egg laying of a colony.

**Queen Bank** = Putting multiple caged queens in a nuc or hive.

**Queen cage** = A special cage in which queens are shipped and/or introduced to a colony, usually with 4 to 7 young workers called attendants, and usually a candy plug.

**Queen cage candy** = Candy made by kneading powdered sugar with invert sugar syrup until it forms a stiff dough; used as food in queen cages.

**Queen cell** = A special elongated cell resembling a peanut shell in which the queen is reared; usually over an inch in length, it hangs vertically from the comb.

**Queen clipping** = Removing a portion of one or both wings of a queen to prevent her from flying or to better identify when she has been replaced.

**Queen cup** = A cup-shaped cell hanging vertically from the comb, but containing no egg; also made artificially of wax or plastic to raise queens

**Queen excluder** = A device made of wire, wood or zinc (or any combination thereof) having openings of .163 to .164 inch, which permits workers to pass but excludes queens and drones; used to confine the queen to a specific part of the hive, usually the brood nest.

**Queen juice** = When retired queens are added to a jar of alcohol, that alcohol becomes "Queen juice". It contains QMP and is good for swarm lure.

**Queenright** = A colony that contains a queen capable of laying fertile eggs and making appropriate pheromones that satisfy the workers of the hive that all is well.

**Queen Mandibular Pheromone aka Queen substance aka QMP** = A pheromone produced by the queen and fed to her attendants who share it with the rest of the colony that gives the colony the sense of being queenright. Chemically QMP is very diverse with at least 17 major components and other minor ones. 5 of these compounds are: 9-ox-2-decenoic acid (9ODA) + cis & trans 9 hydroxydec-2-enoic acid (9HDA) + methyl-p-hydroxybenzoate (HOB) and 4-hydroxy-3-methoxyphenylethanol (HVA). Newly emerged queens produce very little of this. By the sixth day they are producing enough to attract drones for mating. A laying queen makes twice that amount. QMP is responsible for inhibition of rearing replacement queens, attraction of drones for mating, stabilizing and organizing a swarm around the queen, attracting a retinue of attendants, stimulating foraging and brood rearing, and the general moral of the colony. Lack of it also seems to attract robber bees.

**Queen muff** = A screen wire tube that resembles a "muff" to keep your hands warm in shape but is used to keep queens from escaping when marking them or releasing attendants. Available from Brushy Mountain.

***R***

**Rabbet** = In wood working a groove cut into wood. The frame rests in a Langstroth hive are rabbets and the corners are sometimes done as rabbets and sometimes as finger or box joints.

**Races of Bees** = In taxonomy this is actually a variety but in beekeeping it is typically called a "race". All of these are Apis mellifera. The most common currently In the US are Italians (ligustica), Carniolans (carnica) and Caucasians (caucasica). Russians would be either carpatica, acervorum, carnica or caucasica depending on who you are talking to.

**Radial extractor** = A centrifugal force machine to throw out honey but leave the combs intact; the frames are placed like spokes of a wheel, top bars towards the wall, to take advantage of the upward slope of the cells.

**Rauchboy** = A particular brand of smoker that has an inner chamber to provide more consistent oxygen to the fire.

**Raw honey** = Honey that has not been finely filtered or heated.

**Regression** = As applied to cell size, large bees, from large cells, cannot build natural sized cells. They build something in between. Most will build 5.1 mm worker brood cells. Regression is getting large bees back to smaller bees so they can and will build smaller cells.

**Reorientation** = When the bees take note of their surroundings and landmarks to make sure they remember the location of the colony. A variety of things set this off. Young bees will orient (not reorient but it's the same behavior) when they first emerge from the hive. A virgin queen will orient for a day or so before going on her nuptials. Confining tends to set this off. Even short confinements will cause some to reorient. Confining for 72 hours causes virtually all of them to reorient. When it warms up and they can fly, they will hover around the hive and reorient. Reorientation is triggered even by lower times but the amount of it maxes out at 72 hours. More time won't make any noticeable difference. Obstructions add to reorientation (leaves in the entrance, a branch in front etc.) as does general disruption such as drumming or knocking the hive around a bit. On a warm day shaking a frame or two of bees back into the hive from the combs tends to set off Nasonoving which also tends to set off reorienting

**Requeen** = To replace an existing queen by removing her and introducing a new queen.

**Rendering wax** = The process of melting combs and cappings and removing refuse from the wax.

**Retinue** = Worker bees that are attending the queen.

**Reversing aka Switching** = The act of exchanging places of different hive bodies of the same colony;

usually for the purpose of nest expansion, the super full of brood and the queen is placed below an empty super to allow the queen extra laying space.

**Robber screen** = A screen used to foil robbers but let the local residents into the hive.

**Robbing** = The act of bees stealing honey/nectar from the other colonies; also applied to bees cleaning out wet supers or cappings left uncovered by beekeepers and sometimes used to describe the beekeeper removing honey from the hive.

**Ropy** = A quality of forming an elastic rope when drawn out with a stick. Used on capped brood as a diagnostic test for American foulbrood.

**Round sections** = Sections of comb honey in plastic round rings instead of square wooden boxes, usually Ross Rounds.

**Rolling** = A term to describe what happens when a frame is too tight or pulled out too quickly and bees get pushed against the comb next to it and "rolled". This makes bees very angry and is sometimes the cause of a queen being killed.

**Royal jelly** = A highly nutritious, milky white secretion of the hypopharyngeal gland of nurse bees; used to feed the queen and young larvae.

**Russian bees** = Apis mellifera acervorum or carpatica or caucasica or carnica. Some even say they are crossed with Apis ceranae (very doubtful). They came from the Primorsky region of Russia. They were used for breeding mite resistance because they were already surviving the mites. They are a bit defensive, but in odd ways. They tend to head butt a lot while not necessarily stinging any more. Any first cross of any race may be vicious and these are no exception. They are watchful guards, but not usually "runny" (tending to run around on the comb where you can't find the queen or work with them well). Swarminess and productivity are a bit more unpredictable. Traits are not well fixed. Frugality is similar to the Carniolans. They were brought to the USA by the USDA in June of 1997, studied on an island in Louisiana and then field testing in other states in 1999. They went on sale to the general public in 2000.

## *S*

**Sac Brood Virus** = Symptoms are the spotty brood patterns as other brood diseases but the larvae are in a sack with their heads raised.

**Sclerite** = Same as Tergite. An overlapping plate on the dorsal side of a arthropod that allows it to flex.

**Screened Bottom Board** = A bottom board with screen (usually #8 hardware cloth) for the bottom to allow ventilation and to allow Varroa mites to fall through. In Europe this is called an Open Mesh Floor.

**Scout bees** = Worker bees searching for a new source of pollen, nectar, propolis, water, or a new home for a swarm of bees.

**Scutum** = Shield shaped portion of the back of the thorax of some insects including Apis mellifera (honey bees). Usually divided into three areas: the anterior prescutum, the scutum, and the smaller posterior scutellum.

**Sections** = Small wooden (or plastic) boxes used to produce comb honey.

**Self-spacing frames aka Hoffman frames** = Frames constructed so that everything but the end bar (which is the spacer) is a bee space apart when pushed together in a hive body.

**Settling tank** = A large capacity container used to settle extracted honey; air bubbles and debris will float to the top, clarifying the honey.

**Shallow** = A box that is $5^{11}/_{16}$ or $5^{3}/_{4}$" deep with frames that are $5^{1}/_{2}$" deep.

**Shaken swarm** = An artificial swarm made by shaking bees off of combs into a screened box and then putting a caged queen in until they accept her. One method for making a divide. Also the method used to make packages of bees.

**Skep** = A beehive without movable combs, usually made of twisted straw in the form of a basket; its use is illegal in each state in the U.S as the combs are not inspectable.

**Slatted rack** = A wooden rack that fits between the bottom board and hive body. Bees make better use of the lower brood chamber with increased brood rearing, less comb gnawing, and less congestion at the front entrance. Popularized by C.C. Miller and Carl Killion.

**Slumgum** = The refuse from melted combs and cappings after the wax has been rendered or removed; usually contains cocoons, pollen, bee bodies and dirt.

**Small Cell** = 4.9mm cell size. Used by some beekeepers to control Varroa mites.

**Small Hive Beetle** = A pest recently imported to North America, whose larvae will destroy comb and ferment honey.

**Smith method** = A method of queen rearing popularized by Jay Smith, that uses a swarm box as a cell starter and grafting larvae into queen cups.

**Smoker** = A metal container with attached bellows which burns various fuels to generate smoke; used to interfere with the ability to smell alarm pheromone and therefore control aggressive behavior of bees during colony inspections.

**Solar wax melter** = A glass-covered box used to melt wax from combs and cappings using the heat of the sun.

**Sperm cells** = The male reproductive cells (gametes) which fertilize eggs; also called spermatozoa.

**Spermatheca** = A small sac connected with the oviduct of the queen bee in, which is stored, the spermatozoa received by the queen when mating with drones.

**Spiracles** = Openings into the respiratory system on a bee that can be closed at will. These are on the sides of the bee. They are considerably smaller than the Trachea they protect. The first thoracic spiracle is the one that is infiltrated by the tracheal mites as it is the largest. When closed the spiracles are air tight.

**Split** = To divide a colony for the purpose of increasing the number of hives.

**Spur embedder** = A device used for mechanically embedding wires into foundation by employing hand pressure as opposed to using electricity to melt the wires into the wax.

**Starline** = An Italian bee hybrid known for vigor and honey production. It was an F1 cross of two specific lines of Italian bees. Originated by Dadant and sons and produced for many years by York.

**Starter hive aka a Swarm box** = A box of shaken bees used to start queen cells.

**Sting** = An organ belonging exclusively to female insects developed from egg laying mechanisms, used to defend the colony; modified into a piercing shaft through which venom is injected. On workers this has a barb which causes it to catch and pull out.

**Streptococcus pluton** = Deprecated (old) name for the bacterium that causes European foulbrood. The new name is Melissococcus pluton.

**Sucrose** = A polysaccharide. The principal sugar found in nectar. Honey bees break this into Dextrose and Fructose with enzymes.

**Sugar syrup** = Feed for bees, containing sucrose or table (cane or beet) sugar and hot water in various ratios; usually 1:1 in the spring and 2:1 in the fall.

**Sugar roll test** = A test for Varroa mites that involves rolling a cupful of bees in powdered sugar and counting the number of mites dislodged. This was invented as a non-lethal alternative to an alcohol wash or an ether roll.

**Super** = A box with frames in which bees store honey; usually placed above the brood nest. From the Latin *super* meaning "above".

**Supering** = The act of placing honey supers on a colony in expectation of a honey flow.

**Supersedure** = Rearing a new queen to replace the mother queen in the same hive; shortly after the daughter queen begins to lay eggs, the mother queen often disappears.

**Suppressed Mite Reproduction aka SMR** = Queens from a breeding program by Dr. John Harbo that have less Varroa problems probably due to increased hygienic behavior. Lately renamed VSH aka Varroa Sensitive Hygiene.

**Surplus (foundation)** = Refers to thin foundation used for cut comb honey. The name is referring to the extra sheets of foundation you get from a pound of wax.

**Surplus honey** = Any extra honey removed by the beekeeper, over and above what the bees require for their own use, such as winter food stores.

**Survivor stock** = Bees raised from bees that were surviving without treatments. Often feral stock.

**Swarm** = A temporary collection of bees, containing at least one queen that split apart from the mother colony to establish a new one; a natural method of propagation of honey bee colonies.

**Swarm box aka a Starter hive** = A box of shaken bees used to start queen cells.

**Swarm cell** = Queen cells usually found on the bottom of the combs before swarming.

**Swarm commitment** = The point just after swarm cutoff where the colony is committed to swarming.

**Swarm cutoff** = The point at which the colony decides to swarm or not. Past this point they either commit to swarming or they commit to just looking out for colony stores for the coming winter.

**Swarm trap aka Bait hive aka Decoy hive** = A hive placed to attract stray swarms.

**Swarm preparation** = The sequence of activities of the bees that is leading up to swarming. Visually you can see this start at backfilling the brood nest so that the queen has nowhere to lay.

**Swarming** = The natural method of propagation of the honey bee colony.

**Swarming season** = The time of year, usually late spring to early summer, when swarms usually issue.

***T***

**Tanzanian Top Bar Hive** = A top bar hive with vertical sides.

**Telescopic cover** = A cover with a rim that hangs down all the way around it usually used with a inner cover under it.

**Ten frame** = A box made to take ten frames. $16^{1}/_{4}$″ wide.

**Terramycin** = Called oxytet in Canada and other locations. It is an antibiotic that is often used as a preventative for American and a cure for European foulbrood diseases.

**Tested queen** = A queen whose progeny shows she has mated with a drone of her own race and has other qualities which would make her a good colony mother. One that has been given time to prove what her qualities are.

**Tergal** = Pertaining to the Tergum.

**Tergite** = A hard overlapping plate on the dorsal portion of an arthropod that allows it to flex. Also known as sclerite.

**Tergum (plural terga)** = The dorsal portion of an arthropod.

**Thelytoky** = A type of parthenogenetic reproduction where unfertilized eggs develop into females. Usually with bees this is referring to a colony rearing a queen from a laying worker egg. This is very rare, but documented, with European honey bees. It is common with Cape Bees.

**Thin surplus foundation** = A comb foundation used for comb honey or chunk honey production which is thinner than that used for brood rearing. Thinner than surplus.

**Thorax** = The central region of an insect to which the wings and legs are attached.

**Tiger striped (queen)** = Markings of a particular type on a queen. Not striped like a worker (who have very even bands) but more like "flames".

**Top bar** = The top part of a frame or, in a top bar hive, just the piece of wood from which the comb hangs.

**Top Bar Hive** = a hive with only top bars and no frames that allows for movable comb without as much carpentry or expense.

**Top feeder** = Miller feeder. A box that goes on top of the hive that contains the syrup. See Miller Feeder.

**Top supering** = The act of placing honey supers on *top* of the top super of a colony as opposed to putting it under all the other supers, and directly on top of the brood box, which would be *bottom* supering or adding boxes below the brood box which would be nadiring.

**Tracheal Mites** = A mite that infests the trachea of the honey bee. Resistance to tracheal mites is easily bred for.

**Transferring or cut out** = The process of changing bees and combs from trees, houses or bee gums or skeps to movable frame hives.

**Travel stains** = The darkened appearance on the surface of honeycomb caused by bees walking over its surface.

**Triple-wide** = A box that is three times as wide as a standard ten frame box. 48³/₄″.

**Trophallaxis** = The transfer of food or pheromones among members of the colony through mouth-to-mouth feeding. It is used to keep a cluster of bees alive as the edges of the cluster collect food and share it through the cluster. It is also used for communication as pheromones are shared. One very important one is QMP (Queen Mandibular Pheromone) which is shared by trophallaxis throughout the hive.

**Twelve frame** = A box made to take twelve frames. This is $19^7/_8$" by $19^7/_8$".

**Two Queen Hive** = A management method where more than one queen exists in a hive. The purpose is you get more bees and more honey with two queens.

***U***

**Uncapping knife** = A knife used to shave off the cappings of sealed honey prior to extraction; hot water, steam or electricity can heat the knives.

**Uncapping tank** = A container over which frames of honey are uncapped; usually strains out the honey which is then collected.

**Unfertilized** = An ovum or egg, which has not been united with the sperm.

**Uniting** = Combining two or more colonies to form a larger colony. Usually done with a sheet of newspaper between.

**Unlimited Brood Nest aka "food chamber"** = running bees in a configuration where the brood nest is not limited by an excluder and they are usually overwintered in more boxes to allow more food and more expansion in the spring.

***V***

**Varroa destructor used to be called Varroa Jacobsoni** = Parasitic mite of the honey bee.

**Veil** = A protective netting or screen that covers the face and neck; allows ventilation, easy movement and good vision while protecting the primary targets of guard bees.

**Venom allergy** = A condition in which a person, when stung, may experience a variety of symptoms ranging from hives to anaphylactic shock. A person who is stung and experiences systemic (the whole body or places remote from the sting) symptoms should consult a physician before working bees again.

**Venom hypersensitivity** = A condition in which a person, if stung, is likely to experience an anaphylactic shock. A person with this condition should carry an emergency insect sting kit at all times during warm weather

**Virgin queen** = An unmated queen bee.

***W***

**Walter T. Kelley** = A beekeeping supply company out of Clarkson, KY. They have many things no one else does.

**Warré hive =** A type of vertical top bar hive invented by Abbé Émile Warré.

**Washboarding** = When the bees on the landing board or the front of a hive are moving in unison resembling a line dance.

**Warming cabinet** = An insulated box or room heated to liquefy honey or to heat honey to speed extraction.

**Wax Dipping Hives** = A method of protecting wood and also of sterilizing from AFB where the equipment is "fried" in a mixture of wax and gum resin. Usually done with paraffin sometimes done with beeswax.

**Wax glands** = The eight glands located on the last 4 visible, ventral abdominal segments of young worker bees; they secrete beeswax flakes.

**Wax moths** = See chapter *Enemies of the Bees*. Wax moths are opportunists. They take advantage of a weak hive and live on pollen, honey and burrow through the wax.

**Wax scale or flake** = A drop of liquid beeswax that hardens into a scale upon contact with air; in this form it is shaped into comb.

**Wax tube fastener** = A metal tube for applying a fine stream of melted wax to secure a sheet of foundation into a groove on a frame.

**Western** = I have seen this used in two ways. A box that is $6^{5}/_{8}$" in depth and the frames are $6^{1}/_{4}$" in depth. AKA Illinois AKA Medium AKA $^{3}/_{4}$ depth. Or referring to one that is $7^{5}/_{8}$".

**Western Bee Supply** = A beekeeping supply company out of Montana. The company that makes all of Dadant's equipment. Also sell eight frame equipment.

**Windbreaks** = Specially constructed, or naturally occurring barriers to reduce the force of the (winter) winds on a beehive.

**Winter cluster** = A tight ball of bees within the hive to generate heat; forms when outside temperature falls below 50º F.

**Winter hardiness** = The ability of some strains of honey bees to survive long winters by frugal use of stored honey.

**Wire, frame** = Thin 28# wire used to reinforce foundation destined for the broodnest or honey extractor.

**Wire cone escape** = A one-way cone formed by window screen mesh used to direct bees from a house or tree into a temporary hive.

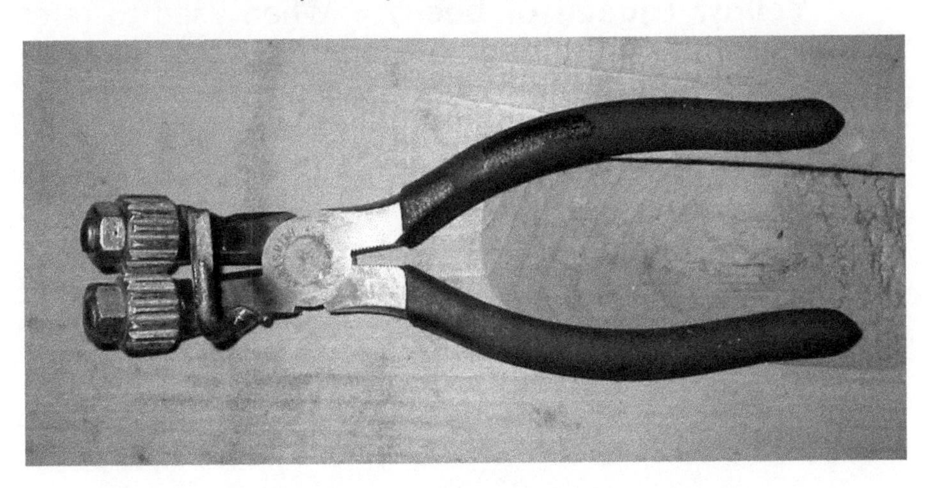

**Wire crimpers** = A device used to put a ripple in the frame wire to both make it tight and to distribute stress better and give more surface to bind it to the wax.

**Worker bees** = Infertile female bee whose reproductive organs are only partially developed, and is anatomically different than a queen and is equipped and responsible for carrying out all the routine duties of the colony.

**Worker comb** = Comb measuring between 4.4mm and 5.4mm, in which workers are reared and honey and pollen are stored.

**Worker Queen aka laying workers** = Worker bees which lay eggs in a colony hopelessly queenless; such eggs are not fertilized, since the workers cannot mate, and therefore become drones.

**Worker policing** = Workers that remove eggs laid by workers.

***Y***

**Yellow (queen or bees)** = When used to refer to honey bees this refers to a lighter brown color. Honey bees are *not* yellow. A Yellow queen is usually a solid light brown.

# Appendix to Volume I: Acronyms

**ABJ** = American Bee Journal. One of the two main bee magazines in the USA.

**AFB** = American foulbrood

**AHB** = Africanized Honey Bees

**AM** = Apis mellifera. (European honey bees)

**AMM** = Apis mellifera mellifera

**APV** = Acute Paralysis Virus. This virus kills both adult bees and brood.

**BC** = Bee Culture aka Gleanings in Bee Culture. One of the two main Beekeeping magazines in the USA

**BLUF** = Bottom Line Up Front. A style of writing where you present the conclusion at the beginning. Common in scientific studies or military correspondence.

**BPMS** = Bee Parasitic Mite Syndrome

**Carni** = Carniolan = Apis mellifera carnica

**Cauc** = Caucasian = Apis mellifera Caucasia

**CB** = Checkerboarding (aka Nectar Management)

**CCD** = Colony Collapse Disorder

**CPV** = Chronic Paralysis Virus

**CW** = Conventional Wisdom

**DCA** = Drone Congregation Area

**DVAV** = Dorsal-Ventral Abdominal Vibrations dance.

**DWV** = Deformed Wing Virus

**EAS** = Eastern Apiculture Society

**EFB** = European Foulbrood

**EHB** = European Honey Bees

**FGMO** = Food Grade Mineral Oil

**FWIW** = For What It's Worth.

**FWOF** = Floor With Out a Floor

**HAS** = Heartland Apiculture Society

**HBH** = Honey Bee Healthy

**HBTM** = Honey Bee Tracheal Mite

**HFCS** = High Fructose Corn Syrup. A common bee feed.

**HSC** = Honey Super Cell (Fully drawn plastic comb in deep depth and 4.9mm cell size)

**HMF** = Hydroxymethyl furfural. A naturally occurring compound in honey that rises over time and rises when honey is heated.

**IAPV** = Israeli Acute Paralysis Virus. The virus currently being blamed for CCD

**IPM** = Integrated Pest Management

**IMHO** = In My Humble Opinion

**IMO** = In My Opinion

**IMPOV** = In My Point Of View

**KTBH** = Kenya Top Bar Hive (one with sloped sides)

**KBV** = Kashmir Bee Virus

**LC** = Large Cell (5.4mm cell size)

**LGO** = Lemon Grass (essential) Oil (used for swarm lure)

**MAAREC** = Mid-Atlantic Apiculture Research and Extension Consortium

**NM** = Nectar Management (aka Checkerboarding)

**NWC** = New World Carniolans

**OA** = Oxalic Acid. An organic acid used to kill Varroa as either a syrup or vaporized.

**OSR** = Oil Seed Rape (aka Canola). A crop that produces honey that is grown to produce oil.

**PC** = PermaComb (Fully drawn plastic comb in medium depth and about 5.0mm cell size)

**PDB** = Para Dichloro Benzene (aka Paramoth wax moth treatment)

**PMS** = parasitic mite syndrome

**QMP** = Queen Mandibular Pheromone

**SBB** = Screened Bottom Board

**SBV** = Sac Brood Virus

**SC** = Small Cell (4.9mm cell size)

**SHB** = Small Hive Beetle

**SMR** = Suppressed Mite Reproduction (usually referring to a queen)

**TBH** = Top Bar Hive

**TM** = Terramycin or Tracheal Mites depending on the context

**T-Mites** = Tracheal Mites

**TTBH** = Tanzanian Top Bar Hive (one with vertical sides)

**ULBN** = Unlimited Brood Nest

**VD** = Varroa destructor

**VJ** = Varroa jacobsoni

**V-Mites** = Varroa Mites

**VSH** = Varroa Sensitive Hygiene. Similar to and appears to be a more specific name for the SMR trait. A trait in queens that is being bred for where the workers sense Varroa infested cells and clean them out.

# Volume II Intermediate

# A System of Beekeeping

***"...avoid the mistake of attempting to follow several leaders or systems. Much confusion and annoyance will be saved if he adopts the teachings, methods, and appliances of some one successful beekeeper. He may make the mistake of not choosing the best system, but better this than a mixture of several systems."—W.Z. Hutchinson, Advanced Bee Culture***

***"In general, the simpler the system, the more efficient and the larger the amount of work which can be accomplished in a given time."—Frank Pellet, Practical Queen Rearing***

In this volume, I am going to try to communicate my system of beekeeping. That is not to say it is the only system, but sometimes, as Hutchinson says, mixing up systems may or may not work depending on how well you understand how the parts of that system are related. First let us talk more about systems in general.

**Context**

One of the problems in giving beekeeping advice is that we beekeepers tend to give advice based on our system of beekeeping. In other words the advice, by our experience, works in our system of beekeeping. The problem is that this assumes that it will work just as well out of that context and in the context of someone else's system. Sometimes it does. But often it does not.

## Examples

For example, if my system is to use both upper and lower entrances and a queen excluder and I tell you to wait until you have some bees working the supers to put the excluder on, and your system is to have only a bottom entrance, and you do this, you'll trap a lot of drones in the supers and plug up the excluder with dead drones trying to get out.

Another obvious example would be if I run all the same sized frames and you run deeps for brood and shallows for supers. I tell you the way to get bees working the supers, is to bait them up with a frame of brood, except your brood frames won't fit. Or I tell you to top off their stores by putting some frames of honey in the brood boxes, except your frames of honey are all in shallows and your brood boxes are all deeps.

## Locale

Local also plays an important role in your system. See the chapter *Locality*. But it seems obvious when talking about cold climates and hot climates. But it does go beyond that as well.

## Summary

These are simple and obvious but there are many less obvious ones. The fact is that picking and choosing beekeeping techniques from several systems can lead to problems. There is nothing wrong with developing your own system of beekeeping eventually but you need to make sure you learn and understand a system first and know why you are doing what you are doing and then tweak it to meet your needs and your philosophy a little at a time.

### Why a system?

Why do we need a system? Why not just pick and choose what you like? Well, you can, it's just that you have to think about all the ramifications. For instance if you decide you want to do a pollen trap, you have to figure out how the drones will get out. The best ones with the cleanest pollen go on top and that's an adjustment if they are used to a bottom entrance. If you decide to put an excluder on, you have to figure out how the drones on both sides of that excluder will get out. Everything you do has its ramifications and those can affect other things. So that's why we need to work out a system, and not just look at the individual pieces.

### Integration and related issues

### Why this system?

I have designed a system that works for me in my location with my problems. Hopefully you can use it for your situation and your problems. There is nothing wrong with making adjustments to it to fit your style, if you adjust for the ramifications. But here's why I picked the things I did.

### Sustainable

I wanted a system that did not require a lot of input from the outside — Bees in an environment that they could survive without my help.

**Workable**

I needed a system that would keep them alive (obviously) and that they could make honey and I could handle the labor involved.

**Efficient**

Back to the labor involved, I needed a system that minimized it especially things that were painful or dangerous like lifting really heavy boxes and time consuming things like wiring frames.

# Decisions, Decisions...

***Kinds of beekeeping***

Many decisions depend on what kind of beekeeping you do.

**Commercial**

Commercial is generally the term used for someone who does beekeeping as their full-time job. There are different methods of doing this. Usually it involves at least 500 to 1,000 hives.

**Migratory**

A migratory beekeeper moves their hives around. Usually they are collecting pollination fees, but sometimes it is just an effort to move south for the winter, so they can build up early and follow the nectar flows north to cash in on as much honey as possible. Pollination is usually something they are paid for.

**Fixed**

I'm simply referring to hives that stay in one place for the most part. Usually the beekeeper finds places to put the hives, often not on their own property, where the hives can remain year around. Usually the beekeeper gives some honey to the landowner every fall when the harvest comes in. How much would depend on several things, such as how many hives, how good the forage is for the bees and how much the landowner likes honey. Some just want the bees there, some are hoping for the honey.

## Sideliner

A sideliner is someone with a full-time job already, but they do make some income from the bees. Usually they have from 50 to 200 hives. It's very difficult to keep any number higher and keep a full time job unless you hire some help. It's difficult to make enough money to live on even with 1,000 hives sometimes, so the transition from Sideliner to full-time can be difficult without hired help.

## Hobbyist

A hobbyist is generally defined as anyone who is not making money on the bees. Most hobbyists seem to have about four hives. Two is pretty much the minimum. More than ten or so is a lot of work so most hobbyists tend to stay below that.

### *Personal Beekeeping Philosophy*

A lot of decisions on equipment or methods, depend on your personal philosophy of life and your personal philosophy of beekeeping. Some people have more faith in Nature or the Creator or Evolution to work things out. Some are more interested in keeping their bee healthy with chemicals and treatments. You'll have to decide where you stand on these kinds of things.

## Organic

If you're the type to take an herbal remedy before you run to the doctor, you probably fall into this category. True organic would be no treatments whatsoever. Some will say this can't be done, but there are many people including me doing it. Many are online and help each other through it. After that there are "soft" treatments like essential oils and FGMO, and then slightly "harder" treatments like formic acid and oxalic acid for Varroa.

### Chemical

If you're the type who runs to the doctor for antibiotics the second you get a sniffle this is probably more your style. Some in this group treat for prevention. IMO the wiser ones treat only when necessary. Most of the recent research shows that treating when for prevention has caused resistance to the chemicals on the part of the pests and has done little to help the hive and often hurt them. Chemical buildup in the wax from coumaphos (CheckMite) and fluvalinate (Apistan) used for Varroa mites, is suspected to be the cause of high supersedure rates, and known to be the cause of infertility in drones and queens.

### Science vs. Art

> ***"Those who are accustomed to judge by feeling do not understand the process of reasoning, for they would understand at first sight and are not used to seek for principles. And others, on the contrary, who are accustomed to reason from principles, do not at all understand matters of feeling, seeking principles and being unable to see at a glance."—Blaise Pascal***

If you see beekeeping as an art or you see it as a science it will change your perspective a lot. I think it's a bit of both, but since bees are quite capable of surviving on their own and since we really can't coerce them into doing anything, I see it as more of an art where you work with the bees natural tendencies to help them and yourself.

### Scale

This is another thing that changes your philosophy on many things. When you have time to spend with the hives and the hives are in your backyard, then methods that require you to do something every week are not a big problem. For instance, when I requeen in my own yard, I don't mind if it takes three trips to the hive to get it done if that improves acceptance. But if it's at an outyard 60 miles away, I want to do something one time and be done. The same is true of the number of hives. If you have only two hives to deal with on a certain issue, you may not mind how complicated it is. When you have hundreds of hives to deal with, you have to have a streamlined system.

### Reasons for beekeeping

A lot of your decisions will be guided by this. If you have bees as pets you have a different agenda than if you have them solely to make a living.

# Locality

***All Beekeeping is Local***

> ***"In my earlier beekeeping years I was often sorely puzzled at the diametrically opposite views often expressed by the different correspondents for the bee journals. In extension of that state of mind I may say that at that time I did not dream of the wonderful differences of locality in its relation to the management of bees. I saw, measured weighted, compared, and considered all things apicutlural by the standard of my own home—Genesee County, Michigan. It was not until I had seen the fields of New York white with buckwheat, admired the luxuriance of sweet-clover growth in the suburbs of Chicago, followed for miles the great irrigating ditches of Colorado, where they give lift to the royal purple of the alfalfa bloom, and climbed mountains in California, pulling myself up by grasping the sagebrush, that I fully realized the great amount of apicultural meaning stored up in that one little word—locality." —W.Z. Hutchinson, Advanced Bee Culture***

It seems rather obvious that beekeeping in Florida won't be the same as beekeeping in Vermont, but what people don't seem to realize is that even in similar winter climates beekeeping is still local. The flows you have in Vermont are not the same as you have in Nebraska. The issues of things like condensation may be very dependent on local climate. For instance, when I was beekeeping in the panhandle of Nebraska, condensation was never a problem. But beekeeping in southeastern Nebraska it is. It's actually colder in the panhandle, and yet, because of differences in humidity, it is not a problem there. All of this seems rather obvious, and yet people continue to ask advice and give advice and contradict advice based on their local experiences without any consideration that warnings given by a beekeeper that they think are unwarranted may be in some locales and not in others. Of course this also applies to things like how many boxes and how much weight do they need to get through the winter and when to manage for swarming and when to start queens and when to do splits and so on.

# Lazy Beekeeping

***"Everything works if you let it"—
Rick Nielsen of Cheap Trick***

***"The master accomplishes more and more by doing less and less until finally he accomplishes everything by doing nothing." —
Laozi, Tao Te Ching***

---

My grandpa used to say that every great invention came from a lazy man. One of my favorite authors said something similar:

***"Progress doesn't come from early risers - progress is made by lazy men looking for easier ways to do things." —Robert Heinlein***

***"It's not the daily increase but daily decrease. Hack away at the unessential."—Bruce Lee***

---

In the past few years I've changed most of how I keep bees. Most of it was to make it less work. As of 2007 I've been keeping about two hundred hives with about the same work I used to put into four hives. Here are some of the things I've changed.

---

***Top Entrances***

I've gone to only top entrances. No bottom entrance. I know there are all kinds of people who either hate top entrances or think they cure cancer, or double your honey crop. I don't think either. But I like them and here's why:

1. I never have to worry about the bees not having access to the hive because the grass grew too tall. I also don't have to cut the grass in front of the hives. Less work for me.

2. I never have to worry about the bees not having access because of the snow being too deep (unless it gets over the tops of the hives). So I don't

have to shovel snow after a snowstorm to open the entrances up.

3. I never have to worry about putting mouse guards on or mice getting into the hive.

4. I never have to worry about skunks or opossums eating the bees.

5. Combined with a SBB I have very good ventilation in the summer.

6. I can save money buying (or making) simple migratory style covers. Most of mine are just a piece of plywood with shingle shims for spacers. But some are wider notches in inner covers that I already had.

7. In the winter I don't have to worry about dead bees clogging the bottom entrance.

8. I can put the hive eight inches lower (because I don't have to worry about mice and skunks) and that makes it easier to put that top super on and get it off when it's full.

9. Lower hives blow over less in the wind.

10. This works nicely for long top bar hives when I put supers on because the bees have to go in the super to get in.

11. With some Styrofoam on the top, there's not much condensation with a top entrance in the winter.

Just remember, if you have no bottom entrance and you use an excluder (which I don't) you will need some kind of drone escape on the bottom for them to get out. A $^3/_8$″ hole will do.

More detail in the Chapter *Top Entrances.*

---

***Uniform frame size.***

> ***"Whatever style (hive) may be adopted, let it by all means be one with movable frames, and have but one sized frame in the apiary."—A.B. Mason, Mysteries of Bee-keeping Explained***

The frame is the basic element of a modern bee-hive. Even if you have various sized boxes (as far as the number of frames they hold) if the frames are all the same depth you can put them in any of your boxes.

Having a uniform frame size has simplified my life. If all your frames are the same size you have a lot of advantages.

You can put anything currently in the hive anywhere else it's needed.

**For instance:**

1. You can put brood up a box to "bait" the bees up. This is useful even without an excluder (I don't use excluders) but it's especially useful if you really want to use an excluder. A couple of frames of brood above the excluder, leaving the queen and the rest of the brood below, really motivates the bees to cross the excluder and start working the next box above it.

2. You can put honeycombs in for food wherever you need it. I like this for making sure nucs don't starve without the robbing that feeding often starts, or bulking up the stores of a light hive in the fall.

3. You can unclog a brood nest by moving pollen or honey up a box or even a few frames of brood up a box to make room in the brood nest to prevent swarming. If you don't have all the same size, where will you put these frames?

4. You can run an unlimited brood nest with no excluder and if there is brood anywhere you can move it anywhere else. You're not stuck with a bunch of brood in a medium that you can't move down to your deep brood chamber. The advantage of the unlimited brood nest is the queen isn't limited to one or two brood boxes, but can be laying in three or four—probably not four deeps, but probably in four mediums.

I cut all my deeps down to mediums.

Typically I hear the question, "do mediums winter as well?" and I say they winter better in my experience as they have better communication between the frames because of the gap between the boxes. Steve of Brushy Mountain used to say there was some research to this effect, but I'm unsure where to find it.

---

***Lighter boxes***

> ***"Friends don't let friends lift deeps"***
> ***—Jim Fischer of Fischer's BeeQuick***

---

The hardest thing for me about beekeeping is lifting. Boxes full of honey are heavy. Deep boxes full of honey are *very* heavy.

There may be some disagreement as to the exact weights of a full box of honey, and there are other factors involved but in my experience this is a pretty good synopsis of sizes of boxes and typical uses for them:

| **10 frame boxes** | | | |
|---|---|---|---|
| Name(s) | Depth | lbs full | Uses |
| Jumbo, Dadant Deep | $11^5/_8$″ | 100-110 | Brood |
| Deep Langstroth Deep | $9^5/_8$″ | 80-90 | Brood & ext |
| Medium, Illinois, $^3/_4$, Western | $6^5/_8$″ | 60-70 | Brood, Ext, Cmb |
| Shallow | $5^3/_4$″, $5^{11}/_{16}$″ | 50-60 | Ext, Cmb |
| Extra Shallow, $^1/_2$ | $4^3/_4$″, $4^{11}/_{16}$″ | 40-50 | Cmb |
| **8 frame boxes** | | | |
| Dadant Deep | $11^5/_8$″ | 80-88 | Brood |
| Deep | $9^5/_8$″ | 64-72 | Brood, Ext |
| Medium | $6^5/_8$″ | 48-55 | Brood, Ext, Cmb |
| Shallow | $5^3/_4$″, $5^{11}/_{16}$″ | 40-48 | Ext Cmb |
| Extra Shallow | $4^3/_4$″, $4^{11}/_{16}$″ | 32-40 | Cmb |

If you want a grasp of these and don't have a hive yet, go to the hardware store and stack up two fifty pound boxes of nails or, at the feed store, two fifty pound bags of feed. This is approximately the weight of a full deep. Now take one off and lift one box. This is approximately the weight of a full eight frame medium.

I find I can lift about fifty pounds pretty well, but more is usually a strain that leaves me hurting the next few days. The most versatile size frame is a medium and a box of them that weighs about 50 pounds is an eight frame.

So, first I converted all my deeps into mediums. It was a huge improvement over the occasional deep full of honey I had to lift. I still got tired of lifting 60 pound boxes, so I cut the ten frame mediums down to eight frame mediums and I am really liking them. They are a comfortable weight to lift all day long and not be in pain for the next week. Any lighter and I might be tempted to try to lift two. Any heavier and I'm wishing it was a shade lighter.

I'm wondering how many aging beekeepers have been forced to give up bees because they hurt themselves lifting deeps and it hasn't occurred to them there are other choices?

Richard Taylor in *The Joys of Beekeeping* says:

> ***"...no man's back is unbreakable and even beekeepers grow older. When full, a mere shallow super is heavy, weighing forty pounds or more. Deep supers, when filled, are ponderous beyond practical limit."***

I often get asked what the down side of using all eight frame mediums is. There is only one I know of.

8 frame medium vs. 10 frame deep = 1.78 times more initial investment for boxes. ($64 for four eight

frame mediums plus frames vs. $36 for two deeps plus frames)

$512 vs. $288 for eight boxes vs. four boxes

Plus lids and bottoms ($20 either way)

$532 vs. $308 = 1.73 times more or $224

100 hives * $224 = $22,400 which should just about cover your first back surgery.

Typically I hear the question, "do they winter as well?" and I say they winter better in my experience as the cluster fits the box better and they don't leave behind frames of honey on the outside as much as they do in the ten frame hives.

The other big plus is being able to treat a box as a unit when splitting instead of a frame.

More details on how to cut down boxes in Volume three Chapter *Lighter Boxes.*

---

***Horizontal hives***

To take not lifting to the next level, how about a hive that's all on one level?

I currently have nine horizontal hives and they have done well. There are some slight adjustments to how to manage them, but the principles are the same. You just can't juggle boxes around. Only frames. But then you can put super on a long hive if you like.

I inherited a few deeps and I already had a Dadant deep, so I currently have three horizontal deeps ($9^5/_8$"), one horizontal Dadant Deep ($11^5/_8$"), four horizontal mediums and one Kenya top bar hive.

I wonder how many old beekeepers, who are being forced to give up their bees, could keep a couple of these without hurting themselves and without much stress?

I wonder how many commercial beekeepers could minimize the labor involved in their operation with these?

I wonder how many hobbyists could just make their life easier with less lifting?

More detail in Volume 3 *Lighter Equipment.*

---

***Top Bar Hive***

Here's another labor saver. How about not even building frames? Or put in foundation—just top bars.

One big long box instead of three separate ones? All the advantages of a horizontal hive. Plus calmer bees because you only face a frame or two of them at a time instead of exposing ten frames of them simultaneously. See Volume 3 *Top Bar Hives* for more detail.

---

***Foundationless frames***

**Making foundationless frames**

You can just break out the wedge on a top bar, turn it sideways and glue and nail it on to make a guide. Or put Popsicle sticks or paint sticks in the groove. Or just cut out the old comb in a drawn wax comb and leave a row at the top or all the way around.

You can cut a triangle off of the corner of a $^3/_4$" board and have a triangle that on its broad side is $1^1/_{16}$". Or buy some chamfer molding and cut it to length. This can be nailed and glued to the bottom of a top bar to make a peak that the bees will attach to. Once you've made these frames you won't need to put starter strips or foundation in them. Or you can just cut a 45° angle on each side of a top bar before you put the frame together.

Also you can put empty frames with no guides between drawn combs and you can put frames with a top row of cells left on the top bar in anywhere you'd put a frame of foundation.

How much time do you spend putting in foundation, wiring it, tearing it out because it sagged and crumpled or fell out of the frame?

I don't do much of that lately. I mostly use foundationless instead.

And that's not even taking into account the cost of foundation, let alone small cell foundation.

It saves me a lot of work.

Yes, I extract them. I can also use them for cut comb.

No, I don't wire them but you can if you like.

For more detail see the chapter *Foundationless*

---

***No chemicals/no artificial feed***

Going to no chemicals saves a lot of work and trouble. All the frames are "clean" so you don't have to worry about residue. If you only feed honey, it's all honey and you don't have to worry what might be syrup instead. You can harvest honey from where ever you find it. And of course you don't have to put in and pull out strips, mix up Fumidil syrup and dust with Terramycin, treat with menthol, make grease patties, fog with FGMO, make up cords, and evaporate oxalic acid. Just think of all the spare time you'll have, and how clean your honey will be.

I've found natural cell size a prerequisite at least for dropping the Varroa mite treatments.

---

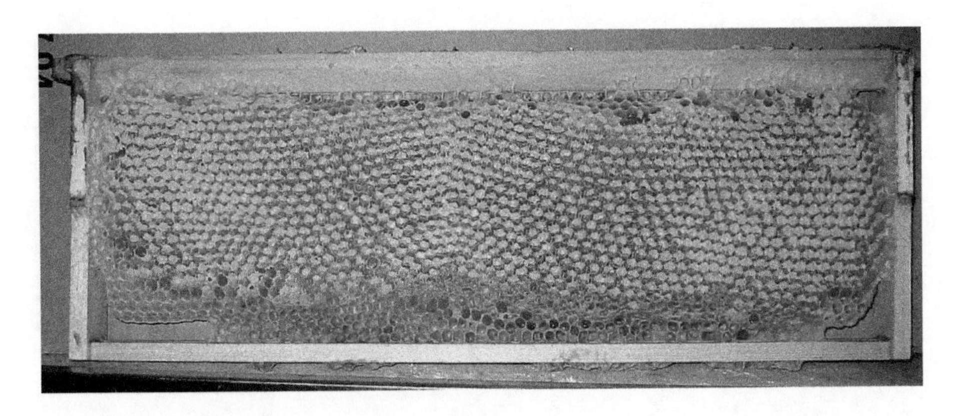

***Leave honey for winter food***

Instead of feeding, just leave them enough. You don't have to harvest it. You don't have to extract it. You don't have to make syrup. You don't have to feed them for winter.

Plus there may be other advantages:

> ***"It is well known that improper diet makes one susceptible to disease. Now is it not reasonable to believe that extensive feeding of sugar to bees makes them more susceptible to American Foul Brood and other bee disease? It is known that American Foul Brood is more prevalent in the north than in the south. Why? Is it not because more sugar is fed to bees in the north while here in the south the bees can gather nectar most of the year which makes feeding sugar syrup unnecessary?"—Better Queens, Jay Smith***

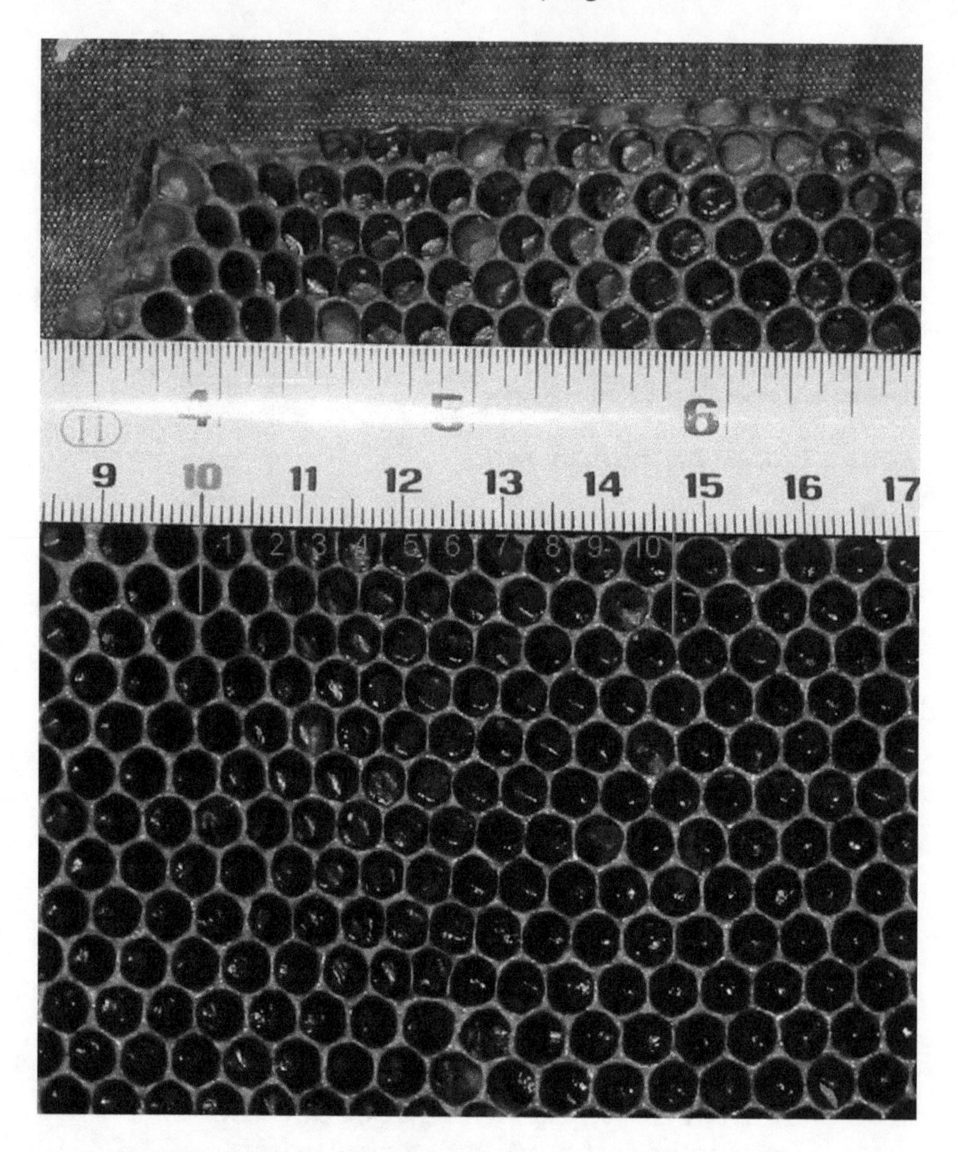


***Natural cell size***

Of course you get this with foundationless frames or top bar hives, but the "side effect" (or the effect if it's what you were looking for) is not only the labor you save wiring wax or buying and inserting foundation, but once the Varroa mites are under control and your mite counts have stayed stable for a couple of years, you might even be able to forget about Varroa. I have.

It is very nice to be back to just worrying about the bees instead of the mites. See *Natural Cell Size* chapter for more information.

***Carts***

Carts have really helped me with my back. My main yard is across the pasture from my house. Moving boxes, both full and empty, back and forth is a lot of work. It's hardly worth loading the boxes in my van to drive around the long way to get to the hives or vice versa. But it's a long carry. I bought three carts and have used all of them to advantage. I mostly use the Mann Lake and Walter T. Kelley ones right now.

I modified both the Mann Lake and Brushy ones a bit because the boxes would rattle off the cart on the way over to the hives and the Mann Lake one was a little too far off the ground, so I moved the axle up to lower the arms. The Brushy Mt one needed a rack (so they wouldn't rattle off) and a bolt for a stop so I can wheel it around empty. More detail in *Carts*.

***Leave the burr comb between boxes***

> ***"Some beekeepers dismantle every hive and scrape every frame, which is pointless as the bees soon glue everything back the way it was." — The How-To-Do-It book of Beekeeping, Richard Taylor***

Here's one I think helps the bees, gives you a chance to monitor for mites on drone pupae and saves work. Leave the burr comb that goes from the bottom of one frame to the top of the one below it. Yes it will break when you separate the boxes, but it makes a nice ladder for the queen to get from one box to the next. Also, they often build some drone comb between the boxes and if you tear them open you'll see the drone pupae and maybe you'll notice mites (you should be looking).

***Stop cutting out swarm cells***

I read the books and I tried to do this when I was young, inexperienced and foolish. The bees soon taught me what a waste of time and effort it was. If the bees have made up their mind to swarm, do a split or put each frame with some swarm cells in a nuc with a frame of honey and get some nice queens. Once they've gone this far, I've never seen them change their mind. Of course the solution was to keep it from getting this far. Keeping the brood nest open while keeping enough expansion room in the supers is the best swarm control I've found. If the brood nest is getting filled with honey, put a couple of empty frames in. Yes, empty. No foundation, nothing. Try it. The bees will build some drone comb, probably the first frame, but after that they'll draw some very nice worker brood and the queen will have it laid up before the whole comb is even drawn or even full depth. You'll be shocked how quickly they can do this and how it distracts them from swarming.

---

***Stop fighting your bees***

> ***"There are a few rules of thumb that are useful guides. One is that when you are confronted with some problem in the apiary and you do not know what to do, then do nothing. Matters are seldom made worse by doing nothing and are often made much worse by inept intervention." —The How-To-Do-It Book of Beekeeping, Richard Taylor***

I don't know how often I see questions on bee forums asking how can I make the bees do this or that. Well, you can't make them do anything. In the end they do what bees do no matter what you try to make them do. You can help them out, by making sure they have the resources they need to do what you think they need to do and by manipulating the hive so they don't swarm. You can fool them into making queens and such. But you'll have a lot more fun and work a lot less if you stop trying to make them do anything.

---

***Stop wrapping your hive.***

> ***"Although we now and again have to put up with exceptionally severe winters even here in the south-west, we do not provide our colonies with any additional protection. We know that cold, even severe cold, does not harm colonies***

> ***that are in good health. Indeed, cold seems to have a decided beneficial effect on bees."—Beekeeping at Buckfast Abbey, Brother Adam***

> ***"Nothing has been said of providing warmth to the colonies, by wrapping or packing hives or otherwise, and rightly so. If not properly done, wrapping or packing can be disastrous, creating what amounts to a damp tomb for the colony" — The How-To-Do-It Book of Beekeeping, Richard Taylor***

I suppose this also includes all the worrying about winter and trying to give them heaters and such. The bees have lived for millions of years with no heaters and no help. If you make sure they are strong and have enough food and adequate ventilation so they don't end up in an icicle from condensation, then you should relax. Work on your equipment and see them in the spring, or at the earliest, late winter.

---

***Stop scraping all the propolis off of everything***

> ***"Propolis rarely creates problems for a beekeeper. Certainly any effort to keep a hive free of it by systematic and frequent scraping, is time wasted." —The How-To-Do-It Book of Beekeeping, Richard Taylor***

Doesn't it feel like a losing battle anyway? The bees will just replace it, so unless it's directly in your way, why bother?

---

***Stop painting your equipment.***

> ***"The hives need no painting, although there is no harm in doing it if their owner wants to please his own eye. The bees find their way to their own hives more easily if the hives do not all look alike. I rarely paint mine, and as a result no two are quite alike. Most have the appearance of many years of use and many seasons of exposure to***

***the elements." —Richard Taylor, The Joys of Beekeeping***

***"I suppose they would last longer if painted, but hardly enough longer to pay for the paint." —C.C. Miller, Fifty Years Among the Bees***

---

You've probably noticed by now, if you looked at pictures of my hives, that a lot of them are not painted. Maybe the neighbors or the wife will complain but the bees won't care. They might not last as long. I don't know because I only stopped painting them about four years ago. But think of all the time you'll save!

Lately I bought a lot of equipment and wanted to keep it as nice as I could for as long as I could so I started dipping them in beeswax and gum rosin.

---

***Stop switching hive bodies.***

***"Some beekeepers, trusting the ways of bees less than I do, at this point routinely 'switch hive bodies,' that is, switch the positions of the two stories of each hive, thinking that this will induce the queen to increase her egg laying and distribute it more widely through the hive. I doubt, however, that any such result is accomplished, and in any case I have long since found that such planning is best left to the bees." –Richard Taylor, The Joys of Beekeeping***

---

In my opinion switching hive bodies is counter-productive. It's a lot of work for the beekeeper and it's a lot of work for the bees. After you swap them the bees have to rearrange the brood nest. It's true it will interrupt swarming, but so will other things. See the chapter *Swarm Control* for what I do.

---

***Don't look for the queen.***

Don't look for the queen unless you have to. It's one of the most time consuming operations. Instead look for eggs or open brood. Nothing wrong with keeping your eye out for her, but trying to find her is time consuming. This even works for things like setting up mating nucs. If you break up a hive for mating nucs and don't look for the queen on the frames and give to the nucs you may lose a queen, but you'll save a lot of time. She'll just get superseded. The only real advantage to finding the queen often is the practice but this could be more easily done with an observation hive.

If you have issues you are concerned about regarding queens, give them a frame of eggs and open brood from another hive and move on. If they are queenless they will raise one. If they are not, you haven't interfered. See the Volume I BLUF the section Panacea for more information.

---

***Don't wait.***

There are many operations where people, including me, will tell you to remove the queen and wait until the next day. This would be things like introducing queen cells to nucs or introducing a new queen to a hive. Waiting will improve the odds of acceptance, But reality is it will only improve it a little. So if you want to save time, don't wait until the next day unless you have to, do it now while you have the hive open.

---

***Feed dry sugar.***

No, they won't take it as well, but if you have to feed it will keep them from starving and you won't have to make syrup and you won't have to buy feeders and you won't have any drowned bees. See *Feeding Bees* for more details.

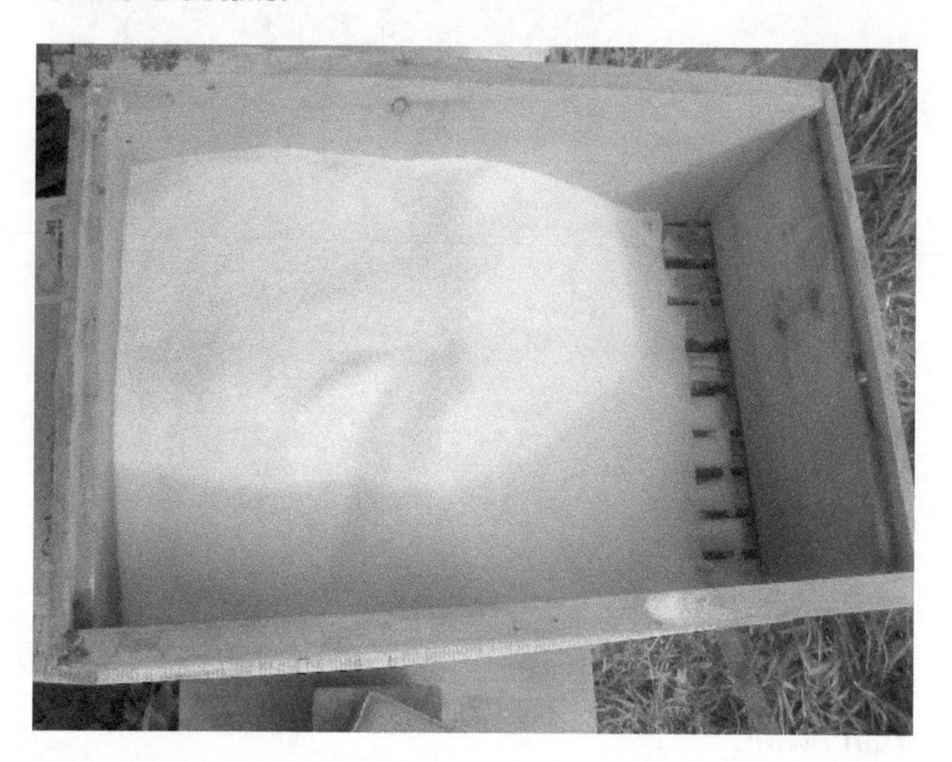

---

***Split by the box.***

If you've got a booming hive you want to split in the spring, don't look for the queen, don't look for brood, just split it by boxes. The bottom two boxes that are seriously occupied by bees probably have brood in them. Of course success is mostly dependent on being able to guess pretty accurately that you have brood and stores in both boxes. If you're wrong, you'll end up with one box empty after only a day or so. But if you are right, you've saved a lot of work. With eight frame mediums (which are half the volume of a ten frame deep) the odds of this working on a hive that is at least four boxes (the equivalent of two ten frame deeps) is twice as good. You just deal the boxes like cards. Put a bottom board on each side and do "one for you and one for you" until you're done. Come back in a month and see how they are doing.

---

***Stop Requeening.***

If you let the bees requeen themselves you'll breed bees that *can* and *do* requeen themselves. Bees in nature have this selective pressure on them. Bees that are constantly requeened by the beekeeper do not have this selective pressure on them. I would only requeen if the hive seems to be failing and I would do so from a hive that is successful at requeening themselves.

Along with this, of course, stop buying queens. Make splits and let the bees raise their own. That way you get bees that are well adapted to your climate and your pests and your diseases; *and* you get diseases and pests that are well adapted to coexist with the bees instead of killing them.

# Feeding Bees

You would think something this simple would not be controversial, but it is—on several fronts.

***First,* when *do you feed?***

> ***"Q. When is the best time to feed the bees?***
>
> ***"A. The best thing is never to feed them, but let them gather their own stores. But if the season is a failure, as it is some years in most places, then you must feed. The best time for that is just as soon as you know they will need feeding for winter; say in August or September. October does very well, however, and even if you haven't fed until December, better feed then than to let the bees starve."***
>
> ***—C.C. Miller, A Thousand Answers to Beekeeping Questions, 1917***

In my opinion there are many reasons to avoid feeding if you can. It sets off robbing. It attracts pests (ants, wasps, yellow jackets etc.) It clogs the brood nest and sets off swarming. It drowns a lot of bees, not to mention it's a lot of work. Then if you use syrup there is the effect of the pH on the microbial culture of the hive and difference in nutritional value compared to what they would have gathered on their own.

Some people feed a package constantly for the first year. In my experience this usually results in them swarming when they are not strong enough and often failing. Some feed spring, fall and dearth regardless of stores. Some don't believe in feeding at all. Some steal all the honey in the fall and try to feed them back up enough to winter.

Personally I don't feed if there is a nectar flow and they have some capped stores. Gathering nectar is what bees do. They should be encouraged to do it. I will feed in the spring if they are light, as they will not rear brood without sufficient stores to do it with. I will feed in the fall if they are light, but I always try to make sure I don't take too much honey and leave them light. Some years, though, the fall flow fails and they are on the verge of starvation if I don't feed. When queen rearing, during a dearth, I sometimes have to feed to get them to make cells and to get the queens to fly out and mate. So while I do try to avoid feeding, I end up doing it very often. In my opinion, there is nothing wrong with feeding if you have a good reason for doing it, but my plan is to try to avoid it and leave the bees enough to live on. Also, while I think honey is the best food for them, it's too much work to harvest it and then feed it back, so when I feed it's either dry sugar or sugar syrup, unless I have some honey I don't think is marketable.

Pollen, if fed, is usually fed before the first available pollen in the spring. Here (Greenwood, Nebraska) that would be about mid February. I have not had luck getting bees to take it any other time except a fall dearth.

***Stimulative feeding.***

A lot of literature out there will act like stimulative feeding is an absolute necessity to get honey production. Many of the greats of beekeeping have decided this is not productive:

> ***"The reader will by now have drawn the conclusion that stimulative feeding, apart from getting the foundations drawn out in the brood chamber, plays no part in our scheme of bee-keeping. This is in fact so." —Beekeeping at Buckfast Abbey, Brother Adam***

> ***"Very many, at the present time, seem to think that brood rearing can be made to forge ahead much faster by feeding the bees a teacupful of thin sweet every day than by any other method; but from many experiments along this line during the past thirty years I can only think this a mistaken idea, based on theory rather than on a practical solution of the matter by taking a certain number of colonies in the same apiary, feeding half of them while the other half are left "rich" in stores, as above, but without feeding and then comparing "notes" regarding each half, thus determining which is the better to go into the honey harvest...results show that the "millions of honey at***

***our house" plan followed by what is to come hereafter, will outstrip any of the heretofore known stimulating plans by far in the race for bees in time for the harvest." —A Year's work in an Out Apiary, G.M. Doolittle.***

***"Probably the single most important step in management for achieving colony strength, and one most neglected by beekeepers, is to make sure the hives are heavy with stores in the fall, so that they emerge from overwintering already strong early in the spring" —The How-To-Do-It Book of Beekeeping, Richard Taylor***

***"The feeding of bees for stimulating brood-rearing in early spring is now looked upon by many as of doubtful value. Especially is this true in the Northern States, where weeks of warm weather are often followed by 'Freeze up.' The average beekeeper in the average locality will find it more satisfactory to feed liberally in the fall— enough, at least so that there shall be sufficient stores until harvest. If the hives are well protected, and the bees well supplied with an abundance of sealed stores, natural brood rearing will proceed with sufficient rapidity, early in the spring without any artificial stimulus. The only time***

***that spring feeding is advisable is where there is a dearth of nectar after the early spring flow and before the coming of the main harvest." —W.Z. Hutchinson, Advanced Bee Culture***

---

***My experiences with stimulative feeding.***

I've tried about every combination over the years and my conclusion is that weather has everything to do with the success or failure of any stimulative feeding attempt. So some years it seems to help some, some years it misleads them into rearing too much brood too early when a hard freeze could be disastrous or having too much moisture in the hive in that precarious time of late winter when a hard freeze could still happen. Plus the really impressive results you get are usually from feeding a hive that is light in stores. Leaving more stores still seems to be a more reliable method of getting a lot of early brood in my climate.

Here in the North it not only makes it difficult to even do, but makes the results vary from disastrous to remarkable. The problem is that beekeeping has enough variables and I'm not interested in introducing more.

I will skip the what to feed issues and distill them down to my experience as relates to stimulating brood production and ignore the issues of honey vs. sugar for the moment.

I have fed really thin (1:2) thin (1:1) moderate (3:2) and thick (2:1) syrup at every time of the year except a honey flow, but again to simplify the issue to stimulating brood rearing, let's stick with the spring.

I see no difference in brood stimulation between any of the ratios. The bees will suck it down if it's warm enough (and here it seldom is in early spring or late fall) and it will induce them sometimes to start brood rearing when the bee's common sense is that it is too early. So for simplifying even further, let's just talk about feeding or not feeding syrup.

Difficulty getting bees to take syrup early in Northern climates:

If you try to feed any kind of syrup to bees in my climate in the late winter or early spring, the results *usually* are that they will not take it. The reason is that the syrup is hardly ever above 50° F (10° C). At night it is somewhere between freezing and sub zero. In the daytimes it's usually not above freezing on those rare occasions when it's actually 50° F in the daytime, the syrup is still below 32° F (0° C) from the night before. So first of all, trying to feed syrup in the late winter and early spring usually doesn't work at all—meaning they won't even take it.

**Down sides to success:**

Then, if you get lucky and get some warm spell somewhere in there that stays warm enough long enough for the syrup to get warm enough that the bees will take it, you manage to get them rearing a huge amount of brood, let's say near the end of February or early March, and then you get a sudden sub zero freeze that lasts for a week and all of the hives that were so induced to raise brood, die trying to maintain that brood. They die because they won't leave it and they die because they can't keep it warm, but they try anyway. We could get a hard freeze (10° or below F) anywhere up to the end of April, and last year we did get one in mid April as did most of the country.

Our record low, here in the warmest part of Nebraska in February is -25° F. In March it's -19° F. In

April it's 3° F (16° C). In May it's 25° F (-31° C). Having freezing weather in May is common enough here. I've seen snowstorms on May 1st. So I seriously doubt, not only the efficacy of feeding syrup, but if you can get it to work, the wisdom of stimulating brood rearing ahead of what is normal for the bees anyway.

**Variable outcomes:**

This might be an entirely different outcome in one year than another year. Certainly if your gamble pays off and you get the bees to brood up in March and you manage to keep them from swarming in April or May (doubtful), don't get any hard freezes that kill some of the hives off, or they are built up so far by the time those freezes hit that they can manage, and you manage to keep that max population for the flow in mid June, maybe you'll get a bumper crop. On the other hand, you get them to brood up heavy in March, get a subzero freeze that lasts a week and most of them die, it's a very different outcome.

In a different climate, this might be an entirely different undertaking. If you live where subzero is unheard of, and clusters don't get stuck on brood from cold and can't get to stores, then the results of stimulative feeding may be much more predictable and possibly much more positive. Then again they may brood up too early and swarm before the flow.

**Dry Sugar:**

This is not good spring feed, except as left over from winter, but in my experience it made a lot of difference overwinter and in the following spring. Most of the hives ate the sugar. Some ate most of the sugar. They did brood up while eating sugar and they could eat it even when it was cold. They don't go as crazy over it nor as crazy on brood rearing, but I see that as a good thing. A moderate build up from stores they can get at even in the cold is a much better survival bet than a huge build up at a time they could get caught in long hard freeze on syrup that they won't be able to get to if it's cold.

**Type of feeder:**

I will admit, that the type of feeder also plays into all of this. A top feeder in the early spring here is worthless. The syrup is hardly ever warm enough for the bees to take it. Baggie feeders, on the other hand, on top of the cluster, they seem to be able to get at, as well as dry sugar. A frame feeder (as much as I don't like them) against the cluster is taken much better than the top feeder. (but not as well as the baggie feeders). In my climate any feeder that is very far from the cluster will not get used until the weather is consistently in the 50's F (10s C) and by then the fruit trees and dandelions will be blooming so it will be irrelevant.

You might get some syrup down them in late March or early April with a baggie feeder or a jar or pail directly over the cluster or if you reheat the syrup regularly, when everything else fails.

***Second,* what *do you feed?***

I prefer to *leave* them honey. Some think you should only feed honey. From a perfectionist view, I like that. From a practical view, it's difficult for me. First, honey sets off robbing a lot worse than syrup. Second, honey spoils a lot more easily if I water it down, and I hate to see honey go to waste. Third, honey is very expensive (if you buy it or just don't sell it) and labor intensive to extract it. It seems wrong to me to go to the trouble of extracting it, only to feed it back. I'd rather leave enough honey on the hives and, in a pinch, steal some from a stronger hive for the weaker hives, rather than feeding. But if it comes down to needing to feed, I feed off, old, or crystallized honey if I have it, otherwise I feed sugar syrup.

## Pollen

The other issue of what, of course, is pollen and substitute. The bees are healthier on real pollen, but substitute is cheap. I try to feed all real pollen, but sometimes I can't afford that and I settle for 50:50 pollen:substitute. On just substitute you get very short-lived bees. I don't notice any difference at 50:50, but I still think 100% pollen is best.

### ***Third, how* much *do you feed?***

It's best to check with local beekeepers on how much stores it takes to get through your winters. Here, with a large cluster of Italians, I'd shoot for a hive weight of 100 to 150 pounds. With Carniolans, it's more like 75 to 100 pounds. With the more frugal feral survivors it might be more like 50 to 75 pounds. It's always better to have too much than too little.

### ***Fourth,* how *do you feed?***

There are more schemes to feed bees than there are options in any other aspect of beekeeping. I have a love/hate relationship with feeding to start with so it's not surprising I have a love/hate relationship with most methods.

***Issues when considering the type of feeder***:

How much labor is involved in feeding? For instance do I have to suit up? Open the hive? Remove lids? Remove boxes? How much syrup will it hold? How many trips will I have to make to an outyard to get them ready for winter? In other words, a feeder that holds five gallons of syrup, I'll only have to fill once. If it only holds a pint or a quart I'll have to fill it many times.

Will the bees take it if it's cold? If the weather is warm most any feeder works. Only a few will work when the weather is marginal. Meaning it's in the 40's or so at night and the 50's or so in the day and none work when it stays too cold all the time.

What does it cost? Some methods are quite expensive (a good hive top feeder could cost $20 to $40 per hive) and some are quite cheap (converting a solid bottom board to a feeder might cost 25¢ per hive).

Does it cause robbing? Boardman feeders, for example are notorious for this.

Does it cause drowning? Can this be mitigated? Frame feeders are notorious for this and most beekeepers have added a float or ladder or both to minimize it. Bottom board feeders are about the same as the frame feeders.

Is it hard to get into the hive with the feeder on or does it get in the way? For instance a top feeder has to be removed to get into the hive and it sloshes and spills a lot.

Is it hard to clean out the feeder? Feed will spoil. Feeders will get mold in them. If bees can drown in them, they will have to be cleaned out from time to time.

***Basic types of feeders***

## Frame feeders

Frame feeder. These vary a lot. The really old ones were wood. The old ones were smooth plastic and drowned a lot of bees. The newer ones are mostly a black plastic trough with some roughness on the sides to act as a ladder. If you put a float in them they work much better with less drowning or a #8 hardware cloth ladder helps. They also take up more than one frame, more like a frame and a half so they don't fit well and they bulge in the middle. Brushy used to have one made one out of Masonite with more limited access, a built in #8 ladder and it only takes up one space and it doesn't bulge. Betterbee has a plastic version with similar features. I haven't had one, but the complaints I've heard are that the ears are too short and it falls off the frame rest. If you make them correctly then they would live up to their other name "division board feeder", but to do that they have to divide the hive into two parts and should have separate access for each side of the hive. Some people make actual "division board feeders" themselves and use them to make a ten frame hive into two four frame nucs with a shared feeder.

### Boardman feeder

These come in all the beginners' kits. They go in the entrance and hold an inverted quart mason jar. I'd keep the jar lid and throw away the feeder. They are notorious for causing robbing. They are easy to check but you have to shake off the bees and open the jar to refill them.

### Jar feeder

Inverted container. These work on the same principle as a water cooler or other upside down containers where the liquid is held in by a vacuum (or for the technically minded among us, held in by the air pressure outside pushing on it). For feeding bees, this can be a quart jar (like the one from the Boardman feeder), a paint can with holes, a plastic pail with a lid, a one liter bottle etc.

It just has to have some way to hold it over the bees and some small holes for the syrup to get out. Advantages vary by how you set it up and how big they are. If they hold a gallon or more you won't have to refill very often. If they are only a quart you will have to refill a lot. If they leak or the temperature changes a lot, they leak and drown or "freeze" the bees. They are usually cheap and usually drown fewer bees than the frame feeder, unless they leak. If the hole it goes over is covered in #8 hardware cloth you won't have any bees on the container when you need to refill.

## Miller feeder

Named after C.C. Miller. There are variations of this. All go on top of the hive and require tight closure so robbers don't get in the top and drown in the syrup. Some of them have open access by the bees to the entire feeder. Some have limited access that is screened in so the bees have just enough room to get to the syrup. They come with the access in various places—sometimes one end, sometimes both, sometimes the center parallel to the frames and sometimes across the frames. The reasoning is either based on being easier to make and fill with only one compartment (ends) or better access for the bees (center) or even better access for the bees (across the frames) so the bees will find it. The taller they are the less they get used when it's cold but the more syrup they hold. Some hold as much as five gallons (great for an outyard during warm weather but not good when it's cold at night). Some hold as little as a couple of quarts. For cool weather the bees will work one that is shallow and has the entrance in the center better than one that is deep and has the entrance on the end. The Rapid feeder is a similar concept but is round and goes over the inner cover hole. The biggest disadvantage is probably having to remove it to get into the hive. Pretty awkward if it's full. The biggest advantages are the volume of syrup they hold and (if it's screened) filling without having to suit up or disrupt the bees.

## Bottom board feeder

## Jay Smith Bottom Board Feeder

Jay Smith Bottom Board Feeder is simply a dam made with a $^{3}/_{4}$" by $^{3}/_{4}$" block of wood put an inch or so back from the where the front of the hive would be (18" or so forward of the very back). The box is slid forward enough to make a gap at the back. The syrup is poured in the back. A small board can be used to block the opening in the back. The bees can still get out the front by simply coming down forward of the dam. The picture is from the perspective of standing behind the hive looking toward the front. This is all empty so you can see where the dam is etc. The edges of the dam have been enhanced and labels put on to try to make more sense. This version doesn't work on a weak hive as the syrup is too close to the entrance. It drowns as many bees as the frame feeders.

*Jay Smith Bottom Board Feeder*

**My version**

*Bottom of the feeder. The block part way across makes a reduced entrance for the hive below it.*

*Top of the feeder. The dam at the front stops the syrup from running out. The support block holds the #8 hardware cloth up so it doesn't sag. The #8 lets me fill the feeder without bees flying out. The drain plug is so I can let condensation out in the winter or rain water if it gets in. It's been dipped in wax and the cracks filled with a wax tube fastener. You could just melt some beeswax and roll it around in the feeder to seal it.*

*With a box on it so you can see where you fill it. If you aren't stacking them the feeder portion could be on the front or back. When doing "apartment style" the filler is in the front.*

*Apartment style where you can see the entrance for the nuc below on the bottom.*

*Apartment style with covers over the filler to keep out most of the rain. These are scraps of $^1/_2$" plywood, but anything works fine. So far they haven't blown off.*

My version of the Jay Smith Bottom Board Feeder I just modified this to make a top entrance and a bottom feeder. These were made from a standard bottom board from Miller Bee Supply. The space on top is $^{3}/_{4}$" and the space on the bottom is $^{1}/_{2}$". This is a nice space for overwintering as I can put some newspaper on and cover with sugar, or I can fit a pollen patty in without squishing bees. I was concerned about water from condensation so I added a drain plug. This could also be used to drain bad syrup. Also this design allows stacking up nucs and feeding all of them without opening or rearranging. So far I have had about the same number of drownings as a standard frame feeder. You do have to pour the syrup in slowly and if the bees are obviously so thick that they are all over the bottom you might want to add a box and lessen the congestion. I am considering making a float out of $^{1}/_{4}$" luan.

**Baggie feeder**

These are just gallon Ziploc baggies that are filled with three quarts of syrup, laid on the top bars and slit on top with a razor blade with two or three small slits. The bees suck down the syrup until the bag is empty. A box of some kind is required to make room. An upside down Miller feeder or a one by three shim or just any empty super will work. Advantages are the cost (just the cost of the bags) and the bees will work it in cooler weather as the cluster keeps it warm. Disadvantages are you have to disrupt the bees to put new bags on and the old bags are ruined. Also the risk of excess space in the hive that could get comb in it.

### Open feeder

These are just large containers with floats ("popcorn peanuts", straw etc.) full of syrup. They are usually kept away from the hives a ways (100 yards or more). Advantages are you can feed quickly as you don't have to go to every hive. Disadvantages are that you are feeding the neighbor's bees and they sometimes set off robbing and sometimes in a feeding frenzy a lot of bees drown.

### Candy board

This is a one by three box with a lid that has candy poured into it. It goes on top in the winter and the bees will use it if they get to the top of the hive and need food. They are very popular around here and seem to work well.

### Fondant

This can be put on the top bars. Again it seems to be more useful for emergency feed. The bees will eat it if there is nothing to eat. The end effect is similar to the candy board.

### Dry Sugar

This can be fed a number of ways. Some people just dump it down the back of the hive (definitely not recommended with screened bottom boards as it will fall through to the ground). Some put it on top of the inner cover. Some put a sheet of newspaper on top of the top bars, add a box on top and put the sugar on the newspaper (as in the photos above). Others put it in a frame feeder (the black plastic trough kind). I've even pulled two frames out of an eight frame box that were empty and dumped the sugar in the gap (with a solid bottom board of course). With screened bottom boards or with a small hive that just needs a little help, I'll pull some empty frames out, put some newspaper in the gap and put a little sugar, spray a little water to clump it so it doesn't run out, a little more sugar until I get it full. Sometimes the house bees carry it out for trash if you don't clump it. If you drizzle some water on it you can get the bees interested in it. The finer the sugar the better they take it. If you can get "bakers" sugar or "drivert" sugar it will be better accepted that standard sugar but harder to find and more expensive.

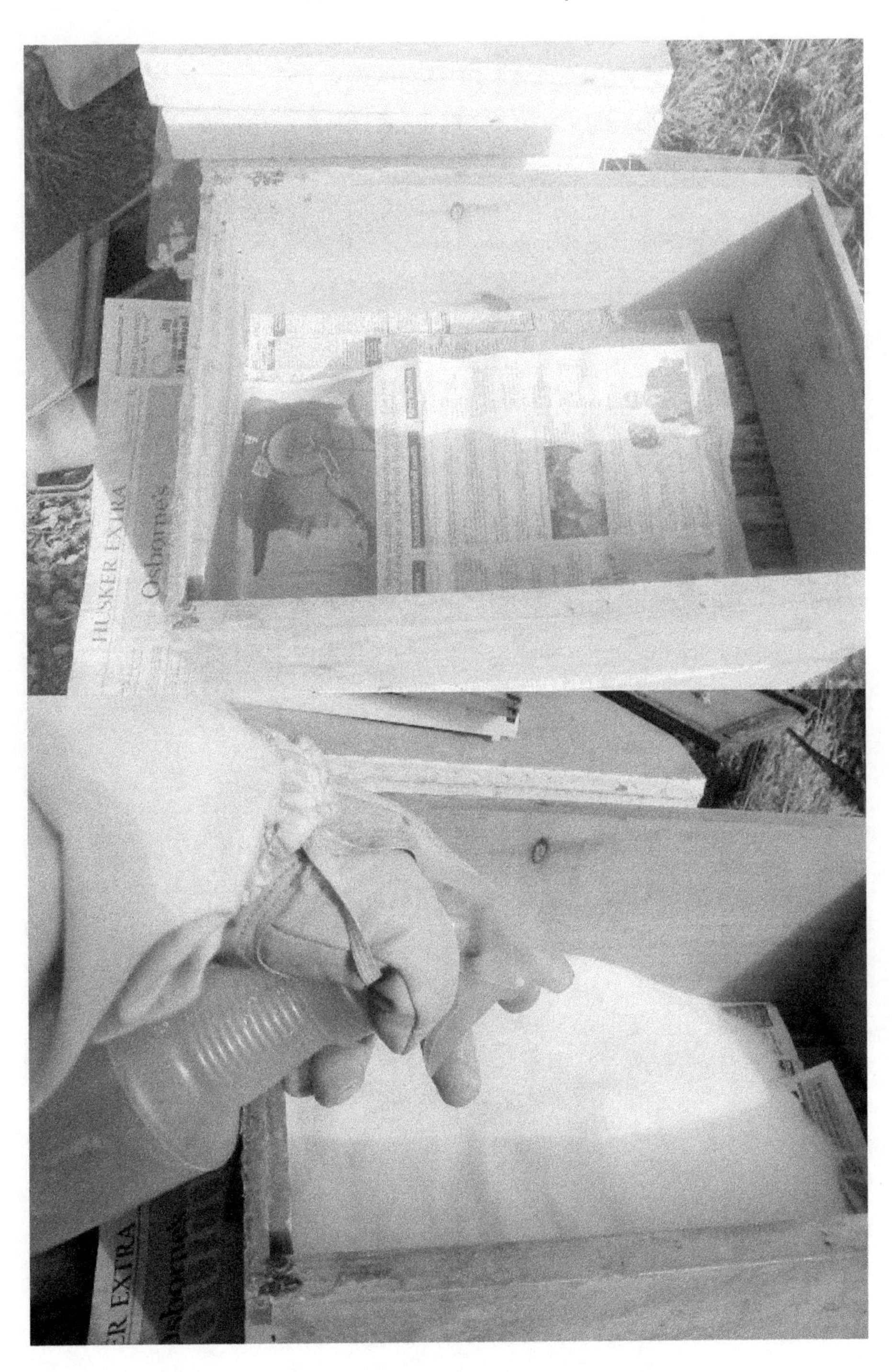
HUSKER EXTRA

**What kind of sugar?**

It matters not at all if it's beet sugar or cane sugar.

It matters a lot if it's granulated white sugar or anything else. Powdered sugar, brown sugar, molasses and any other unrefined sugar is not good for bees. They can't handle the solids.

## Pollen

Pollen is fed either in open feeders for the bees to gather it (dry) or in patties (mixed with syrup or honey into a dough and pressed between sheets of waxed paper). The patties are put on the top bars. A shim is helpful to make room for the patty. I usually do open feeding dry in an empty hive on screen wire on top of a solid bottom so it won't mold.

## Measuring ratios for syrup

The standard mixtures are 1:1 in the spring and 2:1 in the fall (sugar:water). People often use something other than those for their own reasons. Some people use 2:1 in the spring because it's easier to haul around and keeps better. Some people use 1:1 in the fall because they believe it stimulates brood rearing and they want to be sure to have young bees going into winter. The bees will manage either way. I use more like 5:3 (sugar:water) all the time. It keeps better than 1:1 and is easier to dissolve than 2:1.

## Weight or Volume?

The next argument is over weight or volume. If you have a good scale you can find this out for yourself, but take a pint container, tare it (weigh it empty) and fill it with water. The water will weigh very close to a pound. Now take a dry pint container, tare it (weigh it empty) and fill it with white sugar and weight it. It will weigh very close to a pound. So I'll keep this very simple. For the sake of mixing syrup for feeding bees, it just doesn't matter. You can mix and match. "A pints a pound the world around" as far as dry white sugar and water are concerned. At least until you've mixed the syrup. So if you take 10 pints of water, boil it, and add 10 pounds of sugar you'll get the same thing as if you took 10 pounds of water, boil it, and add 10 pints of sugar.

The next confusion seems to be on how much it takes to make how much syrup. The volume of 10 pints of water and 10 pints of sugar will make about 15 pints of syrup, not 20. The sugar and the water fit together.

## How to measure

Don't confuse the issue of how you measure. Measure before you mix. In other words, you can't fill a container $^1/_3$ of the way with water, and add sugar until it's $^2/_3$ full and have 1:1 syrup. You'll get more like 2:1 syrup. Likewise, you can't fill it $^1/_3$ of the way with sugar and then add water until it's $^2/_3$ full and have 1:1 syrup. You'll get more like 1:2. You have to measure both separately and then put them together to get an accurate measurement. I find the easiest is to use pints for water and pounds for sugar since the sugar comes in packages marked in pounds and volume is easy to measure for water. So if you know you are going to add 10 pounds of sugar and you want 1:1 then start with 10 pints of boiling water and add the 10 pounds of sugar.

## How to make syrup

I boil the water and add the sugar and then when it's all dissolved turn off the heat. With 2:1 this can take /some time. Either way, boiling the water makes the syrup keep longer by killing all the microorganisms that might be in the sugar or the water.

## Moldy syrup

I don't let a little mold bother me, but if it smells too funny or it's too moldy I throw it out. If you use essential oils (and I don't) they tend to keep it from molding. Some people add various things to control this. Clorox, distilled vinegar, vitamin C, lemon juice and other things are used by various people to help it keep longer. All of these except the Clorox make the syrup more acidic and closer to the acidity of honey (lower the pH).

# Top Entrances

***Reasons for top entrances***

You can keep bees fine without these, but they do eliminate the following problems: mice, skunks, opossums, dead bees blocking the exit in winter, condensation on the lid in winter, snow blocking the exit in winter, grass blocking the exit the rest of the year. It also allows you to buy inexpensive and very nice Sundance II pollen traps.

> ***"I had a neighbor who used the common box hive; he had a two inch hole in the top which he left open all winter; the hives setting on top of hemlock stumps without any protection, summer or winter, except something to keep the rain out and snow from beating into the top of the hive. he plastered up tight all around the bottom of the hive for winter. his bees wintered well, and would every season swarm from two to three weeks earlier than mine; scarcely any of them would come out on the snow until the weather was warm enough for them to get back into the hive.***
>
> ***"Since then I have observed that whenever I have found a swarm in the woods where the hollow was below the entrance, the comb was always bright and clean, and the***

***bees were always in the best condition; no dead bees in the bottom of the log; and on the contrary when I have found a tree where the entrance was below the hollow, there was always more or less mouldy comb, dead bees &c.***

***"Again if you see a box hive with a crack in it from top to bottom large enough to put your fingers in, the bees are all right in nine cases out of ten. The conclusion I have come to is this, that with upward ventilation without any current of air from the bottom of the hive, your bees will winter well..."—Elisha Gallup, The American Bee Journal 1868, Volume 3, Number 8 pg 154***

*Regular migratory covers with tapered shims to make top entrances with the opening the long way.*

***How to make top entrances***

*My current ones are these. These are $^{3}/_{4}$″ plywood cut to the size of the box (no overhang or cleats) with shims to make the opening the short way.*

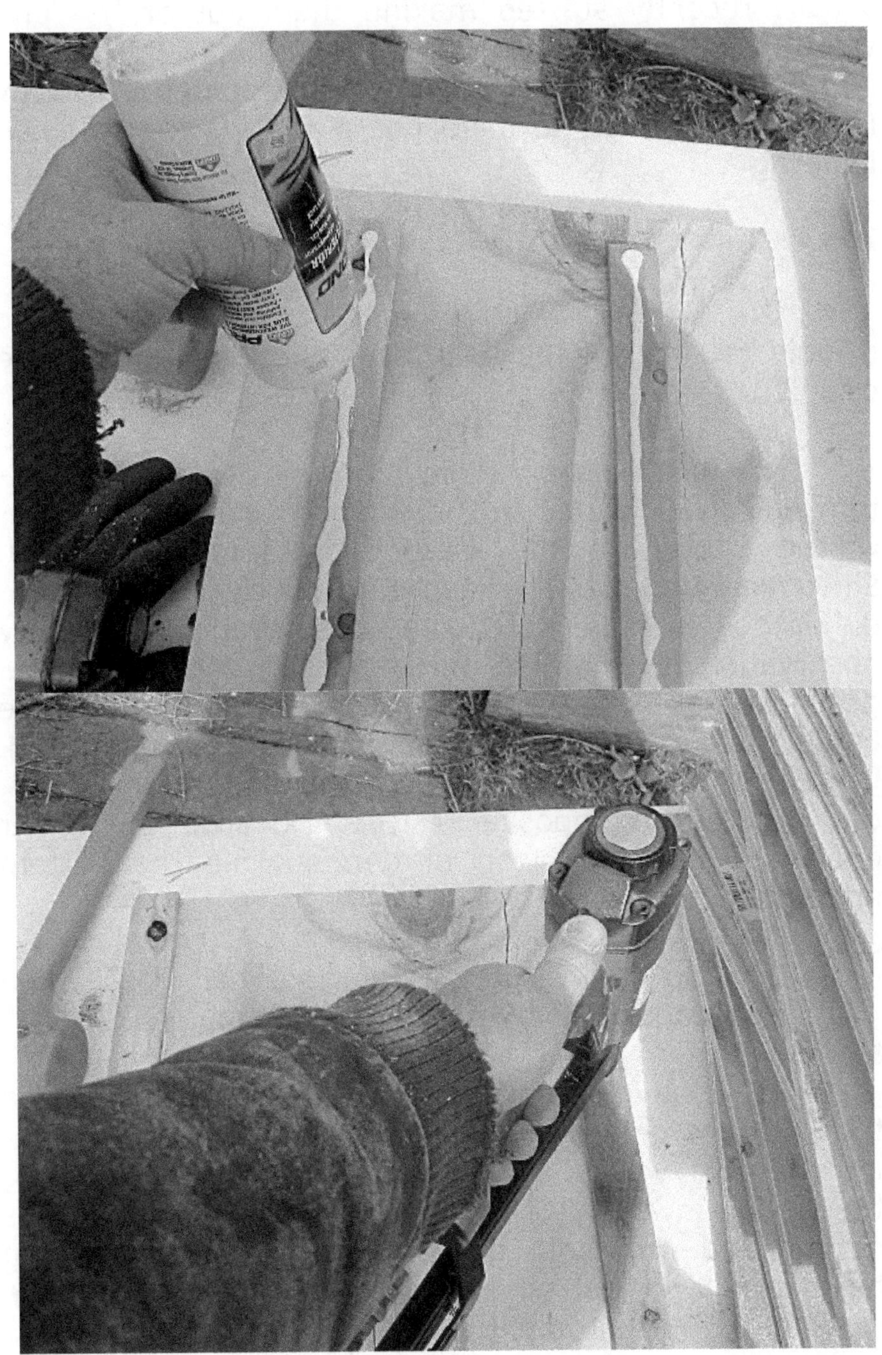

*Making the top entrances.*

I recently started making them out of $^{1}/_{2}$″ plywood.

The idea of using shims was presented to me by Lloyd Spears who says he got it from a man named Ludewig

***Top Entrance Frequently Asked Questions:***

**Q:** Without a bottom entrance, don't they have trouble hauling out the dead bees and keeping the hive clean?

**A:** In my observation, no more than with a bottom entrance. Either way dead bees accumulate over winter. Either way they accumulate some in the fall. Either way they usually keep it pretty clean in the middle of the year. I've watched a house keeping bee in my observation hive (which has a bottom entrance), haul dead bees all over the hive from top to bottom before finally finding the entrance at the bottom. I don't think it matters at all. According to Elisha Gallup (see previous quote) the opposite is true. He says the upper entrance ones are clean of debris while the bottom entrance ones are full of debris.

**Q:** Do the returning foragers get irate when you're working the hive?

**A:** I haven't noticed any difference. Whether a top entrance or a bottom entrance, while you're working the hive you're disrupting things just by standing there. You always, in both cases, have confused bees circling and with both bottom and top entrances you have bees who just go back into the hive while you're working. With the top entrance they just go in the top.

**Q:** When removing supers don't they get confused?

**A:** The most confusion is when you remove them from only one and it's right next to a similar height hive. Then they do get confused about which hive is theirs. But I think they do the same with a bottom entrance for the same reason except you don't notice. They use the height of the hive as one of their landmarks so they continue to fly into the tall white hive nearest where they remember it instead of the short one next to it. In a day things go back to normal.

**Q:** Why do some people recommend not using them in town because of bees being confused when working the hive?

**A:** Similar to above answer. In my experience any hive being opened causes confusion for the returning foragers because the height of the hive is often changed because of removing boxes, and the beekeeper's presence changes the landmarks. I see no increase in the confusion of a top entrance only hive to a bottom entrance only hive. In my opinion, advice that top entrances should not be used in urban areas are misplaced but seem to be often repeated by those who have no experience with top entrances. Wintering will be much improved by a top entrance and it prevents issues such as and overheating as well. These advantages should not be sacrificed merely because of a commonly held belief about hive disruption that is so often repeated.

**Q:** Do you use an entrance reducer?

**A:** On some of them I have them and some I don't. I use a $^{1}/_{4}$" thick piece of wood (a piece of screen molding works well) cut 2" short of the width of the opening with one nail in the center to make a pivot so you can pivot it open or pivot it closed.

# Carts

In my pursuit of easier beekeeping, I bought and modified these carts.

I modified two of the beekeeping carts I have. This is the Brushy Mt one. I added the perforated angle iron rack on the front so I can haul six empty boxes around without them sliding off. I also added the bolt to the stop so I can move it when it's empty. Unfortunately I'll have to drill another hole for the pin if I want to haul 8 frame boxes with it.

Here's the rack on the Mann Lake beekeeping cart. Again, so I can haul six empty boxes across the pasture without them falling off. The pin in the hole at the top is used too, to keep the boxes from tipping forward when you pick them up. I had to lower the axle by adding the angle iron on top here so it would slip into a medium and pick it up without fighting with it tipping forward. I also had to cut off some of the angle iron on the bottom so it wouldn't catch in the grass. I seem to use this one the most because you can just slide into a stack of boxes and pick them up.

This one, by the way, was invented by beekeeper Jerry Hosterman of Arizona. I've seen some of his work that are obviously much older than Mann Lake's.

Here's the classic Walter T. Kelley "Nose Truck" designed for beekeeping. It requires some kind of bottom board, preferably with some cleats on the end, to act as a pallet. It's heavy duty and will haul six FULL supers. I did no modifications on it.

# Swarm Control

*Photo by Judy Lillie*

Swarming is when the old queen and part of the bees leave to start a new colony. Afterswarms are after the old queen has left and there are still too many bees so some of the swarm queens (which are unmated queens) leave with more swarms. Sometimes a colony has a several afterswarms.

Generally swarming is considered a bad thing because you usually lose those bees. But if you catch them it's a bonus because swarms are notorious for building up quickly. The bees are focused on it already and it's in the natural order of things. Back in the days of skeps and box hives it was always considered a good thing. It was a chance to make increase.

## Causes of swarming

It's good to realize that swarming is the normal response of a hive to success. It means they are doing well enough to reproduce the hive. It is the natural order of things. However, it is inconvenient for the beekeeper to have them swarm, so let's think about what causes them to want to swarm.

First there are two main types of swarms. There are reproductive swarms and there are overcrowding swarms. There are a variety of pressures that push them toward swarming.

## Overcrowding swarm

Since it's the simplest and can happen anytime, let's briefly look at the overcrowding swarm. The factors that seem to contribute are:

No place to put nectar so it gets stored in the brood nest. Prevention: add supers.

Honey or pollen clogging the brood nest so that the queen has nowhere to lay. Prevention: remove combs of honey and add empty frames so that the bees will be occupied drawing wax and the queen will have somewhere to lay and the bees will have more room to cluster in the brood nest.

No place to cluster near the brood nest. The bees like to cluster near the queen (who is in the brood nest) and this clogs the brood nest making it crowded. Prevention: Slatted racks give room to cluster under the brood nest. Follower boards on the outside give room to cluster on the sides of the brood nest. These are a $^{3}/_{4}$" wide top bar with a sheet of plywood or Masonite or similar material in the middle the size of a frame. One on each end replaces one frame in the brood nest.

Too much traffic congesting the brood nest. Prevention: a top entrance will give foragers a way in without going through the brood nest.

So basically, if you keep supers on and provide ventilation you can prevent an overcrowding swarm.

**Reproductive swarm**

The bees have been working toward this goal since last winter when they tried to go into winter with enough excess stores to build up in the spring before the flow enough to cause a swarm that will then have the optimum chance to build up enough to survive the following winter.

The first mistake people make about preventing swarms is they think you can just throw on some supers and they won't swarm. But they will. Yes, it's nice to have room for them to store the honey, so the supers are helpful, but the bees intend to swarm and the supers will not deter them from the plan to do a reproductive swarm.

Back to the sequence in the spring, the bees, during winter, rear little spurts of brood. The queen lays a little and they start rearing that batch, but they don't start any new brood until that brood emerges and they take a break. Then they rear another little batch. When pollen starts coming in they start to rear more brood to build up. They also start using up the honey they have stored. This is used to feed brood and also it makes room for more brood.

When the bees think they have enough bees they start filling all of that back in with honey, both to stop the queen from laying, and to have adequate stores in case the main flow doesn't pan out. As the brood nest gets backfilled it makes more and more unemployed nurse bees. These nurse bees start doing a keening buzz that is quite different from the typical harmonious buzz you usually hear—more of a warble. Once the brood nest is mostly full of honey they start swarm cells. About the time they get capped the old queen leaves with a large number of bees. Even if you catch the swarm, the hive has still stopped brood production and has lost (to the swarm) a lot of bees. It's doubtful it will make honey. If there are still enough bees, the hive will throw afterswarms with virgin queens heading them.

If I don't catch them in time, once they make up their mind I always make splits because not much will dissuade them. Destroying queen cells only postpones the inevitable, at best and most likely will leave them queenless. My guess is that most people destroy the queen cells *after* the hive has swarmed without realizing it.

If you catch them trying to swarm between about two weeks and just before the main flow, a cut down split with the old queen and all but one frame of the open brood in a new location is a nice swarm prevention method. Leave the old hive with all the capped brood, one frame of eggs/open brood, no queen and empty supers. Usually, the old hive won't swarm because they have no queen and hardly any open brood. Usually the new hive won't swarm because they have no foragers. This is best done just before the main honey flow.

I often just put every frame that has some queen cells on it with a frame of honey in a two frame nuc to get good queens.

But, of course, the real object is to avoid the swarm and the split (unless you want to do the cut down split) so you'll have a bigger stronger hive that will make more honey.

### *Preventing swarming*

I do love to catch swarms but who has time to watch the hives all the time to catch them? And if you have that much time, then you have the time to prevent them.

## Opening the broodnest

This, of course is what we want to do. What we need to do is interrupt the chain of events. The easiest way is to keep the brood nest open. If you keep the brood nest from backfilling and if you occupy all those unemployed nurse bees then you can change their mind. If you catch it before they start queen cells, you can put some empty frames in the brood nest. Yes, empty. No foundation. Nothing. Just an empty frame. Just one here and there with two frames of brood between. In other words, you can do something like: BBEBBEBBEB where B is brood comb and E is an empty frame. How many you insert depends on how strong the cluster is. They have to fill all those gaps with bees. The gaps fill with the unemployed nurse bees who begin festooning and building comb. The queen will find the new comb and about the time they get about $^{1}/_{4}$" deep, the queen will lay in them. You have now "opened up the brood nest". In one step you have occupied the bees that were preparing to swarm with wax production followed by nursing, you've expanded the brood nest, and you've given the queen a place to lay. If you don't have room to put the empty combs in, then add another brood box and move some brood combs up to that box to make the room to add some to the brood nest. In other words, then the top box would probably be something like EEEBBBEEEE and the bottom one

BBEBBEBBEB. The other upside is I get good natural sized brood comb.

A hive that doesn't swarm will produce a *lot* more honey than a hive that swarms.

## Checkerboarding aka Nectar Management

Checkerboarding is a technique originated by Walt Wright that involves interspersing drawn and capped honey *over* the brood nest. It in no way involves the brood nest itself. If you'd like to know about this technique and a *lot* more detail about swarm preparation and what goes on in a hive at any given time in the buildup, I would contact Walt Wright. This is a method that also fools the bees into believing that the time has not yet come to swarm. It works without disturbing the brood nest. Basically it's putting alternating frames of empty drawn comb and capped honey directly *above* the brood nest. If you would like to purchase a copy of Walt's manuscript, it's about 60 pages long and last I heard was $8 in a pdf by email or $10 on paper. You can contact him at this address: Walt Wright; Box 10; Elkton, TN 38455-0010(WaltWright@hotmail.com).

# Splits

***What is the desired outcome?***

I would choose my method for doing a split depending on what you want for an outcome.

Reasons for doing a split:

- To get more hives.
- To requeen.
- To get more production.
- To get less production (for people who don't want too many hives or too many bees).
- To raise queens.
- To prevent swarms.

***Timing for doing a split:***

As soon as commercial queens are available, or as soon as drones are flying, depending on if you want to buy or raise queens, you *can* do a split. It depends again on what you want for an outcome.

There are an infinite variety of methods for doing a split. Many of these are because of the desired outcome (swarm prevention, maximizing yields, maximizing bees etc.) Some of the variations are also due to buying queens or letting the bees raise queens.

The simple version is to make sure you have some eggs in each of the deeps and put them facing toward the old location. In other words put a bottom board on the left facing the left side of the hive and one on the right facing the right side of the hive and put one deep on each and maybe an empty deep on top of that. Put the tops on and walk away.

There are an infinite number of variations of this.

***The concepts of splits are:***

- You have to make sure that both of the resulting colonies have a queen or the resources to make one (eggs or larvae that just hatched from the egg, drones flying, pollen and honey, plenty of nurse bees).
- You have to make sure that both of the resulting colonies get an adequate supply of honey and pollen to feed the brood and themselves.
- You have to make sure that you account for drift back to the original site and insure that both resulting colonies have enough population of bees to care for the brood and the hive they have.
- You need to respect the natural structure of the brood nest. In other words, brood combs belong together. Drone brood goes on the outside edge of the brood and pollen and honey go outside that.
- You need to allow enough time at the end of the season for them to build up for winter in your location.
- The old adage is that you can try to raise more bees or more honey. If you want both, then you can try to maximize honey in the old location and bees in the new split. Otherwise most splits are either a small nuc made up from just enough to get it started, or an even split.
- The size greatly impacts how quickly it builds from there. You can make a split as small as a frame of brood and a frame of honey. But you can't expect that to raise a well nourished queen. You also can't expect that nuc to build up to a hive by winter. But it makes a good mating nuc or a good place to hold a queen for a while. On the other hand you can make a split that is a minimum of 10 deep frames of bees and brood and honey or 16 medium frames of bees and brood and honey and it will build up rapidly because it has enough "income" and workers to cover its overhead and make a

good "profit". They are at "critical mass" and can really grow rapidly rather than struggle to get by. It's more productive and will build up more quickly to do a strong split, let both double in size and do another strong split than to do four weak splits and wait for them to build up.

***Kinds of splits***

### An even split

You take half of everything and divide it up. That's an even split. I would face both of new hives at the sides of the old hive so the returning bees aren't sure which one to come back to. In a week or so, swap places to equalize the drift to the one with the queen.

### A walk away split

Mostly this refers to not giving them a queen and just doing a split by whatever method and walking away and letting them sort things out. Come back in four weeks and see if the queen is laying. But it could also be an even split.

### Swarm control split

Ideally you want to prevent swarming and not have to split. But if there are queen cells I usually put every frame with any queen cells in its own nuc with a frame of honey and let them rear a queen. This usually relieves the pressure to swarm and gives me very nice queens. But even better, put the old queen in a nuc with a frame of brood and a frame of honey and leave one frame with queen cells at the old hive to simulate a swarm. Many bees are now gone and so is the old queen. Some people do the other kinds of splits (even walk away etc.) in order to prevent swarming. I think it's better to just keep the brood nest open.

***A cut down split***

## Concepts of a cut down:

The concepts of a cut down are that you free up bees to forage because they have no brood to care for, and you crowd the bees up into the supers to maximize them drawing comb and foraging. This is especially useful for comb honey production and more so for cassette comb honey production, but will produce more honey regardless of the kind of honey you wish to produce.

This is very timing critical. It should be done shortly before the main honey flow. Two weeks before, would be ideal. The purpose is to maximize the foraging population while minimizing swarming and crowding the bees into the supers. There are variations on this, but basically the idea is to put almost all the open brood, honey and pollen and the queen in a new hive while leaving all the capped brood, some of the honey and a frame of eggs with the old hive with less brood boxes and more supers. The new hive won't swarm because it doesn't have a workforce (which all returns to the old hive). The old hive won't swarm because it doesn't have a queen or any open brood. It will take at least six weeks or more for them to raise a queen and get a decent brood nest going. Meantime, you still get a lot of production (probably a lot *more* production) from the old hive because they are not busy caring for brood. You get the old hive requeened and you get a split. Another variation is to leave the queen with the old hive and take *all* the open brood out. They won't swarm right away because the open brood is gone. But I think it's riskier as far as swarming to crowd a hive with a queen.

### Confining the queen

Another variation on this is to just confine the queen two weeks before the flow so there is less brood to care for and free up nurse bees to forage. This also helps with Varroa as it skips a brood cycle or two. This is a good choice if you don't want more hives and you like the queen. You can put her in a regular cage or put her in a #5 hardware cloth push in cage to limit where she can lay. They will eventually chew under the hardware cloth cage, but it should set her back for a while.

### Cut down Split/Combine

This is a way to get the same number of hives, new queens and a good crop. You set up two hives right next to each other (touching would be good) early in the spring. Two weeks before the main flow you remove all the open brood and most of the stores from both hives, and the queen from one hive, and put it in a hive at a different location (the same yard is fine, but a different place). Then you combine all the capped brood, the other queen, or a new queen (caged), or no queen and one frame with some eggs and open brood (so they will raise a new one) into one hive in the middle of the old locations so all the returning field bees come back to the one hive.

***Frequently Asked Questions about splits***

## How early can I do a split?

It's very difficult for a split to build up unless it has an adequate number of bees to keep the brood warm and reach critical mass of workers to handle the overhead of a hive. For deeps this is usually ten deep frames of bees with six of them brood and four of them honey/pollen in each part of the split. For mediums this is usually sixteen medium frames of bees with ten of them brood and six of them honey/pollen. I'd say you can split as early as you can put together nucs that are this strong. Half this size can work but a stronger split will take off better. Later in the year when it's not frosting occasionally at night, you could get by with somewhat less, but you'll still do better with this much.

## How many times can I split?

Some hives you can't do any splits as they are struggling and never get on their feet. Some hives are such boomers that you can do five splits in a year, although you probably won't get a honey crop.

The object shouldn't be how many can you make, but to keep all the splits you make at critical mass. Critical mass is that point where they are no longer living hand to mouth and they have enough stores, workers, nurse bees and brood to have a surplus. Think of it as economics. If you have barely enough money to pay your bills (or even fall behind on them) you are struggling. When you get to the point where you can pay your bills, you can start to get ahead. When you get to the point where you have some money in the bank and you have a surplus of cash, then life gets pretty easy. Prosperity tends to lead to more prosperity as you can now do things right instead of just getting by. Try it another way. If you run a store you're not really coming out ahead until you cover your overhead.

A hive needs a certain amount of workers to feed the brood (it takes a lot of nurse bees to keep up with a prolific queen), haul the water, pollen, propolis and nectar to feed the brood, build the comb, guard the nest from ants and hive beetles, guard the entrance from skunks and mice and hornets etc.

Once that overhead has been met they can start working on a surplus. If your splits are strong enough to meet their overhead they can take off quickly. If they have barely the resources and workers to survive, they will struggle and take a long time to start really building up.

If you make strong splits and you don't weaken your hives too much you have a shot at getting more splits because they grow faster and more efficiently. Also if you don't weaken your main hives you have more surplus bees to make a surplus crop.

If you take only a frame of brood from each of your strong hives every week they will tend to just make up the difference very quickly with hardly a noticeable lull. One frame of brood and one of honey from each hive put together to fill a ten frame box has a good chance of taking off quickly as opposed to only a few frames of bees.

### How late can I do a split?

What you really need to ask yourself is "when is the best time to do a split". By the bee's example that would be sometime before the main flow so they have a flow to get established on. However this tends to cut into your harvest, so you could do them right after the main flow and probably still have time to build up for the fall, if you make them strong enough and give them a mated queen. Of course this depends on the typical flow where you are. If you typically have a dearth after the flow, you may have to feed if you do this

I'm in Greenwood, Nebraska. In a year with a good fall flow, I can do a split on the 1st of August that may build up enough to overwinter in one or two eight frame medium boxes. But if the fall flow fails they may not build up at all.

## How far?

The question often seems to come up, how far away to put the split. Mine are usually touching. You need to account for drift if it is less than 2 miles. I've been beekeeping since about 1974 and I've never taken a split 2 miles away unless that's where I wanted to take them anyway. I just do the split and shake in some extra bees or do the split and face both hives to the old location. In other words where the old hive was is where both of the new hives face. Returning bees have to choose. Sometimes I swap those after a few days if one is a lot stronger Usually the one with the queen is stronger.

I say all of this, mostly because it's "the right thing to do", but really since I went to eight frame mediums and since I expanded to 200 hives, I just split by the box and I do nothing about drift. I put two bottom boards where ever there is room on the stand and "deal" the boxes like cards. "One for you and one for you". I add as much empty room as I have boxes full of bees (in other words I double their actual space). So if there are three boxes full of bees on each stand I add three empty supers with frames. But these are strong splits from booming hives with at least two eight frame medium boxes full of bees in each resulting hive.

# Natural Cell Size

***And its implications to beekeeping and Varroa mites***

> ***"Everything works if you let it"— Rick Nielsen of Cheap Trick***

There has been much talked about and written about small cell and natural cell in recent times and the relationship of small cell to Varroa. Let's clarify a few points about natural cell size.

***Does Small Cell = Natural Cell?***

Small cell has been purported by some to help control Varroa mites. Small cell is 4.9 mm cell size. Standard foundation is 5.4 mm cell size. What is natural cell size?

---

**Baudoux 1893**

Made bees larger by using larger cells. Pinchot, Gontarski and others got the size up as large as 5.74 mm. But AI Root's first foundation was 5 cells to an inch which is 5.08 mm. Later he started making it 4.83 cells per inch. This is equivalent to 5.26 mm. (*The ABC and XYZ of Bee Culture*, 1945 edition, pages 125-126.)

---

**Eric Sevareid's Law**

> ***"The chief cause of problems is solutions."***

## Foundation Today

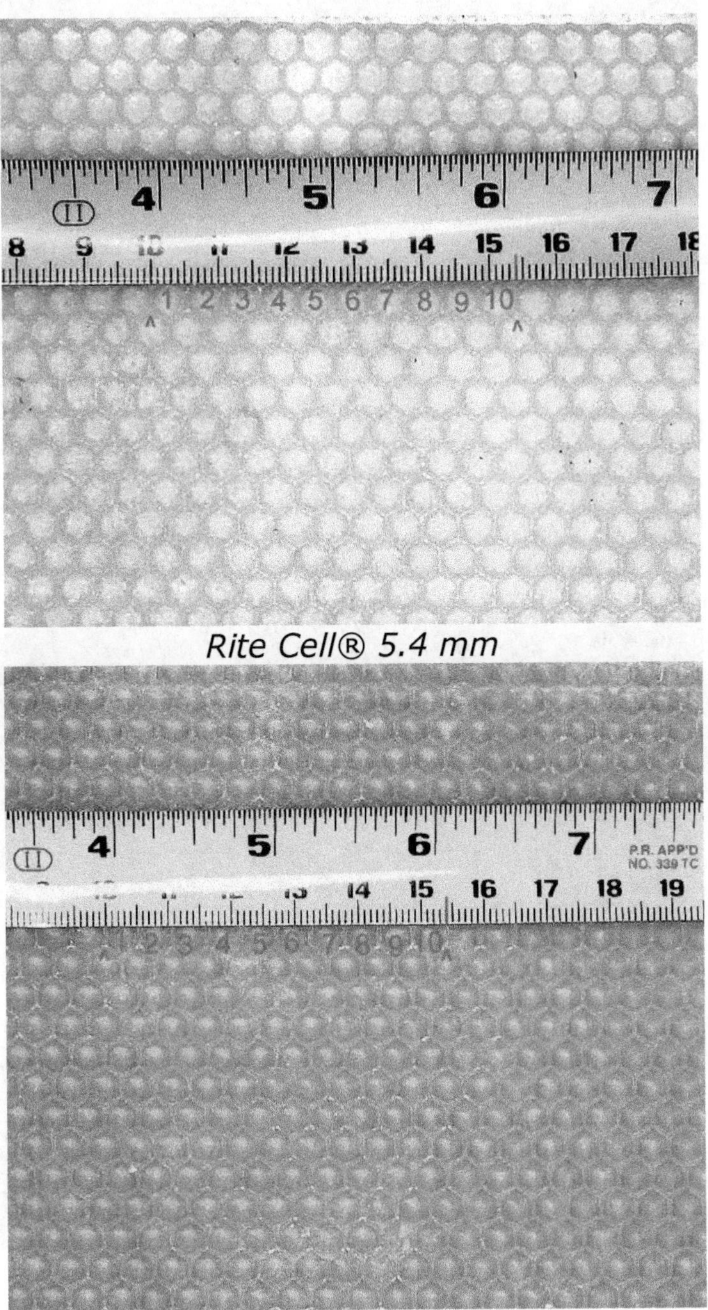


*Rite Cell® 5.4 mm*

*Dadant normal brood 5.4 mm*

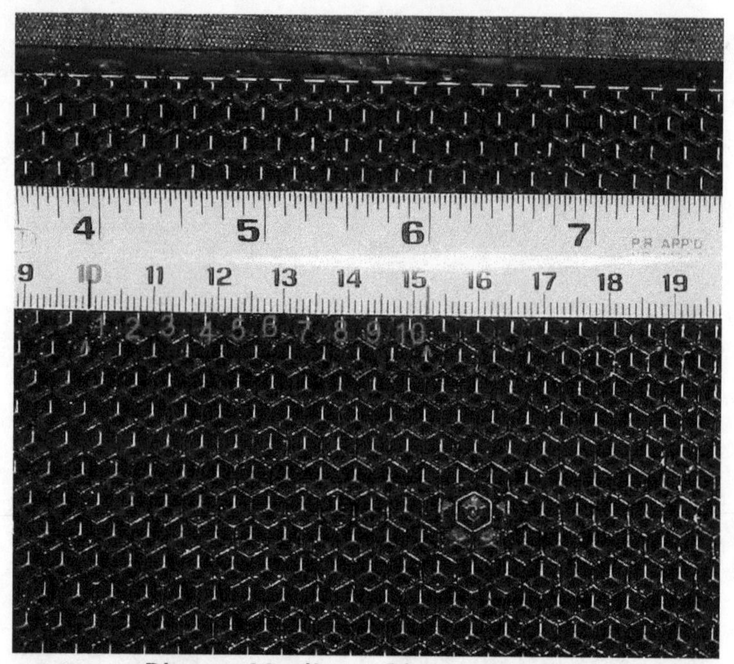


*Pierco Medium Sheet 5.2mm*

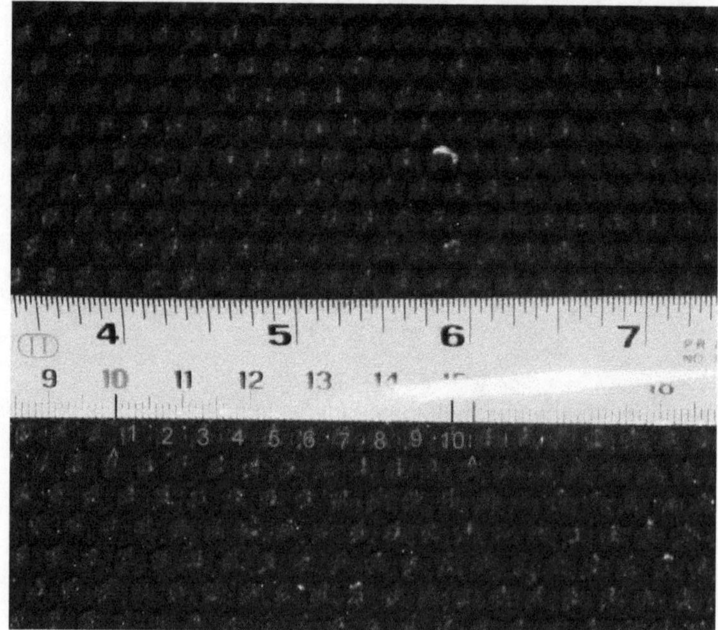


*Pierco Deep Frame 5.25mm*

*Mann Lake PF120 Medium frame*

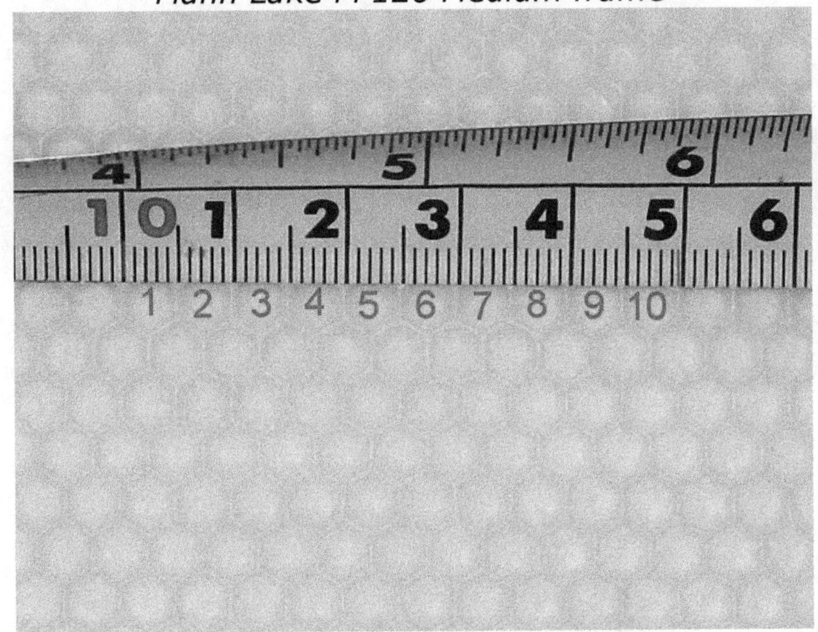

*Mann Lake PF100? Deep? frame*

*NOTE: The Mann Lake PF100 and PF120 are not the same cell size as Mann Lake PF500 and PF520 frames which are 5.4mm.*

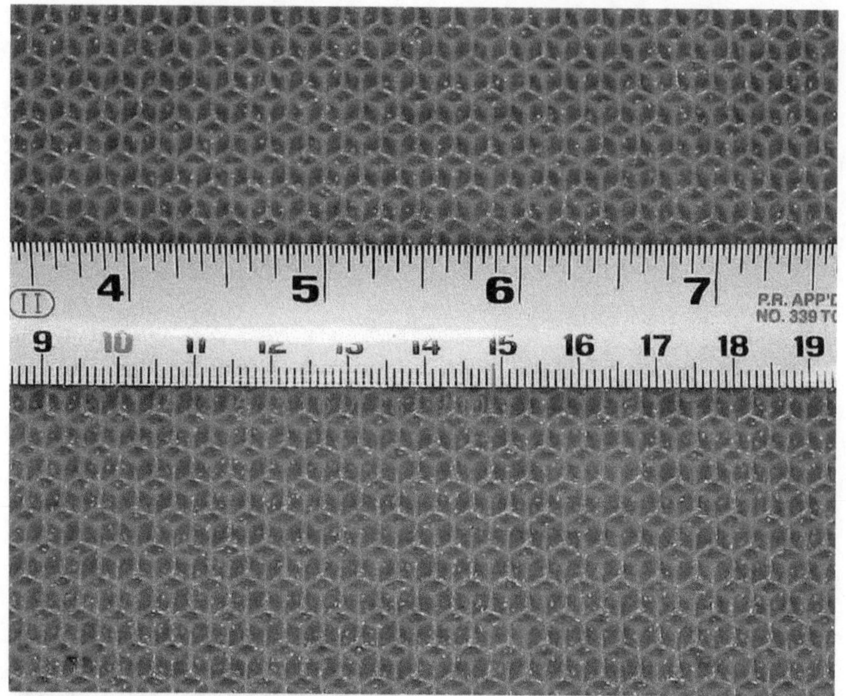


*Dadant 4.9mm Measured*

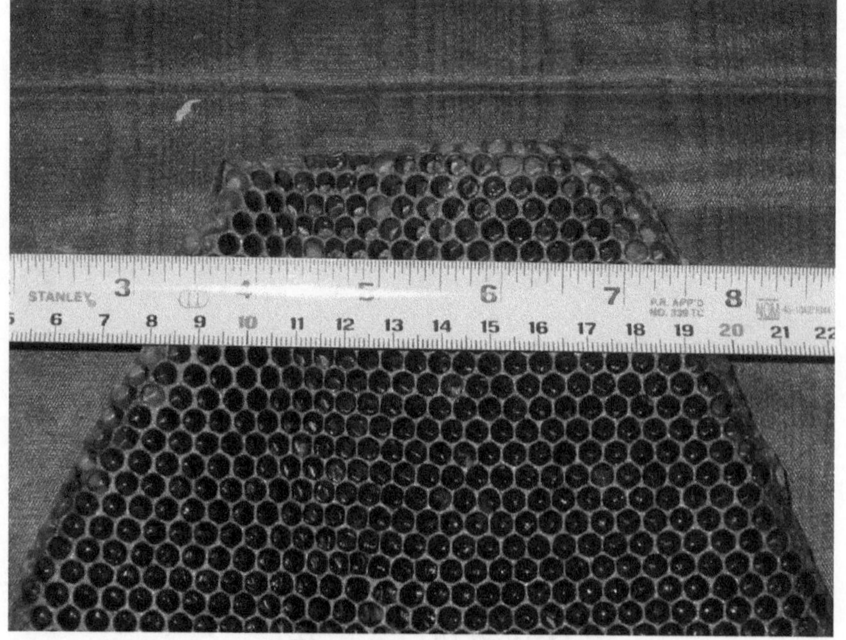


*4.7mm natural comb*

*4.7mm Comb Measurement*

---

***Chart of Cell Sizes***

| | |
|---|---|
| Natural worker comb | 4.6 mm to 5.1 mm |
| Lusby | 4.83mm average |
| Dadant 4.9mm Small Cell | 4.9 mm |
| Honey Super Cell | 4.9 mm |
| Wax dipped PermaComb | 4.9 mm |
| Mann Lake PF100 & PF120 | 4.95 mm |
| 19th century foundation | 5.05 mm |
| PermaComb | 5.05 mm |
| Dadant 5.1mm Small Cell | 5.1 mm |
| Pierco foundation | 5.2 mm |
| Pierco deep frames | 5.25 mm |
| Pierco medium frames | 5.35 mm |
| RiteCell | 5.4 mm |
| Standard worker foundation | 5.4 to 5.5mm |
| 7/11 | 5.6 mm |
| HSC Medium Frames | 6.0 mm |

Drone 6.4 to 6.6 mm

Note: fully drawn plastic (PermaComb and Honey Super Cell) is always .1mm larger at the mouth than the bottom and you have to allow for the thicker cell wall to come up with an equivalent. So the actual equivalent is pretty much the inside diameter of the mouth.

---

What I've done to get natural comb

- Top Bar Hive
- Foundationless Frames
- Blank Starter Strips
- Free Form Comb
- Empty Frame Between Drawn Combs

---

How much difference between natural and "normal"? Keep in mind that "normal" foundation is 5.4 mm and natural cell is between 4.6 mm and 5.0 mm.

***Volume of cells***

According to Baudoux:

| Cell Width | Cell Volume |
|---|---|
| 5.555 mm | 301 $mm^3$ |
| 5.375 mm | 277 $mm^3$ |
| 5.210 mm | 256 $mm^3$ |
| 5.060 mm | 237 $mm^3$ |
| 4.925 mm | 222 $mm^3$ |
| 4.805 mm | 206 $mm^3$ |
| 4.700 mm | 192 $mm^3$ |

From *The ABC and XYZ of Bee Culture*, 1945 edition, p. 126.

---

***Things that affect cell size***

- Worker intention for the comb at the time it was drawn:
  - Drone brood
  - Worker brood
  - Honey storage
- The size of the bees drawing the comb
- The spacing of the top bars

---

***What is Regression?***

Large bees, from large cells, cannot build natural sized cells. They build something in between. Most will build 5.1 mm worker brood cells.

The next brood cycle will build cells in the 4.9 mm range.

The only complication with converting back to natural or small cell is this need for regression.

---

***How do I regress them?***

To regress, cull out empty brood combs and let bees build what they want (or give them 4.9 mm foundation)

After they have raised brood on that, repeat the process. Keep culling out the larger combs.

How do you cull out the larger combs? Keep in mind it is normal procedure to steal honey from the bees. It is frames of brood that are our issue. The bees try to keep the brood nest together and have a maximum size in mind. If you keep feeding in empty frames in the center of the brood nest, put them between straight combs to get straight combs, they will fill these with comb and eggs. As they fill, you can add another frame. The brood nest expands because you keep spreading it out to put in the frames. When the large cell frames are too far from the center (usually the outside wall) or when they are contracting the brood nest in the Fall, they will fill them with honey after the brood emerges and then you can harvest them. You could also move the capped large cell brood above an excluder and wait for the bees to emerge and then pull the frame.

***Please*** do not confuse this issue of regression. I seem to get questions constantly asking whether to install a package on 5.4mm foundation first since they can't draw 4.9mm foundation well. If you want to get back to natural or small cell size, it is ***never*** to your advantage to use the already too large foundation they are already using. That is simply going nowhere at all. With a package, if you do so, you will have missed the opportunity to get a full step of regression. Dee Lusby's method is to do shakedowns (shake all the bees off of all the combs) onto 4.9mm foundation and then another shakedown onto 4.9mm to finish the main regression and then cull out the large comb until they have all 4.9mm in the brood nest. Shakedowns are the fastest method but also a stressful method and when you buy a package you already *have* a shakedown. I would take advantage of it. If you intend to get back to natural size then *stop* using large cell foundation all together. The main challenge is getting all the large cell comb *out* of the hive, so don't make that harder by putting more *in*.

Another misconception seems to be that there are large losses in regressing. Dee Lusby went cold turkey, no treatments and only did shakedowns. She lost a lot of bees in the process. Many who tried the same also did. But this is not necessary.

First of all, there is no stress in letting them build their own comb. It's what they have always done. Second, it's not necessary to do shakedowns, it's just quicker. Third, you don't have to go cold turkey on treatments. You can monitor mites (and I would) until things are stable. Meanwhile you could use some non-contaminating treatment *if* the numbers get too high. I have seen no losses from Varroa from regressing in this manner and no increase in losses to stress related problems and I found no need for any treatments.

---

### ***Observations on Natural Cell Size***

First there is no one size of cells nor one size of worker brood cells in a hive. Huber's observations on bigger drones from bigger cells was directly because of this and led to his experiments on cell size. Unfortunately, since he couldn't get foundation at all, let alone different sizes, these experiments only involved putting worker eggs in drone cells which, of course, failed. The bees draw a variety of cell sizes which create a variety of bee sizes. Perhaps these different subcastes serve the purposes of the hive with more diversity of abilities

The first "turnover" of bees from a typical hive (artificially enlarged bees) usually builds about 5.1 mm cells for worker brood. This varies a lot, but typically this is the center of the brood nest. Some bees will go smaller faster.

The next generation of bees, given the opportunity to draw comb will build worker brood comb in the range of 4.9 mm to 5.1 mm with some smaller and some larger. The spacing, if left to these "regressed" bees is typically 32 mm or $1^{1}/_{4}$" in the center of the brood nest. Subsequent generations may go slightly smaller.

---

***Observations on Natural Frame Spacing***

## $1^1/_4$" spacing agrees with Huber's observations

> ***"The leaf or book hive consists of twelve vertical frames... and their breadth fifteen lines (one line= $^1/_{12}$ of an inch. 15 lines = $1^1/_4$"). It is necessary that this last measure should be accurate." François Huber 1789***

---

## Comb Width (thickness) by Cell Size

According to Baudoux (note this is the thickness of the comb itself and not the spacing of the comb on centers)

| Cell Size | Comb width |
|---|---|
| 5.555 mm | 22.60 mm |
| 5.375 mm | 22.20 mm |
| 5.210 mm | 21.80 mm |
| 5.060 mm | 21.40 mm |
| 4.925 mm | 21.00 mm |
| 4.805 mm | 20.60 mm |
| 4.700 mm | 20.20 mm |

*The ABC and XYZ of Bee Culture* 1945 edition Pg 126

---

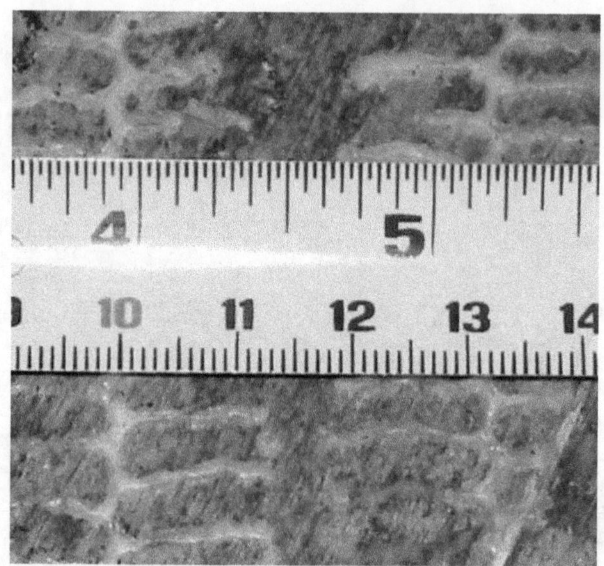


*Wild Comb in Top Feeder Comb Spacing Comb Spacing 30mm*

Here is a brood nest that moved into a top feeder even with plenty of room in the boxes and the inner cover after removing the comb. Spacing on naturally drawn brood comb is sometimes as small as 30 mm but typically 32 mm.

---

***Pre and Post Capping Times and Varroa***

8 hours shorter capping time halves the number of Varroa infesting a brood cell.

8 hours shorter post-capping time halves the number of offspring of a Varroa in the brood cell.

---

Accepted days for capping and post capping (based on observing bees on 5.4 mm comb):

Capped 9 days after egg laid
Emerges 21 days after egg laid

---

### ***Huber's Observations***

Huber's *Observations on Capping and Emergence on Natural Comb*.

Keep in mind that on the 1st day no time has elapsed and on the 20th 19 days have elapsed. If you have doubts about this add up the elapsed time he refers to. It adds up to $18^1/_2$ days.

> ***"The worm of workers passes three days in the egg, five in the vermicular state, and then the bees close up its cell with a wax covering. The worm now begins spinning its cocoon, in which operation thirty-six hours are consumed. In three days, it changes to a nymph, and passes six days in this form. It is only on the twentieth day of its existence, counting from the moment the egg is laid, that it attains the fly state."—François Huber 4 September 1791.***

### ***My Observations***

My Observations on Capping and Emergence on 4.95mm Comb.

I've observed on commercial Carniolan bees and commercial Italian bees a 24 hour shorter pre capping and 24 hour shorter post capping time on 4.95 mm cells in an observation hive.

My observations on 4.95 mm cell size
  Capped 8 days after laid
  Emerged 19 days after laid

---

### *Why would I want natural sized cells?*

Less Varroa because:

- Capping times shorter by 24 hours resulting in less Varroa in the cell when it's capped
- Postcapping times shorter by 24 hours resulting in less Varroa reaching maturity and mating by emergence
- More chewing out of Varroa

---

### *How to get natural sized cells*

Top Bar Hives:
Make the bars 32 mm (1 $^{1}/_{4}$") for the brood area
Make the bars 38 mm (1 $^{1}/_{2}$") for the honey area

Foundationless frames:
Make a "comb guide" like Langstroth did (see *The Hive and the Honey-Bee*)
Also helpful to cut down end bars to 32 mm (1 $^{1}/_{4}$") or
Make blank starter strips
Use a brine-soaked board and dip it in wax to make blank sheets. Cut these into $^{3}/_{4}$" wide strips and put in the frames.

---

### *How to get small cells*

Use 4.9 mm foundation or
Use 4.9 mm starter strips

---

***So what Are natural sized cells?***

I have measured a lot of natural drawn combs. I have seen worker brood in the range of 4.6 mm to 5.1 mm with most in the 4.7 to 4.8 ranges. I have not seen any large areas of 5.4 mm cells. So I would have to say:

***Conclusions:***

Based on my measurements of natural worker brood comb:

- There is nothing *un*natural about 4.9 mm worker cells.
- 5.4 mm worker cells are not the norm in a brood nest.
- Small cell and natural cell have been adequate for me to have hives that are stable against Varroa mites with no treatments.

---

***Frequently asked questions:***

**Q:** Doesn't it take longer for them to draw their own combs?

**A:** I have not found this to be true. In my observation (and others who have tried it), they seem to draw plastic with the most hesitation, wax with a little less hesitation and their own comb with the most enthusiasm. In my observation, and some others including Jay Smith, the queen also prefers to lay in it.

**Q:** If natural/small cell size will control Varroa, why did all the feral bees die off?

**A:** The problem is that this question typically comes with several assumptions.

The first assumption is that the feral bees have all but died out. I have not found this to be true. I see a lot of feral bees and I see more every year.

The second assumption is that when some of the feral bees did die, that they all died from Varroa mites. A lot of things happened to the bees in this country including Tracheal mites, and viruses. I'm sure some of the survival from some of this is a matter of selection. The ones that couldn't withstand them died.

The third assumption is that huge numbers of mites hitchhiking in on robbers can't overwhelm a hive no matter how well they handle Varroa. Tons of crashing domestic hives were bound to take a toll. Even if you have a fairly small and stable local population of Varroa, a huge influx from outside will overwhelm a hive.

The fourth assumption is that a recently escaped swarm will build small cell. They will build something in between. For many years most of the feral bees were recent escapees. The population of feral bees was kept high by a lot of recent escapees and, in the past, those escapees often survived. It's only recently I've seen a shift in the population to be the dark bees rather than the Italians that look like they are recent. Large bees (bees from 5.4 mm foundation) build an in between sized comb, usually around 5.1 mm. So these recently swarmed domestic bees are not fully regressed and often die in the first year or two.

The fifth assumption is that small cell beekeepers don't believe there is also a genetic component to the survival of bees with Varroa. Obviously there are bees that are more or less hygienic and more or less able to deal with many pests and diseases. Whenever a new disease or pest comes along the ferals have to survive them without any help.

The sixth assumption is that the feral bees suddenly died. The bees have been diminishing for the last 50 years fairly steadily from pesticide misuse, loss of habitat and forage, and more recently from bee paranoia. People hear about AHB and kill any swarm they see. Several states have killing all feral bees as their official policy.

**Q:** If bees are naturally smaller why didn't anyone notice? Also why are the bee scientist saying they are larger?

**A:** I don't know why, they are saying they are larger, perhaps some of it comes back to the regression issue. If you take bees from large cell comb and let them build what they want, what will they build? Is this the same as natural comb? Sometimes we just have differences in observations because of a variety of factors being involved.

I really don't think it should be hard to accept that they are naturally smaller since there have been plenty of measurements taken over the centuries. Dee Lusby's writings (available on www.beesource.com have references to many articles and discussions on the size of bees and comb and the concept of enlarging it. We have plenty of easy to find evidence that bees used to be smaller.

Find *ABC & XYZ of Bee Culture* books and look under "Cell Size".

Here are some quotes from them.

*ABC & XYZ of Bee Culture*, 38th edition (1980), page 134:

---

> ***"If the average beekeeper were asked how many cells, worker and drone comb, there were to the inch, he would undoubtedly answer five and four, respectively. Indeed some text books on bees carry that ratio. Approximately it is correct, enough for the bees, particularly the queen. The dimensions must be exact or there is a protest. In 1876 when A.I. Root, the original author of this book, built his first roll comb foundation mill, he had the die faces cut for five worker cells to the inch. While the bees built beautiful combs from this foundation, and the queen laid in the cells, yet, if given a chance they appeared to prefer their own natural comb not built from comb foundation. Suspecting the reason, Mr. Root then began measuring up many pieces of natural comb when he discovered that the initial cells, five to the inch, from his first machine were slightly too small. The result of his measurements of natural comb showed slightly over 19 worker cells to four inches linear measurement, or 4.83 cells to one inch."***

---

Roughly this same information is in the 1974 version, page 136 and the 1945 version, page 125. The 1877 version, page 147 says:

> ***"The best specimens of true worker-comb, generally contain 5 cells within the space of an inch, and therefore this measure has been adopted for the comb foundation."***

All of the following historic references list that same measurement, 5 cells to the inch and can be reviewed at Cornell's Hive and the Honey Bee Collection online (http://bees.library.cornell.edu/):

- *Beekeeping*, Everett Franklin Phillips pg 46
- *Rational Bee-keeping*, Dzierzon pg 8 and again on pg 27
- *British Bee-keeper's Guide Book*, T.W. Cowan pg 11
- *The Hive and the Honey Bee*, L.L. Langstroth pg 74 of the 4th edition but is in all of them

This "5 cells to the inch" in *ABC XYZ* is followed in all but the 1877 version with a section on "will larger cells develop a larger bee" and information on Baudoux's research.

***So let's do the math:***

Five cells to an inch, the standard size for foundation in the 1800s and the commonly accepted measurement from that era, is five cells to 25.4mm which is ten cells to 50.8 mm which is, of course, 5.08mm per cell. This is 3.2 mm smaller than standard foundation is now.

A.I. Root's measurement of 4.83 cells to an inch is 5.25 mm which is 1.5 mm smaller than standard foundation. Of course if you measure comb much you'll find a lot of variance in cell size, which makes it very difficult to say exactly what size natural comb is. But I have measured (and photographed) 4.7 mm comb from commercial Carniolans and I have photographs of comb from bees on natural comb in Pennsylvania that are 4.4mm. Typically there is a lot of variance with the core of the brood nest the smallest and the edges the largest. You can find a lot of comb from 4.8 mm to 5.2 mm with most of the 4.8 mm in the center and the 4.9 mm, 5.0 mm and 5.1 mm moving out from there and the 5.2 mm at the very edges of the brood nest.

> ***"Until the late 1800s honeybees in Britain and Ireland were raised in brood cells of circa 5.0 mm width. By the 1920s this had increased to circa 5.5 mm."— John B. McMullan and Mark J.F. Brown, The influence of small-cell brood combs on the morphometry of honeybees (Apis mellifera)—John B. McMullan and Mark J.F. Brown***

Hubersaid in Volume two of *Huber's Observations on Bees* (see translation by C.P. Dadant) that worker cells are 2-$^{2}/_{5}$ lines which is equal to 5.08mm which is identical to the early ABC XYZ of Bee Culture.

The 41st edition of ABC XYZ of Bee Culture on Page 160 (under Cell Size) says:

> ***"The size of naturally constructed cells has been a subject of beekeeper and scientific curiosity since Swammerdam measured them in the 1600s. Numerous subsequent reports from around the world indicate that the diameter of naturally constructed cells ranges***

***from 4.8 to 5.4mm. Cell diameter varies between geographic areas, but the overall range has not changed from the 1600s to the present time."***

---

And further down:

***"reported cell size for Africanized honey bees averages 4.5-5.1mm."***

---

Marla Spivak and Eric Erickson (Do measurements of worker cell size reliably distinguish Africanized from European honey bees (Apis mellifera L.)?*American Bee Journal*, April 1992, p. 252-255 says:

***"...a continuous range of behaviors and cell size measurements was noted between colonies considered "strongly European" and "strongly Africanized". "***

***"Due to the high degree of variation within and among feral and managed populations of Africanized bees, it is emphasized that the most effective solution to the Africanized "problem", in areas where Africanized bees have established permanent populations, is to consistently select for the most gentle and productive colonies among the existing honey bee population" —Identification and***

***relative success of Africanized and European honey bees in Costa Rica..***

In my observation, there is also variation by how you space the frames, or variation on how *they* space the combs. 38 mm (1 1/2") will result in larger cells than 35 mm (1 3/8") which will be larger than 32 mm (1 1/4"). In naturally spaced comb the bees will sometimes crowd the combs down to 30 mm in places with 32 mm more common in just brood comb and 35mm more common where there is drone on the comb.

So what is natural comb spacing? It is the same problem as saying what natural cell size is. It depends.

But in my observation, if you let them do what they want, for a couple of comb turnovers, you can find out what the range of these is and what the norm is. The norm was (and is) *not* the standard foundation size of 5.4 mm cells and it is *not* the standard comb spacing of 35 mm.

# Ways to get smaller cells

***How to get natural sized cells***

**Top Bar Hives**

Make the bars 32 mm ($1^1/_4$") for the brood area
Make the bars 38 mm ($1^1/_2$") for the honey area

**Foundationless frames**

Make a "comb guide" like Langstroth did (see Langstroth's *The Hive and the Honey-Bee*)

Also helpful to cut down end bars to 32 mm (1 $^1/_4$") or

**Make blank starter strips**

Use a brine soaked board and dip it in wax to make blank sheets. Cut these into $^3/_4$" wide strips and put in the frames.

---

***How to get small cells***

Use 4.9 mm wax foundation or
Honey Super Cell (see www.honeysupercell.com)
PermaComb or PermaPlus (5.0mm cell size)
Mann Lake PF100s or PF120s (4.95mm cell size).

# Rationalizations on Small Cell Success

This chapter is *not* to talk about my theories of why small cell works or others who are doing it, but the theories of those who want to explain away the success of small cell beekeepers with theories that are more in line with their model of the world. There seem to be many theories from those who are not doing small cell and who want to explain the success of small cell beekeepers in some other frame of reference that makes sense to them. I will address a few of these here.

***AHB***

One explanation, which is consistent with other beliefs held by these individuals is that small cell beekeepers must have Africanized honey bees. Since they believe that AHB build smaller cells and EHB do not, in their model of the world, that explains both the size of the cells, and the success with Varroa as well as early emergence and other issues to do with Varroa. The problem with this theory is that many of us are keeping bees in Northern climates, where we are told AHB can't survive, are selling them to others, who comment on how gentle our bees are, have them regularly inspected, without any complaints of aggressiveness or suspicions of AHB from inspectors, and indeed most of us are collecting local survivor stock when we can, which supposedly could not survive in the North if it was AHB. And I have had samples tested at the request of someone doing a study on bee genetics which says they are not. The fact is at least those of us not in AHB areas are definitely not raising AHB and don't want to. Whether or not Dee Lusby, or others in AHB areas end up with some AHB genes, is a different discussion, but it's irrelevant to the fact that most of us small cell beekeepers do not live in AHB areas and are not raising AHB and are not interested in raising AHB yet our bees are surviving.

***Survivor stock***

While it's true that many small cell and natural cell beekeepers try to breed from survivors, this is simply the logical thing to do. You raise bees that can survive where you are. Many people are doing that even if they are not doing small cell and even if it's not for Varroa issues, but just wintering issues. Typically the people using this argument quote the losses that the Lusby's had while regressing as evidence that they just bred stock that could survive the Varroa. This seems plausible if the Lusbys were the only example, but I had no large losses while regressing and started with commercial stock and when I did the same thing on large cell, I lost all of them to Varroa several times over. Starting again with new commercial stock on small cell I have lost none to Varroa. Considering how many people are working so diligently to try to breed resistant stock, I think it's beyond believability that so many of us small cell beekeepers just blundered into Varroa-resistant stock with so little effort. If these people really believe genetics is the cause of our success then they should be begging us to sell them breeder queens. Since they are not, I do not think even they believe this. I certainly don't believe this, although I would love to. It would greatly increase the value of my queens. Since I regressed and since my Varroa issues went away, I then did start breeding from survivor stock I could find around, because I want bees acclimatized to my environment. I have better wintering when I do this. I did not see any change in Varroa issues when doing this as Varroa problems had already disappeared.

***Blind faith***

This isn't so much a reason being given that it works, as much as discounting that it does work and trying to find a reason people *think* it works. It seems that a lot of detractors of small cell think that the whole group of small cell beekeepers are fanatically religious followers of Dee Lusby suffering from mass hysteria. The implication is that we are deluded into believing it is working when it is not. Anyone who comes to one of the many organic meetings where Dee Lusby, Dean Stiglitz, Ramona Herboldsheimer, Sam Comfort, Erik Osterlund, I and others speak would see the absurdity of this. As would anyone who participates in the organic beekeepers Yahoo group. We often have different observations and often disagree, as all honest beekeepers do. If we all spouted some standard party line, then this might be a legitimate concern, but while we agree on the basic concepts, we often disagree on details and we have all had different experiences probably caused our locations and our climate as well as just chance. While I have great respect for all of the above listed speakers and particularly for Dee, as she and her late husband Ed pioneered this work, I have never been in total agreement with her or the rest.

The four things I think we all agree on are: No treatments, natural or small sized cells, local adapted stock, and avoiding artificial feed. But while Sam and I are pretty happy with simple foundationless, Dee is more focused on actual specific cell size. While Dee will feed barrels of honey to her bees, I have neither the time nor the honey for such things and will, if they are faced with not enough honey for winter stores, feed sugar. While Dean and Ramona like natural comb, their experience has been that they had to force the bees down with some Honey Super Cell first to get them regressed, while I've often had good luck with just foundationless regressing quickly. This may be related to the genetics or the cell size in the hives that are the source of my packages and their packages. It is difficult to say. The point is, there is no "party line".

### *Resistance*

Personally, I have never been able to figure out the resistance to the concept of small cell or natural comb. While the large cell beekeepers are obsessed with Varroa, I get to just keep bees. While the large cell beekeepers are still searching for a solution to Varroa, I get to work on my queen rearing and finding easier ways to do less work. Since letting the bees build comb is easier than using foundation, and since those of us doing that are not having Varroa issues, I would think there would be a lot more interest in doing the same. The battle cry of the detractors, of course, is either that there is no study to prove it works, or that there are studies that show that it doesn't. All of this is, of course, irrelevant to me since I'm still not having Varroa issues anymore. I've been hearing such arguments about things not being proved scientifically all my life and yet have lived to see many of those things proved eventually. In the end it's about what works, not what has been proven. In the end it's not about mite counts, although mine have dropped to almost none over time, it's about survival. No one seems to want to count living hives instead of mites, but it's a much easier thing to count and much more meaningful. If you put one bee-yard on small cell and leave another on large cell, then it seems like the "last man standing" would be an easy way to decide. If one yard dies out and the other does well, that would seem a much better way to decide than counting mites.

### *Small Cell Studies*

There are a few positive small cell studies, but also several that show higher mite counts on small cell and people always ask why. I don't know for sure, as it is inconsistent with my experience, but let's look at that. Let's assume a short term study (which all of them have been) during the drone rearing time of the year (which all of them have been) and make the assumption for the moment that Dee Lusby's "pseudodrone" theory is true, meaning that with large cell the Varroa often mistake large cell workers for drone cells and therefore infest them more. The Varroa in the large cell hives during that time would be less successful at reproducing, but cause more damage, because they are in the wrong cells (workers). The Varroa, during that time would be more successful at reproducing but cause less damage to the workers on the small cell because they are in the drone cells. But later in the year this may shift dramatically when, first of all the small cell workers have not taken damage from the Varroa and second of all the drone rearing drops off and the mites, looking for drone cells (or "pseudodrone" cells) have nowhere to go.

In the end, as Dann Purvis says, "It's not about mite counts. It's about survival". No one seems interested in measuring that. What I do know is that after a couple of years the mite counts dropped to almost nothing on small cell. But that did not take place in the first three months.

# Foundationless

***Why would one want to go foundationless?***

How about no chemical contamination of the combs and natural Varroa control from natural cell size? As far as contamination, some of my queens are three years old and laying well. I don't think you'll find anyone who is using chemicals in their hives with that kind of longevity and health in their queens. You can also get clean wax combs with natural cells in a top bar hive.

*Comb On Blank Starter Strip. The cells are 4.5mm. The frames were spaced 1 $^{1}/_{4}$"*

***How do you go foundationless?***

Bees need some kind of guide to get them to draw straight comb. Any beekeeper has seen them skip the foundation and build combs between or out from the face of the comb, so we know that sometimes they ignore those clues. But a simple clue like a beveled top bar or a strip of wax or wood or even a drawn comb on each side of an empty frame will work most of the time. You can just break out the wedge on a top bar, turn it sideways and glue and nail it on to make a guide. Or put Popsicle sticks (jumbo craft sticks) or paint sticks in the groove. Or just cut out the old comb in a drawn wax comb and leave a row at the top or all the way around.

*Foundationless Frame*

I made these by ordering frames from Walter T. Kelley with no grooves in the top and bottom bars and cutting the top bars at a 45 degree angle on both sides. Kelley is now offering them already made with the bevel on them. The bees tend to follow the sloped top bar.

*Foundationless Frame*

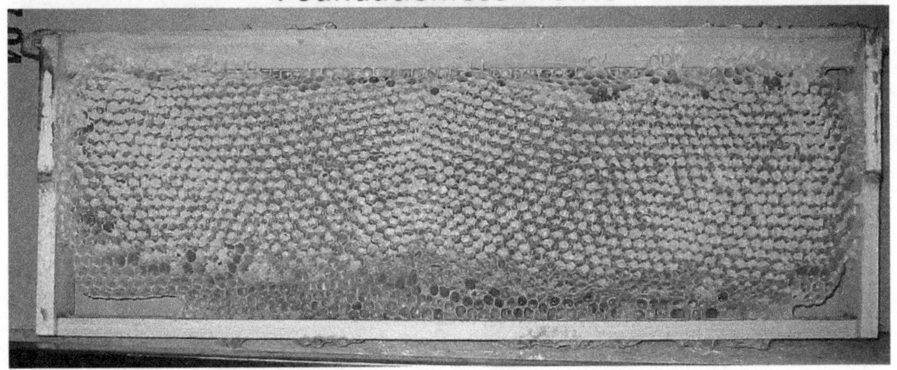

*Drawn Foundationless Frame*

Note the picture of *Drawn Foundationless Frame.* You can see the corners are often open, the bottom seems to be the last to get attached, but this is attached on all four sides and ready to be uncapped and extracted.

*Dadant Deep Foundationless Frame ($11^1/_4$ in.)*

Here is a Dadant Deep foundationless with a comb guide all the way around and a $^1/_{16}$" steel rod for support horizontally in the center. This allows cutting six pieces of 4" by 4" comb honey out without fighting with wires. Langstroth also used the comb guides on the side like this.

*Beveled Top Bar Frame*

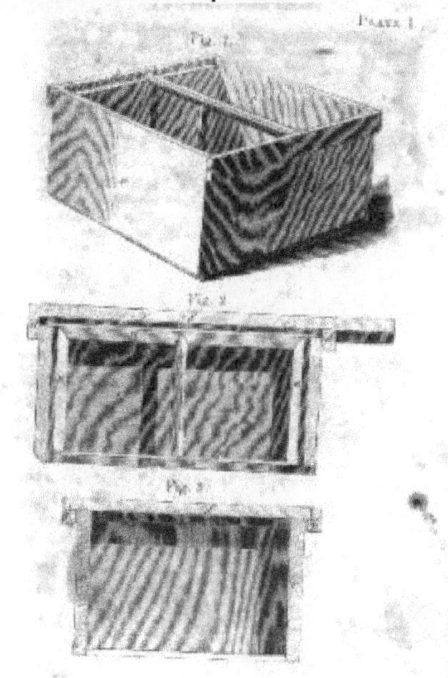

*Langstroth's Foundationless Frame*

L.L. Langstroth has pictures of this design in the original "Langstroth's Hive and the Honey Bee" which you can still buy as a reprint.

### *Foundationless frames*

In my experience the bees will draw their own comb faster than they will draw foundation. I'm not the only one to make the observation that bees are not attracted to foundation.

> ***"Foundation, even composed of pure beeswax, is not intrinsically attractive to bees. Swarming bees offered the opportunity to cluster on foundation or some branch, show no preference for foundation." —The How-To-Do-It Book of Beekeeping, Richard Taylor***

### *Historic References*

Most of these can be found online in Cornell's Hive and the Honey Bee collection (http://bees.library.cornell.edu/).

> ***"HOW TO SECURE STRAIGHT COMBS. "The full advantages of the movable comb principle is only secured by getting all the combs built true within the frames. Upon the first introduction of movable frames, bee-keepers frequently failed in this although much care***

***and attention were given. Mr. Langstroth, for a time, used for guides strips of comb attached to the under side of the top bar of the frame. This is a very good practice when the comb can be had, as it usually secures the object besides giving the bees a start with worker comb. Next followed the triangular comb guide consisting of a triangular piece of wood tacked to the under side of the top bar, leaving a sharp corner projecting downwards. This is a valuable aid and is now universally adopted." —Facts in Bee Keeping by N.H. King and H.A. King 1864, pg. 97***

***"If some of the full frames are moved, and empty ones placed between them, as soon as the bees begin to build powerfully, there need be no guide combs on the empty frames, and still the work will be executed with the most beautiful regularity." —The Hive and the Honeybee by Rev. L.L. Langstroth 1853, pg. 227***

***"Improved Comb Bar.—Mr. Woodbury says that this little contrivance has proved very effectual in securing straight combs when guide combs are not obtainable. The lower angles are rounded off whilst a central rib is***

***added of about $^1/_8$ of an inch in breadth and depth. This central rib extends to within $^1/_2$ an inch of each end, where it is removed in order to admit of the bar fitting into the usual notch. All that is necessary to insure the regular formation of combs is, to coat the underneath surface of the central rib with melted wax. Mr. Woodbury further says, "my practice is to use plain bars, whenever guide-combs are attainable, as these can be attached with much greater facility to a plain than to a ribbed bar; but whenever I put in a bar without comb, I always use one of the improved ones. By this method , crooked and irregular combs are altogether unknown in my apiary." Most of our bars are made with the ridge; but should any of our customers prefer the flat ones, we keep a few to supply their requirements"—Alfred Neighbour, The Apiary, or, Bees, Bee Hives, and Bee Culture pg 39***

***"Top bars have been made by some hive manufacturers from one-fourth-inch to three-eighths-inch strips, strengthened somewhat by a very thin strip placed edgewise on the underside as a comb guide; but such bars are much too light and will sag when filled with honey or with brood and honey..."—Frank***

***Benton, The Honey Bee: A Manual of Instruction in Apiculture pg 42***

***"Comb Guide.—Generally a wooden edge, or a strip of comb or fdn., in the top of a frame or box, on which comb is to be built...As the comb guide is 9-16, and the cut in the end bar $^3/_4$, we have 3-16 left for whole wood in the top bar, as at A, and the table should be set, as to leave just this amount of wood uncut. Even if the fdn. is fastened in the frames with melted wax as many do, I would have such a comb guide, because it adds so much to the strength of the frame, and obviates the necessity of having a very heavy top bar. The bees will, in time, build their combs right over such a comb guide, and use the cells above the brood for honey."— A.I. Root, ABC of Bee Culture 1879 edition pg 251***

***"A comb guide proper is a sharp edge or corner in the frame, from which the comb is to depend, the bees usually choosing to follow this edge, rather than diverge to an even surface; portions of comb are sometimes used for the same purpose."—J.S. Harbison, The bee-keeper's directory, footnote at the bottom of page 280 and 281***

---

***FAQs***

**Box of empty frames?**

**Q:** You mean I can just put a box of empty frames on the hive?

**A:** No. The bees need some kind of guide.

**What is a guide?**

**Q:** What is a comb guide?

**A:** It can be any of several things. You can use an empty frame with nothing added *if* you have a drawn brood comb on each side as the brood comb will act as a guide. You can put popsicle sticks in the groove to make a sort of wooden strip, or cut a piece of wood to make a wood starter strip. You can turn the wedge on end and glue it in. You can cut a triangular piece and put on the bottom of the top bar. You can buy chamfer molding and cut it to fit and put it on the bottom of the top bar. You can cut the top bars on a bevel. You can make a sheet of empty wax and cut it into $^{3}/_{4}$″ wide strips and put in the groove of the top bar and wax it in. You can cut strips of regular foundation into $^{3}/_{4}$″ wide strips and wax that in the groove or nail it with the cleat. If the frame already had comb in it, you can just leave the top row of cells on the top bar for a guide. Any of these work fine.

**Best guide?**

**Q:** Which comb guide do you like best?

**A:** I like most them fine, but I like the durability of the beveled top bar and I think the comb is attached a bit better. Next I'd probably go for the wood strip. Last I'd go for the starter strips as they sometimes get hot and fall out if the bees haven't used them yet. But I also feed empty frames into brood nests all the time as I have a lot of old frames around. Bottom line is, I do whatever is the easiest at the time. The worst comb guide is filling a groove with just a wax bead. Wax in the groove is barely a suggestion and not at all a good guide. You need something that protrudes significantly. $^{1}/_{4}$" is good.

**Extract?**

**Q:** Can I extract them?

**A:** Yes. I extract them all the time. Just make sure they are attached on all four sides and the wax isn't so new that it's still soft, like putty. Once the wax is mature and the comb is attached at least some on all four sides, it extracts fine. Of course you should always be gentle with any wax combs (wired or not) when extracting.

**Wire?**

**Q:** Do I need wire in them?

**A:** I don't use wire but I don't use deeps either.

**Q:** *Can* I use wire in them?

**A:** Sure. The bees will incorporate the wire into the comb. Of course you need the hive level anyway, but this becomes more obvious with wire in the comb.

Wire is probably more useful when doing deeps than mediums. I run all mediums.

## Wax them?

**Q:** Do I need to wax them?

**A:** I find wax to be counterproductive. It is more work, it often falls off, and it is never attached to the bar as well as the bees will attach their own comb. I not only *don't* recommend that you wax them, I recommend that you *not* wax them.

## Whole box?

**Q:** Can I put a whole box of foundationless frames on a hive?

**A:** Assuming we mean frames with comb guides, yes, you can. Usually this works fine. Sometimes because of a lack of a comb to use as a "ladder" to get up to the top bars, the bees start building comb up from the bottom bar. For this reason I prefer to have one frame of drawn comb or a full sheet of foundation in a super being added on. This isn't a problem when installing a package. Another reason for the one comb, though, is it's good insurance at getting the combs in the right direction. Another solution to them trying to build comb up, is to put the empty box under the current box so they can work down.

## Will they mess up?

**Q:** Won't the bees mess it up without foundation?

**A:** Sometimes. But they mess it up sometimes even with wax and even more often with plastic. I've seen no more bad combs doing foundationless than I have using plastic foundation. Some of this appears to be genetic as some hives build good comb even when you do everything wrong. Other hives build messed up comb even when you do everything right and simply repeat the "mistakes" when you remove them.

I said it before, but it bears repeating. The most important thing to grasp with any natural comb hive is that because bees build the next comb parallel to the current one, one good comb leads to another in the same way that one bad comb leads to another. You cannot afford to not be paying attention to how they start off. The most common cause of a mess of comb is leaving the queen cage in as they always start the first comb from that and then the mess begins. I can't believe how many people want to "play it safe" and hang the queen cage. They obviously can't grasp that it is almost a guarantee of failure to get the first comb started right, which without intervention is guaranteed to mean every comb in the hive will be messed up. Once you have a mess the most important thing is to make sure the *last* comb is straight as this is always the guide for the *next* comb. You can't take a "hopeful" view that the bees will get back on track. They will not. You have to put them back on track.

This has nothing to do with wires or no wires. Nothing to do with frames or no frames. It has to do with the last comb being straight.

## Slower?

**Q:** Won't it set the bees back having to build their own comb?

**A:** In my experience, and many others who have tried it as well, the bees build their own comb much more quickly than they build on foundation. Using foundation sets them back in many ways. First they draw foundation more slowly. Second, the foundation is all contaminated with fluvalinate and coumaphos. Third, unless you're using small cell foundation, you're giving them cells that are larger than they want and giving the advantage to the Varroa.

## Beginners

**Q:** Is it a good idea for a beginner to use foundationless?

**A:** In my opinion it's easier for the beginner who has no habits to adjust to foundationless. It's much more difficult for the seasoned beekeeper to adjust to keeping hives perfectly level, not turning comb flatways, not shaking bees vigorously off of a comb that's still new and not well attached etc. Beginners will often break one comb and learn their lesson. Experienced beekeepers will keep falling back into habits and breaking combs for a while until they finally get it ingrained as a new habit.

## If they mess up?

**Q:** What if they mess it all up?

**A:** It's doubtful but possible that they will. I've seen this occur more often when a box full of frames with wax foundation collapses in the heat. I suppose this seems much more frightening to someone who has never done a cutout. If you've ever cut all the combs out of a wild hive and tied them into frames, then you already know what to do. You cut the wild combs and you put them in an empty frame and use rubber bands or string to hold them in the frame. The bees will take care of the rest. They do this just as often with plastic foundation and it's often more difficult to fix.

## Dimensions

**Q:** If I make my own what dimensions should they be?

**A:** You can make them out of standard frames, but I do prefer them with smaller end bars and slightly smaller top bars. See the *Narrow Frames* chapter.

# Narrow Frames

***Observations on Natural Frame Spacing***

## 1 $^{1}/_{4}$" spacing agrees with Huber's observations

> ***"The leaf or book hive consists of twelve vertical frames... and their breadth fifteen lines (one line= $^{1}/_{12}$ of an inch. 15 lines = $1^{1}/_{4}$"). It is necessary that this last measure should be accurate." François Huber 1806***

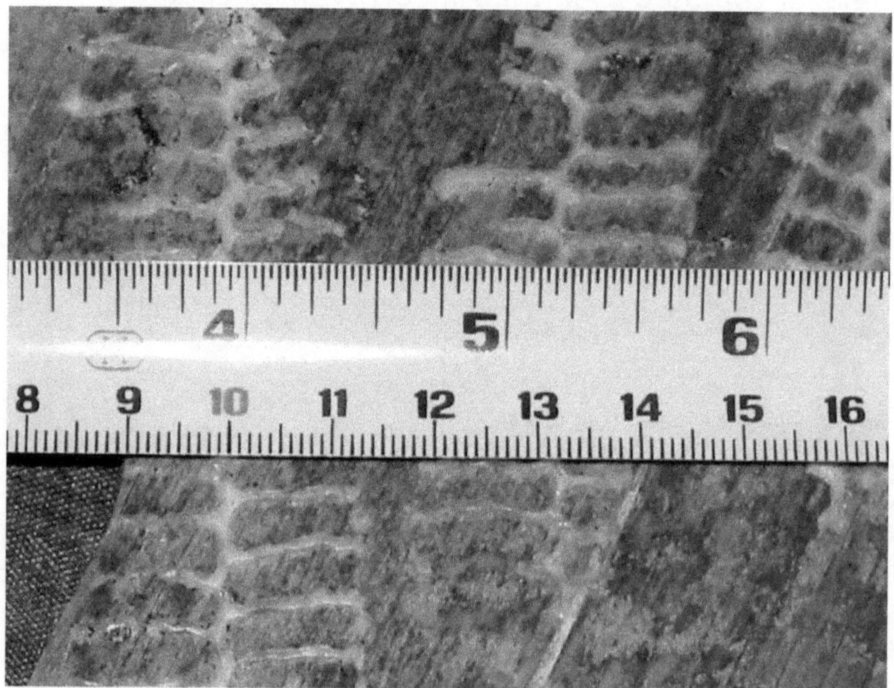


*Brood nest that moved into a top feeder. Inner cover after removing the comb. Spacing on naturally drawn brood comb is sometimes as small as $1^{1}/_{8}$" (30mm) but typically $1^{1}/_{4}$" (32mm).*

## Comb Width by Cell Size

According to Baudoux (note this is the thickness of the comb itself and not the spacing of the comb on centers)

| Cell Size | Comb width |
| --- | --- |
| 5.555 mm | 22.60 mm |
| 5.375 mm | 22.20 mm |
| 5.210 mm | 21.80 mm |
| 5.060 mm | 21.40 mm |
| 4.925 mm | 21.00 mm |
| 4.805 mm | 20.60 mm |
| 4.700 mm | 20.20 mm |

ABC XYZ of Bee Culture 1945 edition Pg 126

---

***Historic references to narrower frame spacing***

> ***"...are placed the usual distance, so that the frames are $1\frac{9}{20}$ inch from centre to centre; but if it is desired to prevent the production of drone brood, the ends of every other frame are slipped back as shown at B, and the distance of $1\frac{1}{4}$ inch from centre to centre may be maintained."—T.W. Cowan, British bee-keeper's Guide Book pg 44***

> ***"On measuring the combs in a hive that were regularly made, I found the following result, viz; five worker-combs occupied a space of***

> ***five and a half inches, the space between each being three-eights of an inch, and allowing for the same width on each outer side, equals six and a quarter inches, as the proper diameter of a box in which five worker-combs could be build...The diameter of worker-combs averaged four-fifths of an inch; and that of drone-combs, one and one-eight of an inch."—T.B. Miner, The American Bee Keeper's Manual, pg 325***

If you take off the extra $^{3}/_{8}$" on the last one this is $5^{7}/_{8}$" for five combs divided by five is 1.175" or $1^{3}/_{16}$" on center for each comb.

> ***"Frame.—As before mentioned, each stock hive has ten of these frames, each 13 inches long by $7^{1}/_{4}$ inches high, with a $^{5}/_{8}$ inch projection either back or front. The width both of the bar and frame is $^{7}/_{8}$ of an inch; this is less by $^{1}/_{4}$ of an inch than the bar recommended by the older apiarians. Mr.Woodbury,—whose authority on the modern plans for keeping bees is of great weight,—finds the $^{7}/_{8}$ of an inch bar an improvement, because with them the combs are closer together, and require fewer bees to cover the brood. Then too, in the same space that eight old fashioned bars***

***occupied the narrower frames admit of an additional bar, so that, by using these, increased accommodation is afforded for breeding and storing of honey."— Alfred Neighbour, The Apiary, or, Bees, Bee Hives, and Bee Culture...***

***"I have found it to be just that conclusion in theory that experiment proves a fact in practice, viz: with frames 7/8 of an inch wide, spaced just a bee-space apart, the bees will fill all the cells from top to bottom with brood, provided deeper cells or wider spacing, is used in the storage chamber. This is not guess-work or theory. In experiments covering a term of years. I have found the same results, without variation, in every instance. Such being the fact, what follows? In answer, I will say that the brood is invariably reared in the brood-chamber — the surplus is stored, and at once, where it should be, and no brace-combs are built; and not only this, but the rearing of drones is kept well in hand, excess of swarming is easily prevented, and, in fact, the whole matter of bee-keeping work is reduced to a minimum, all that is required being to start with sheets of comb just 7/8 of an inch thick, and so spaced that they cannot be built any deeper. I***

***trust that I have made myself understood; I know that if the plan indicated is followed, beekeeping will not only be found an easier pursuit, but speedy progress will be made from now on."—"Which are Better, the Wide or Narrow Frames?" by J.E. Pond, American Bee Journal: Volume 26, Number 9 March 1, 1890 No. 9. Page 141***

---

Note: 7/8" plus 3/8" (max beespace) makes 11/4". 7/8" plus 1/4" (min beespace) makes 11/8".

***"But those who have given special attention to the matter, trying both spacing, agree almost uniformly that the right distance is 1 $^{3}/_{8}$ or, if anything, a trifle scant, and some use quite successfully 1$^{1}/_{4}$ inch spacing." — The ABC and XYZ of Bee Culture by Ernest Rob Root Copyright 1917, Pg 669***

***"With so many beginners wanting to know about eleven deep frames in a 10 frame deep Langstroth brood chamber I will have to go into further details. But first this letter from Anchorage, Alaska of all places. For that is as far north as you can keep bees. He writes, I'm a new beekeeper with one season's experience with two hives. A good friend is in the same boat he had***

***read one of your articles on "Squeezing" the bees and tried one of his hives that way result a hive full of bees and honey. This year we will have eight hives with eleven frames in the brood chamber."***

***"If you, too, want to have eleven frames in the brood chamber do this. In assembling your frames besides nails use glue. It' a permanent deal anyway. Be sure your frames are the type with grooved top and bottom bars. After assembling the frames, plane down the end bars on each side so that they are the same width as the top bar. Now drive in the staples. As I mentioned last month make them by cutting paper clips in half. They cost but little and don't split the wood. Drive the staples into the wood until they stick out one quarter inch. The staples should be all on one side. This prevents you from turning the frame around in the brood nest. It's a bad practice and it upsets the arrangement of the brood nest. It is being done, but it leads to chilling of brood and it disturbs the laying cycle of the queen. I am talking to beginners, but even old timers should not commit this bad practice. As for the foundation, if you use molded plastic foundation just snap it into the frame and you are ready***

***to go."— Charles Koover, Bee Culture, April 1979, From the West Column.***

---

The standard frame width on Hoffman frames is $1^3/_8$". That means that from center to center combs are spaced $1^3/_8$" apart. This makes a comb about 1" thick and a beespace between the combs about $^3/_8$". This spacing works pretty well as an all around spacing and yet beekeepers usually space the frames in the supers further, like $1^1/_2$" or more apart. The $1^3/_8$" was already a compromise between honey storage, drone brood comb and worker brood comb. Natural worker brood comb being spaced $1^1/_4$" while natural drone comb is more like $1^3/_8$" and honey storage typically is about $1^1/_2$" or more ($1^1/_4$"=32mm, $1^3/_8$" = 35mm and $1^1/_2$"=38mm).

***Spacing frames $1^1/_4$" has advantages***

Among them:

- Less drone comb.
- More frames of brood in a box.
- More frames of brood can be covered with bees to keep them warm as the layer of bees is only one bee deep instead of two.
- According to some research back in the 70's in Russia, there was less Nosema.
- It's more natural spacing for smaller cells.
- It incites the bees to build smaller cells. The smaller spacing contributes towards them viewing the comb on it as worker comb.

***Frequent misconceptions:***

- That $1^1/_4$" (32mm) is only right for Africanized honey bees. I've let European honey bees build their own comb and they space worker brood comb as small as $1^1/_8$" (30mm) but typically $1^1/_4$" for the core of the brood nest. Wider at the outside edges when they want drones and even wider when they want to store honey.
- That your frames won't be interchangeable with 1 $^3/_8$" frames. I interchange them all the time. Many of the historical references above show that people often spaced them tighter in the center and wider on the outside edges. There is nothing stopping you from putting a $1^3/_8$" frame in the middle of $1^1/_4$" frames or vice a versa.
- That it simply doesn't matter. Well, it probably doesn't matter a lot but see the above advantages.

***Ways to get narrow frames***

- Assuming no nails from the outsides of the end bars, you can plane off the end bars of regular frames until they are $1^1/_4$" wide. If you do this before assembling the frames, you can also cut the top bar down to 1" wide on a table saw.
- You can make or buy frames built from scratch. Either by adjusting the dimensions and building Hoffman frames or by building Killion style frames and simply changing the spacing (see "Honey in the Comb" by Carl Killion or later editions Eugene Killion).
- You can intersperse PermaComb (which has no spacers) with regular Hoffman combs and then space them a little further by hand.

- You can build Koover frames (see old 70's Gleanings in Bee Culture articles or plans on nordykebeefarm.com)

***FAQs***

**Q:** Won't the top bars be too close if I plane off the end bars?

**A:** A little, but you can get by with it. It does cramp them down to about $^{3}/_{16}$″ between the top bars, but bees can get through a $^{5}/_{32}$″ hole. I prefer to have more space but not enough to cut down the top bars on regular frames. I do prefer them enough that I make them smaller when I make frames or order them smaller if I can get someone to make them.

**Q:** Why not put 9 frames in the brood box of a ten frame box? Won't that keep things the same (since I want to run nine in my supers) and give them more space so they don't swarm and I don't roll bees pulling out frames?

**A:** In my experience you'll roll more bees with this arrangement (9 in a 10 frame box) because the surface of the comb will be very uneven due to the thickness of the brood being consistent while the thickness of honey storage varies. This means that frame spaced nine in a ten frame box have an uneven surface. That uneven surface is more likely to catch bees between two protruding parts and roll them than when they are even. It also takes more bees to cover and keep warm the same amount of brood when you have 9 frames instead of 10 or 11.

***"...if the space is insufficient, the bees shorten the cells on the side of one comb, thus rendering that side useless; and if placed more than the usual width, it requires a greater amount of bees to cover the brood, as also to raise the temperature to the proper degree for building comb, Second, when the combs are too widely spaced, the bees while refilling them with stores, lengthen the cells and thus make the comb thick and irregular—the application of the knife is then the only remedy to reduce them to proper thickness."—J.S. Harbison, The Bee-keeper's Directory, p. 32***

---

# Yearly Cycles

Beekeeping, like any farming, follows the seasons. It is cyclic in nature and the bigger cycle is the year. Smaller cycles are 21 day worker brood cycles etc. but the big picture for beekeeping is a year.

In my view the beekeeper's year starts, as it does for the bees, in preparing the colony for winter. A colony that has a good footing for surviving the winter and prospering in early spring has a good start on the year.

My view, of course will be colored by my experiences in a cold northern climate. You may need to adjust things for your climate.

***Winter***

From a beekeeper's point of view Winter starts at the first killing frost. From this point on the bees will have no resources coming in. No nectar. No pollen. Before this happens they need to be in pretty good shape. Some winters come early and set in early and there are no other opportunities to prepare.

**Bees**

Basically for winter they need to have a sufficient quantity of bees. Lacking this they should either be babied in some way (difficult at best) or combined with another weak hive to make one strong enough to winter. This will vary by race of bee and by climate. Here with Italians I'd want at least a basketball sized cluster. With Carnis, a soccer ball sized cluster and with ferals something between a soccer ball and a softball.

### Stores

They should have enough food to last the winter. I try to leave them enough, but sometimes with a dearth or a poor fall flow they can end up light. Here, in Greenwood, Nebraska, with Italians you need a hive to weigh about 150 pounds. With ferals that's about a 90 pound hive. A light hive can be fed syrup or you can put sugar on top of newspaper on the top bars to make up the deficit. Some people feed pollen or substitute in the late fall as well. Fall syrup is usually 2:1 (sugar:water)

### Setup for winter

They should have no queen excluder and if they have a bottom entrance they should have a mouse guard. A reduced entrance is helpful to prevent robbing. They need to have some kind of top entrance.

### *Spring*

Spring for the beekeeper starts at the blooming of the maples. Here where I live that's late February or early March. This is when the bees start rearing brood in earnest. It's important from this point on that the supply of pollen and stores is not interrupted as this can interrupt brood rearing. Pollen patties are a common solution for this. Mix pollen with honey to make a dough and roll between waxed paper to make patties. Or feed it open in an empty hive. Feed 1:1 or 2:1 syrup if they are light on stores. On a warm day do a full inspection and check for eggs and brood. Mark the queenless ones to requeen or combine. Clean off the bottom boards and inspect them for dead Varroa mites. If you're using Walt Wright's Nectar management, it's time to checkerboard. If you're not you need to keep an eye on things to prevent early swarms. When the weather starts staying warm enough, open up the brood nest by putting some empty frames in the middle of the brood nest. If it's a booming hive with lots of bees, two or three frames. If it's a moderate hive, one. If it's a weak hive, leave it alone. Don't add a lot of room as the weather is still chilly and too much space is still a stressful thing. The hive is trying to build up enough to swarm before the main flow. Brood rearing has kicked in. Drone rearing will kick in soon.

***Summer***

Summer, from a beekeepers point of view, is when swarm season hits or just a few weeks before the flow. The flow is when you start seeing white wax and new comb. This is a time to watch for swarm preparations (backfilling the brood nest) and keep the brood nest open. If swarm preparations have progressed to swarm cells, do splits to get spare queens. Add supers for honey storage. By this point, too much room isn't an issue so pile them on the strong hives. Here this would be mid to late May. If you want to do cut down splits or confine a queen for a better crop or to help with Varroa this would be the time. Two weeks before the main flow would be almost perfect timing.

***Fall***

Fall, from a beekeepers point of view, is when the main summer flow is over and it's time to harvest the honey. The flowers with darker stronger tasting nectar will be blooming soon—goldenrod, smartweed, asters, sunflowers, partridge peas and chicory. It's a good time to requeen as queens are better mated and more available. Also a good time to rear queens, unless there's a bad drought. Towards the end of fall is when you get them settled in for winter. Put on mouse guards. Remove excluders. Remove empty boxes. Reduce entrances. Equalize stores or feed. In other words we are back to setting up for winter.

# Wintering Bees

I have hesitated to write on wintering bees and so far had resisted the temptation because wintering is so tied to locale. But it is a critical issue and I get questions all the time and so I wish to state what I think on many of the issues. Please read all of this with *locale* in mind. I will try to cover what I do in my locale (Southeast Nebraska) in detail and why I do what I do, but that does not mean it is the best for your locale or that some other methods might not work in other or even my location.

I will break this down into topics or manipulations that are commonly discussed whether I do or do not do them.

Another thing that matters is the race or the breeding. Mine are all mutts, but they run from brown to black and are Northern bred survivor stock.

I'll break it down by items and actions:

***Mouse Guards***

Typical questions are what to use and when to use them. I have only upper entrances so mouse guards are not an issue anymore. Back when I had lower entrances I used $^{1}/_{4}$″ hardware cloth for mouse guards, but I might consider, if I were still using lower entrances, a popular device here in Southeast Nebraska. The device is a 3″ to 4″ wide piece of $^{3}/_{8}$″ plywood cut to fit the width of the entrance and three $^{3}/_{8}$″ laths cut to the 3″ or 4″ width of the plywood. This slides into the entrance reducing it to $^{3}/_{8}$″ and forming a baffle so that the wind doesn't blow in. People who use it say there is no problem with mice as the $^{3}/_{8}$″ gap being several inches long seems to deter the mice. They leave them on all year around.

As far as when, I'd try to get them on by or shortly after the first frost. Here we get some warm weather after the first frost, so the mice usually don't move in until it stays cold for several days. You want them on before then or the mice may already be in the hive. The other nice thing about the "baffle" type of entrance reducer/mouse guard is you can leave it in all year around and you don't have to worry about remembering to get the mouse guards on.

### *Queen Excluders*

I don't use excluders, but when I did, I would remove them before winter as they can cause the queen to get stuck below the excluder when the bees move up. The excluder will not stop the bees from moving up, but will keep the queen from joining them. You can store it on top of the inner cover or at the top of the hive I you like, but don't leave it between any boxes.

### *Screened bottom boards (SBB)*

I have these on about half of my hives. If the stand is short enough and enough grass blocks the wind, I sometimes leave out the tray, but usually I put the tray in. Some people in some climates seem to think it's good to leave them open year round, but I don't think it works well in a cold windy climate like mine. I also don't think the SBB helps much with Varroa, but it does help with ventilation in the summer and it keeps the bottom board dry in the winter. On the other hand a solid bottom board can double as a feeder and a cover.

***Wrapping***

I don't. I tried it once, but it seemed to seal in all the moisture and cause the boxes to remain soaking wet all winter, so I quit doing it. If I were to try it again, which I probably won't, I'd put some wood on the corners to create an air space between the wood and the wrap.

***Clustering hives together***

I put my hives on stands that hold two rows of seven (eight frame) hives. Basically they are eight foot long treated two by fours with four foot ends on them so the entire stand is 99" long (8' 3") because of the end pieces. The rails (the eight foot long pieces) are such that the outside ones are 20" from the center and the inside ones are 20" from the outside. This allows the hives (which are $19^7/_8$") to be all the way forward in the summer to maximize convenience of manipulating them, and all the way back in winter to minimize exposed area. So during the winter 10 of the hives are touching on three sides and the four on the outside ends are touching on two sides. This minimizes exposed walls. Sort of like huddling together for warmth.

***Feeding Bees***

Contrary to popular belief, winter feeding honey or syrup does not work in Northern climates. Once the syrup doesn't make it above 50º F during the day (and it takes a while to warm up after a chilly night) the bees won't take it anymore anyway. The time to feed if needed is September, if necessary and if you're lucky you may be able to continue into October some years.

The questions always seem to be what concentration and how much.

When feeding honey, I don't water it down at all. Watered down it spoils quickly and I can't see wasting honey. When feeding syrup (because you have no honey or don't want to feed what you already went to the work of harvesting) the concentration should not be below 5:3 nor above 2:1. Thicker is better as it will require less evaporation, but I have trouble getting 2:1 to dissolve.

"How much" is not the right question. The right question is "what is the target weight?" For a large cluster in four medium eight frame boxes (or two ten frame deep boxes) should be between 100 and 150 pounds. In other words if the hive weighs 100 pounds, I might or might not feed, but if it weighs 150 I won't. If it weighs 75 pounds I'll try to feed 75 pounds of honey or syrup. Once the target weight is reached I would stop.

My management plan is to leave them enough honey and steal capped honey from other hives if they are light. But some years when the fall flow fails, I have to feed. I like to wait until the weather turns cold before harvesting as it solves several issues. 1) no wax moths to worry about. 2) the bees are clustered below so no bees to remove from supers. 3) I can assess better what to leave and what to take as the fall flow did or did not occur. Another option for a light hive, if it's not too light, is to feed dry sugar. The down side is that sugar is not stored like syrup, so it's more of an emergency ration, but the up side is you don't have to make syrup, buy feeders, etc. But it not being stored is also the up side. If they don't need it, you don't have syrup stored in your combs. You just put an empty box on the hive with some newspaper on the top bars and pour the sugar on top of the newspaper. I wet it a bit to clump it and wet the edge to get them to see it is food. If the hive is only a little light this is nice insurance. But if it's very light, I think they need to have some capped stores and I'd feed them honey or syrup.

A solid bottom board can be converted to a feeder. This makes sense to me because feeding isn't my normal management plan, leaving honey is. Why buy feeders for all your hives if feeding isn't a normal situation? This is not the best feeder, but it is the cheapest (basically free). If I need to feed, I don't have to buy a feeder for each hive. They hold about as much as a frame feeder.

Around here candy boards are popular, but the dry sugar on top is easier as you don't have to make the boards, and make the candy. You just use your standard boxes and sugar. I've also been known to spray syrup into drawn comb to give a light hive to get them through.

### *Insulation*

Sometimes I insulate the tops and sometimes I don't. I gave up insulating anything else. I think it's a good idea to insulate the top, but I just don't always get it done. Since I run a simple top with a top entrance, when I do insulation it's just a piece of Styrofoam on top of the cover with the brick on top of that. This will reduce condensation on the top, as does the top entrance. Any thickness of Styrofoam will do. The main issue is condensation on the lid. When I have tried insulating the entire hive the moisture between the insulation and the hive became a problem.

***Top Entrances***

I think this is essential to reducing condensation in my climate. It was not necessary when I was in Western Nebraska which is a much drier climate. It doesn't have to be a large top entrance, just a small one will do. The notch that comes on the notched inner covers is fine. This also provides a way for the bees to exit for cleansing flights on warm snowy days when the bottom entrance (which I don't have) would be blocked with snow. I have only top entrances and no bottom entrances.

***Where the cluster is***

Usually around here it's in the top box going into and coming out of winter, with or without a top entrance. Sometimes it's not, but that seems to be the norm, despite what all the books seem to say. I leave them where they are and I don't try to make them be where I think they should be. Usually they spend the entire winter there. I would move them to one end in a horizontal hive, though, so they don't get to one end and starve with stores at the other end.

***How strong?***

This question comes up a lot. I used to combine weak hives and I seldom lost a hive over winter. However, since I started trying to overwinter nucs I've realized how well a small hive takes off if it does make it through the winter. So I've overwintered much smaller clusters. Also if you have local queens, instead of southern queens, they do better as well as the darker bees overwintering on smaller clusters than the lighter colored bees. So, while I've never seen a softball sized cluster of southern package Italians get through the winter, I've seen that size of feral survivor stock, Carniolans and even Northern raised Italians make it. This is actually going into winter on a cold day (tight cluster). There is some attrition in the fall, and if they are this size in September and there is no flow and they are rearing no brood, they probably wouldn't make it. A strong Italian hive going into winter would be a basketball sized cluster or more, while Carniolans or Buckfasts are usually more like soccer ball sized or smaller, and feral survivors tend to be even smaller.

### ***Entrance reducers***

I do like them on all the hives. On the strong hives they create a traffic jam in the case of a robbing frenzy which will slow things down, and on a weak hive they create a smaller space to guard. On all the hives they create less of a draft than a wide open entrance. In fact when I have forgotten to open up the reducers in the spring, even the strong hives with the traffic jams because of it seem to do better than the ones that are wide open. I do try to remember to open them up on the strong hives for the main flow.

### ***Pollen***

I have, in recent years, started feeding pollen in the fall during a dearth so they are well stocked with pollen going into winter and so they have one more turnover of brood before winter sets in. There is no point in doing this while real pollen is coming in. I feed real pollen if I have enough. I have sometimes mixed it 50/50 with substitute or soybean flour when I'm desperate and don't have enough. I never mix it at less than 50% real pollen. You can trap this yourself or buy it from one of the suppliers like Brushy Mountain I feed it in the open. I put it on a SBB on top of a solid bottom board in an empty hive. This would be in September usually.

### *Windbreak*

Some people use straw bales to get a windbreak. I hate mice and they seem to me to be mouse nests waiting to happen, so I don't. But if you kept them back a ways maybe they would work. I suppose one could use corn cribbing or snow fence for a wind break as well as any kind of privacy fence. Mel Disselkoen uses a ring of sheet metal around four hives to make a windbreak for them. This looks like a good setup to me but requires buying the metal and storing it during the rest of the year and then setting it up again in the fall.

### *Eight frame boxes*

I find that eight frame boxes overwinter better than ten frame boxes. The width is more the size of a tree and the size of a cluster, so there is less food left behind. This is not to say that you can't winter bees in ten frame boxes, just that they seem to do slightly better in eight frame boxes.

### *Medium boxes*

I find that medium boxes overwinter better than deeps as there is better communication between frames because of the gap between the boxes. If you picture what is in the hive when the bees cluster in the winter there are combs making walls between parts of the cluster. With a sudden cold snap a group of bees often get trapped on the other side of a deep frame when the cluster contracts as they can't get to the top or bottom and over, where with the medium the cluster usually spans the gap between the boxes providing communication between frames throughout the hive. Again, this is not to say you can't overwinter them in deeps, but only that they seem to do slightly better in mediums.

### *Narrow frames*

I find they winter better on narrow frames ($1^1/_4$″ on center instead of the standard $1^3/_8$″ on center or the 9 frame arrangement in a ten frame box which is about $1^1/_2$″ on center) because it takes less bees in the late winter to cover and keep the brood warm than it does with larger gaps. Again, this is not to say you can't overwinter them on $1^3/_8$″ frames, only that they seem to do slightly better, build up earlier, get less chilled brood and less chalkbrood on narrow frames.

### *Wintering Nucs*

I have tried overwintering nucs every winter since 2004. I can't claim to be good at it, but when I get nucs through they are my best hives the next year. I've tried many things from wrapping, huddling, heating, feeding syrup all winter etc. I've come to these conclusions. First, wrapping just made them too wet. Feeding syrup all winter did also. Insulating top and bottom and huddling were helpful. A heater if not too hot, down the middle of this arrangement was helpful, except every year someone unplugs it during the coldest spell, so it really hasn't helped. My nucs are a bit backwards of most as mine are combines of mating nucs rather than splits from my strong hives or requeening and splits from my weak hives. I've concluded that one mistake I've been making is I need to combine them soon enough for them to get reorganized as their own colony before the cold weather sets in. Which means about the end of July or the first of August. This also lets them get some stores put away and arranged the way they want. But assuming you're making splits of your weak hives and requeening them, the same rule holds true. You want them to have time to get organized as a colony. I'm liking the sugar on top more and more for these as feeding syrup has the problem of too much moisture. But if you feed early this isn't so much of a problem. Rather than spend a lot of time making special equipment for overwintering nucs, I think it's more practical to figure out how to overwinter them in your standard equipment. Granted, this makes more sense when your typical box is the size of a five frame deep nuc (my eight frame mediums are exactly that volume), but I hate having a lot of specialized equipment around when I can have equipment that is more multipurpose. My bottom board feeders work well for wintering nucs as you can stack up the nucs and see if they need to be fed and feed any of them without unstacking them.

***Banking queens***

I've tried overwintering a queen bank. I have not had really great success but these are the things that helped. You have to keep it warm enough to keep them from clustering or they will contract to the point that many of the queens will die. The best way I found to do this was a terrarium heater under the bank. You also have to repopulate the hive part way through the winter. This means either sacrificing one of the nucs or stealing some bees from a really strong hive. If you pull out a frame that is well covered in bees, but not too close to the center you have a better chance of *not* getting the queen and then you add that frame to the queen bank. If you get half of the queens through the winter, I think you're doing well. But if you do, you have a bunch of queens in the spring for queenless hives, splits and for selling at the time when the demand is high.

### *Indoor wintering*

I have not tried it other than the observation hive I typically winter. I have corresponded with many people who have tried it and it is far trickier than one would think. Bees need a cleansing flight now and then so they need to be free flying. They need temps down around 30° to 40° F to keep them inactive so they don't burn up all their stores and burn out from activity (inactive bees live longer than active bees). Ventilation and keeping bees cool enough seem to be the bigger issues with this than keeping them warm.

### *Wintering observation hives*

I have wintered an observation hive many times. The issues are to make sure they are strong enough going into winter. Have some way to feed them syrup. Have some way to feed them pollen. Don't' over feed the pollen. Make sure they are free flying (check the tube to make sure they haven't clogged it with dead bees and pollen). No, they won't all fly out and die because they are warm and confused about the weather outside. Some will no matter what, but that's just normal. They are quite aware of the weather outside. If they get too weak in the spring you may have to boost them with some bees. A handful or two of bees in an empty box that is connected to the tube will usually result in those bees moving into the hive without you having to take it outside and open it.

# Spring Management

### *Tied to climate*

Next to wintering this seems to be the next biggest topic of discussion. And, next to wintering, this seems to be the most tied to climate. I can really only share with any confidence what I've actually experienced in my climate. Most places I've had bees are similar (cold winters etc.) but some were a bit colder (Laramie) and some a bit drier (Laramie, Brighton and Mitchell). But all in all most of my experience is in either the Panhandle of Nebraska or Southeast Nebraska. So keep that in mind.

### *Feeding Bees*

Spring is a very volatile and unpredictable time here. We could have warm sunny flying weather and tree pollen as early as late February, but sometimes it stays cold until April. Our first actual nectar availability of any size, is the early fruit trees somewhere between early and late April, with mid April being most likely. The thing that seems to set off spring build up the most is pollen. Feeding syrup is iffy at best. If you feed syrup in February or March (if it every warms up enough to do so) and they decide to brood up a lot and we get a hard freeze (sub zero would not be unusual around here) then they could die from trying to keep the brood warm. On the other hand if they don't get going before the first nectar flow in mid April they won't build up enough to make a good crop. I like to just make sure they have pollen and stores. Dry sugar can stave off starvation. If the weather stays warm enough and they are light enough I might try syrup. I would still stick with 2:1 or 5:3 and not 1:1. 1:1 is just too much moisture in the hive and it doesn't keep well. So my main spring management up until the first blooms is to make sure they have pollen and they don't starve from lack of honey. Once the early flow starts, there is no need to feed really, but if it stays rainy for long periods it might pay. My bottom board feeders are easy enough to feed with on the fly like this. Just put in the plugs and fill with syrup even if it's raining. It helps to have a cover to keep the rain out of the syrup if it's really pouring, but if it's just drizzling, the 2:1 will work well and even if it gets watered down the bees still seem pretty interested as it gets diluted, all the way up to 1:2 or more.

***Swarm Control***

The next issue in spring is heading off swarming. Of course you keep enough supers on that they don't run out of room. But in my experience, this alone will not head off swarming. You need some way to convince them that swarm preparation is not what is happening. If my bees had overhead honey, as Walt Wright's seem to in Tennessee, then I think I would do Checkerboarding/Nectar Management. But since mine are virtually always in the top box and I don't have capped honey to checkerboard above them, I just try to keep the brood nest open. In April, they are usually too small to swarm, but if they get going a lot, I'd put more boxes on. They only seem to swarm in April if they get overcrowded. In May is when I have to deal with swarm prevention in my location. The ideal is to keep them from swarming without splitting so you can have a maximum work force to make honey. In order to do this, I recommend keeping the brood nest open. Checkerboarding is fine for this, but as I say I don't seem to have the same conditions that lend well to this. So if a hive is getting really booming and strong from about early May on, I open up the brood nest. I do this with empty frames. No foundation. Just empty frames. Put these in the middle of the brood nest and they are quickly drawn and filled with brood. How many will depend on the strength of the hive. But if the nights aren't that chilly anymore and they can easily fill the gap where I intend to put the empty frame with festooning bees, then I can put another in. The maximum, which should only be done on a really strong hive, is an empty frame every other frame. The minimum, other than none, is one frame.

For more information on swarm prevention see the chapter *Swarm Control*.

### *Splits*

If you want more bees and honey isn't your prime consideration then do splits. Sometime on some warm days in April I will try to get all the way to the bottom board and clean it off while looking through the hive for brood, eggs, etc. to make sure things are going well. Other than that I just judge the strength and rate at which the population is increasing. Until you get good at judging this at a glance, look for swarm cells. Usually you can tip a box up and find them hanging down from the bottom of the frames. In the long run, this will give you an idea how much critical mass causes them to swarm and you can judge better how much to intervene. If you have swarm cells though, you already missed the opportunity for a large crop and now you need to worry about making splits.

***Supering***

Of course you need to add supers. You don't want to do this when the hive is still struggling and the weather is cold, but once they are building up you need to add them. Doubling the space of the hive is my goal. If they are two boxes full, then I add two boxes. If they are four boxes full, then I add four boxes. Of course you eventually may, in a bumper crop year, get so tall you can't do this anymore, but it's a good way to try not to run out of room without giving them more room than they can handle.

# Laying Workers

***Cause***

When the hive is queenless, and therefore broodless, for several weeks sometimes some workers develop the ability to lay eggs. It's not actually the lack of a queen, but the lack of brood. But the lack of brood is caused by the lack of a queen. These are usually haploid (infertile with a half set of chromosomes) and will all develop into drones.

***Symptoms***

Laying workers lay eggs in worker cells, in addition to drone cells and usually lays several in each cell. Laying worker eggs are usually on the side of the cell instead of the bottom except in drone cells. A hive with lots of drones is a symptom of laying workers as are the multiple eggs in the cell and eggs on top of pollen.

Sometimes a queen, when she starts laying after a time of not laying, will lay a few double eggs but she usually stops after a day or two. The laying workers will lay three or four or more to a cell in almost every cell. The difficulty is that the bees think they have a queen (the laying workers) and will not accept one. The laying workers are virtually impossible to find. I have found one in a two frame nuc by studying every bee until I saw one lay, but this is impractical in a full sized hive since there would be too many bees and too many laying workers.

***Solutions***

## Simplest, least trips to the beeyard

### Shakeout and forget

In my opinion there are only two practical solutions. The simplest solution if you have several hives and especially if the laying worker hive is a long trip, is just shake all the bees in front of the various other hives and divvy all the combs out to the other hives. This is my preferred method for an outyard or a small hive. It doesn't waste your time and money trying to requeen a hive that is going to reject the queen anyway. This is the method of least time spent on interventions and most predictable outcome.

If you really want to have that many hives, you can pull some frames from them several weeks after the shake out and do a split with some brood from all or several of your hives. A frame of open brood and emerging brood and honey and pollen from each and you'll have a nice split.

## Most successful but more trips to the beeyard

### Give them open brood

The only other really practical method, in my opinion, is to add a frame of open brood every week until they rear a queen. Usually by the second or third frame of open brood they will start queen cells. This is simple enough when the hive is in your backyard. Not so easy in an outyard 60 miles away.

## Other less successful or more tedious methods

I would do one of the above, but if you want to know every possible method that I've tried, here are the things I have done that sometimes work. Note some appear to be, and are, slight variations of the same theme.

1) If you have several weak laying worker hives and at least one strong queenright hive, put all the laying worker hives on the strong queenright hive. The resulting confusion between several hives will usually settle down to one queenright hive.

2) Any setup where a queen right hive is on the other side of a double screen so the brood pheromones get to the laying workers for two or three weeks will work to suppress them and then any introduction method will work get them queenright.

3) Put a queen cell in (either a frame from a hive trying to supersede or swarm or one that you made by queen rearing techniques). Sometimes they will let the queen emerge. Sometimes they will tear it down.

4) Put a virgin queen in. Just smoke it heavily and run her in. Sometimes they will accept her. Sometimes they will ball her.

5) Put a frame of emerging brood with a queen in a push in cage in the laying worker hive. When they are no longer biting the cage and killing the emerging attendants, release her. This usually works. Sometimes they will kill the queen.

***More info on laying workers***

**Brood pheromones**

It's the pheromones from open brood that suppress the laying workers from developing, but some do anyway. It is *not* the queen pheromone as many of the older books suggest.

See page 11 of Wisdom of the Hive:

> ***"the queen's pheromones are neither necessary nor sufficient for inhibiting worker's ovaries. Instead, they strongly inhibit the workers from rearing additional queens. It is now clear that the pheromones that provide the proximate stimulus for workers to refrain from laying eggs come mainly from the brood, not from the queen (reviewed in Seeling 1985; see also Willis, Winston, and Slessor 1990)."***

There are always multiple laying workers even in a queenright hive

"Anarchistic bees" are ever present but usually in small enough numbers to not cause a problem and are simply policed by the workers *unless* they need drones. The number is always small as long as ovary development is suppressed.

See page 9 of "The Wisdom of the Hive"

***"All studies to date report far fewer than 1 % of workers have ovaries developed sufficiently to lay eggs (reviewed in Ratnieks 1993; see also Visscher 1995a). For example, Ratnieks dissected 10,634 worker bees from 21 colonies and found that only 7 had moderately developed egg (half the size of a completed egg) and that just one had a fully developed egg in her body."***

If you do the math, in a normal booming queen-right hive of 100,000 bees that's 70 laying workers. In a laying worker hive it's much higher.

# More than Bees

A honey bee colony is more than just bees. There is a whole ecology from microscopic to fairly large there are many symbiotic plus some benign relationships in the ecology of a bee colony. Even those benign relationships often crowd out pathogenic organisms.

### *Macro and Microfauna*

For instance, there are over 32 kinds of mites that live in harmony with bees. When these are allowed to live (instead of being killed by acaracides) there are insects in the hive that eat them, such as the pseudoscorpion which also eat the malignant mites.

An examination of feral colonies shows just in the macroscopic arena the colony is full of life forms as diverse as mites, beetles, waxworms, ants and roaches.

### *Microflora*

There are many microflora that live in the bees and in the colony. These vary from fungi to bacteria to yeasts. Many are necessary for the digestion of pollen or the maintenance of a healthy digestive tract by crowding out pathogens that would otherwise take over. Even seemingly benign ones and sometimes even mildly pathogenic ones often serve a beneficial purpose by supplanting otherwise deadly ones.

Many of the Lactobacillus genus are needed to properly digest the pollen and many of the Bifidobacterium and Gluconacetobacter genus are beneficial in the sense that they crowd out Nosema and other pathogens and probably contribute to digestion as well.

***Pathogens?***

Even some seemingly pathogenic organisms such as Aspergillus fumigatus, which causes stonebrood, supplants worse pathogens, in this case Nosema. Or Ascosphaera apis, which causes chalkbrood but prevents European foulbrood.

***Upsetting the Balance***

How much do we upset the balance of this rich ecosystem when applying anti-bacterials such as tylan or terramycin and anti-fungals such as Fumidil? Even essential oils and organic acids have anti-bacterial and anti-fungal effects. Then we kill off many of the mites and insects with acaracides.

After totally unbalancing this complex society of diverse organisms with no regard for benefit or not and contaminating the wax that we reuse and put in the hives as foundation, we are surprised to find that the bees are failing. Under such circumstances I would be surprised to find them flourishing!

## For More Reading

Try an internet search on the following phrases and read some of what comes back:

bees microflora (10,900 hits)
bees "symbiotic mites" (30 hits)
bees symbiotic bacteria (25,100 hits)

Here are a few of the specific strains and groups you might want to research further:

Bifidobacterium animalis
Bifidobacterium asteroides

Bifidobacterium coryneforme
Bifidobacterium cuniculi
Bifidobacterium globosum
Lactobacillus plantarum
Bartonella sp.
Gluconacetobacter sp.
Simonsiella sp.

# Bee Math

All of the numbers about the life cycle of bees may seem irrelevant, so let's put them in a chart here and talk about what they are useful for.

| Caste | Days Hatch | Cap | Emerge | |
|---|---|---|---|---|
| Queen | $3^1/_2$ | 8 +-1 | 16 +-1 | Laying 28 +-5 |
| Worker | $3^1/_2$ | 9 +-1 | 20 +-1 | Foraging 42 +-7 |
| Drone | $3^1/_2$ | 10 +-1 | 24 +-1 | Flying to DCA 38 +-5 |

If you find eggs, and no queen how long ago do you *know* there was a queen? At least there was one three days ago and possibly is one now.

If you find just hatched larvae and open brood but no eggs when was there a queen? Four days ago.

If you put an excluder between two boxes and come back in four days and find eggs in one and not the other, what do you know? That the queen is in the one with eggs.

If you find a capped queen cell, how long before it should have emerged for sure? 9 days, but probably eight.

If you find a capped queen cell, how long before you should see eggs from that queen? Probably 20 days. Possibly as much as 29.

If you killed or lost a queen, how long before you'll have a laying queen again? Probably 24 days.

If you start from larvae and graft, how long before you need to transfer the larvae to a mating nuc? 10 days. (day 14 from when it was laid)

If you confine the queen to get the larvae how long before you graft? Four days.

If you confined the queen to get the larvae how long before we have a laying queen? 28 days.

# Races of Bees

### *Italian*

Apis mellifera ligustica. This is the most popular bee in North American. These, as all of the commercial bees, are gentle and good producers. They use less propolize than some of the darker bees. They usually have bands on their abdomen of brown to yellow color. Their biggest weakness is that they are prone to rob and drift. Most of these (as all of the queens) are bred and raised in the south, but you can find some northern breeders.

### *Starline*

These are just hybrid Italians. Two strains of Italians are kept separate and their hybrid is what the Starline queen is. They are very prolific and productive, but subsequent queens (supersedures, emergency and swarms) are disappointing. If you buy Starlines every year to requeen they will give you very good service. Unfortunately I don't know of any available anymore. They used to come from York and before that Dadant.

### *Cordovan*

These are a subset of the Italians. In theory you could have a Cordovan in any breed, since it's technically just a color, but the ones for sale in North American that I've seen are all Italians. They are slightly more gentle, slightly more likely to rob and quite striking to look at. They have no black on them and look very yellow at first sight. Looking closely you see that where the Italians normally have black legs and head, they have a purplish brown legs and head.

### *Caucasian*

Apis mellifera caucasica. They are silver gray to dark brown. They do propolis extensively. It is a sticky propolis rather than a hard propolis. The build up a little slower in the spring than the Italians. They are reputed to be more gentle than the Italians. Less prone to robbing. In theory they are less productive than Italians. I think on the average they are about the same productivity as the Italians, but since they rob less you get less of the really booming s that have robbed out all their neighbors.

### *Carniolan*

Apis mellifera carnica. These are darker brown to black. They fly in slightly cooler weather and in theory are better in northern climates. They are reputed by some to be less productive than Italians, but I have not had that experience. The ones I have had were very productive and very frugal for the winter. They winter in small clusters and shut down brood rearing when there are dearths.

### *Midnite*

These are, sort of, to the Caucasians what the Starline is to the Italians. At first they were two lines of Caucasians that were used to make an F1 cross. Later when the lines were hard to maintain, they were a Carniolan line crossed with a Caucasian line. They have that hybrid vigor that disappears in the next generation of queen. York used to sell them and before them Dadant. I don't know where they are available anymore.

***Russian***

Apis mellifera acervorum or carpatica or caucasica or carnica. Some even say they are crossed with Apis ceranae (very doubtful). They came from the Primorksy region of Russia. They were used for breeding mite resistance because they were already surviving the mites. They are a bit defensive, but in odd ways. They tend to head butt a lot while not necessarily stinging any more. Any first cross of any race may be vicious and these are no exception. They are watchful guards, but not usually "runny" (tending to run around on the comb where you can't find the queen or work with them well). Swarminess and productivity are a bit more unpredictable. Traits are not well fixed. Frugality is similar to the Carniolans. They were brought to the USA by the USDA in June of 1997, studied on an island in Louisiana and then field testing in other states in 1999. They went on sale to the general public in 2000.

***Buckfast***

These are a mixture of bees developed by Brother Adam of Buckfast Abbey. I had them for years. They were gentle. They built up rapidly in the spring, produced awesome crops and dropped back in population in the fall. They are just like the Italians as far as robbing. They are resistant to the tracheal mites. They are more frugal than the Italians, but not as much as the Carniolans.

***German or English native bees***

Apis mellifera mellifera. These are the bees native to England or Germany. They have some of the characteristics of the other dark bees. They do well in damp cold climates. They tend toward being runny (excitable on the combs) and a bit swarmy, but also seem to be well adapted to Northern climates. Some of the ones that were here in the US were very unmanageable as far as temperament possibly because of crosses with the Italians.

### *LUS*

Small black bees similar to Carniolans or Italians in production and temperament but have mite resistance and have the ability of a laying worker to raise a new queen. This ability is called thelytoky. Several studies were done on them by the USDA in the 80's and 90's.

### *Africanized Honey Bees (AHB)*

I have heard these called Apis mellifera scutelata But Scutelata are actually African bees from the Cape. Dr. Kerr, who bred them thought they were Adansonii. AHB are a mixture of African (Scutelata) and Italian bees. They were created in an attempt to increase production of bees. The USDA bred these at Baton Rouge from stock obtained from Kerr from July 1942 until 1961. From the records I've seen it looks like the USDA shipped these queens to the continental US at about 1,500 queens a year from July 1949 until July of 1961. The Brazilians also were experimenting with them and the migration of those bees has been followed in the news for some time. They are extremely productive bees that are extremely defensive. If you have a hot enough that you think they are AHB you need to requeen them. Having angry bees where they might hurt people is irresponsible. You should try to requeen them so no one (including you) gets hurt.

# Moving Bees

***Moving hives two feet***

If you want to move a hive two feet, just stack the boxes off onto some kind of board (top, bottom etc.) and restack on the new location. Stacking them off and then restacking is so they are in the right order.

***Moving hives two miles***

If you want to move a hive two miles or more, you need to anchor the hive together for the trip and you need to load it. Since I am usually doing this by myself I will give instructions from that view.

I do this when the bees are flying. First I put my transportation as close as I can get to the hive. Directly behind it is best. I have a small trailer I often use, but a pickup would work too. I put a bottom board in the trailer where I think I want the hive to be. I put a strap under it so I can strap the hive together. You can buy small ones at the hardware store but they also sell them at bee supply places. I stack the boxes on the bottom board as I take them off. This leaves the hive in reverse order which will get reversed back when we unload. After all the boxes are on you need to nail all of the boxes together somehow. They sell 2" wide staples that can be used, or you can cut small ($2^1/_2$") squares of plywood and nail it between the parts of the hive to attach it all together. Cut a piece of #8 hardware cloth the length of the entrance and fold it into a 90 degree. It should fit tight enough to keep the bees in. Leave the entrance open until you are ready to leave.

Strap it together tightly and tie it anyway you need to or wedge it with empty bee boxes so that the hive can't shift or tip over on a curve or a sudden stop.

Next, you need to take into account your situation. If you have other hives at this location and the hive you are moving could lose a few foragers without hurting it much, just close it up and go. The returning foragers will find another hive. If this is your only hive or you are really concerned about losing foragers, then wait for dark and then close it up and go.

When you get to the new location, if it's already daylight, just unload the hive by putting a bottom board on the new location, removing the staples or plywood and stacking the boxes off onto it. If it's dark, wait for daylight and do the same thing.

Put a branch in front of the entrance so any bee leaving notices it. A green sapling with some leaves is nice so they have to fly through the middle of it. It causes them to stop and pay attention and reorient. This is useful at any distance of moving.

Other variations on this are a board (as mentioned in Dadant's The Hive and the Honey Bee) or grass plugging the entrance as mentioned many places.

***"Bees moved less than a mile are likely to return in considerable numbers to their old location. This can be minimized by throwing grass or straw over their entrances to force them to take note of the change when they emerge for the first time from the hive at its new location" —The How-To-Do-It book of Beekeeping, Richard Taylor***

### *More than 2 feet and less than 2 miles*

This is a subject apparently full of controversy. There is an old saying that you move a hive 2 feet or two miles. I often need to move them 100 yards more or less. I've never seen that it was a problem. I move hives as seldom as I need to because anytime you move a hive even two feet, it disrupts the hive for a day. But if I need to, I move them. I didn't invent all of the concepts here, but some of them I refined for my uses. Here is my technique.

It occurs to me that a lot of detail that is intuitively obvious to me may not be to a newbie. So here is a detailed description of how I usually move hives single handedly. This is assuming the hive is too heavy to move in one piece or I lack the help to do so. But it works so well, I don't even think about using other methods. But if you have help and can lift it, you can block the entrance and move it all at once at night and put a branch in front. I know every time I tell any version of this method, someone quotes the "2 feet or 2 miles" rule and says you can't do it and you can only move them two feet or you'll lose all your bees. I've done this many times with no noticeable loss of workforce and no bees clustering at the old location by the second night.

### *Moving hives 100 yards or less by yourself.*

### Concepts

#### Reorientation

When bees fly out of the hive, normally, they pay no attention to where they are. They know where they live and don't even consider it on the way out. When they fly back they look for familiar landmarks and follow them home. They orient when they first leave the hive as a young bee, but only certain conditions cause them to reorient after that. One is confinement. Any confinement will cause some. 72 hours causes about the maximum reorientation. Any length of time more than that is difficult to tell any difference. A blockage of the exit causes reorientation. People sometime stuff the entrance with grass. This combines the act of removing it, which sets off reorientation, with some confinement, which causes some reorientation. An obvious obstruction that causes them to deviate from their normal exit will set off reorientation. A branch or a board in front of the entrance that causes them to have to fly around it, will cause them to pay attention to where they are. Some oldtimers would just bang the hive around really well to indicate to the bees that something has happened and they need to pay attention.

**Autopilot**

When a bee is returning to the hive they tend to be on "autopilot". It's like you driving home from work. You don't think about where the turns are, you just make them. If they have done no reorientation, they will see landmarks and return to the old hive and have no idea where to go. If they have reoriented, they will still fly back to the old location, but when they see the hive isn't there, they think back to when they left and remember.

**Finding the new hive**

Assuming they did not reorient and they have to figure out where the new hive is, then they have to do increasing spirals out until they smell the hive. Odds are they will move into the first hive they find doing this. How long it takes to find the new location is exponential to the distance. In other words if it's twice as far away it will take them four times as long to find it.

**Weather**

Keep in mind that cold weather can complicate things in odd contradictory ways. On the one hand if they have been confined for 72 hours and you move them, they are most likely to reorient. On the other hand if they fly back to the old location they have to find the hive again before they get too chilled or they will die.

**Leaving a box**

Leaving a box at the old location is another of those complicated things. If you leave one from the start they all return and just stay there. If you leave nothing at the old location they will look for the new location, but some may get stuck at the old location. If you wait until just before dark to put a box there you will motivate them to find the new location, but still give them somewhere to go. You can move that to the new location, and in warm weather, just set it beside the hive. In cold weather you may need to put this box on top, but that's not a pleasant thing to do in the dark.

**Materials:**

- Second bottom board. If you don't have one, some board big enough to set the hives on will do.
- Third bottom board.
- A cover cloth is useful but not necessary. If you don't have one, some board big enough to set the hives on will do.
- Second lid. If you don't have one, any board big enough to put on top of the hive will work.
- Smoker.

- Veil.
- Gloves (optional but nice)
- Bee Suit (optional but nice)
- A branch that will stick up nicely and disrupt the flight of the bees leaving the hive.

**Method**

Suit up to your comfort level. Remember we will not be manipulating frames so the gloves are not a big disadvantage.

I usually put a puff of smoke in the entrance, then pull off the lid and put a puff in the inner cover (unless you don't have an inner cover).

Then I put four or five good strong puffs of smoke in the entrance and wait a minute. Then repeat four or five puffs and wait a minute. I do this until I see just a whiff of smoke out the top. This is more smoke than I usually use, but we will be rearranging this hive twice and I need it calm all the way through. If they are getting irate or you are moving an exceptionally strong and large hive and it is taking some time, feel free to smoke some more from time to time.

Wait about three minutes before opening the hive.

Set the second bottom board next to the hive. Take the top box off, lid and all and put it on the bottom board. Remove the lid and move each box from the old location to the new bottom board until you reach the last box. You don't need to restack the last one because we are moving it first. You now have reversed the order of the boxes so when we move them to the new location they will be in the correct order.

Put the second lid on the stack of boxes to keep the bees calm and the lid on the last brood box so they won't fly in your face. Carry the last brood box, with the lid and bottom board to the new location.

Put the branch in front of the entrance so that the bees have to fly through the branch. It doesn't have to be so thick they have trouble getting through it, just enough that they can't miss seeing it. This is to cause them to reorient when they leave. If you watch them they will start by circling the hive, then make larger circles until they have placed the hive in their mental map of their world. Since you have moved the hive to a new place and that place is within their known world they do this fairly quickly.

Remove the lid, if you want to use a cloth cover, put it on the brood box. It will help keep the bees calm, but you have to get it off with a box in your hands when you come back. That is why I like a cloth instead of a cover. Take the lid back to the old location. Take the top box and lid off and put in on the third bottom board. Put the lid you that you brought back on the stack of boxes. Again this is so there is always a lid on the stack of boxes and a lid on the box you are moving. This helps keep the bees calm. You may be thinking, that the bottom is exposed while you're carrying it. Yes, but the bees don't move down when they are getting jostled, they move up. Not that I'd wear shorts while moving the boxes.

Carry the second box over to the new location and catch the cloth (if you used one) with one finger while still holding the box and lift the cloth off and set the box down. Remove the lid and replace it with the cloth.

Go back to the old location with the lid and repeat until all of the boxes are at the new location.

We want nothing at the old location that looks like home. When it’s almost dark we will take that last box back, to the old location with its own lid and bottom so you can bring it back to the old location just after dark.

After dark, block the entrance, or pull out the stick and carry it to the new location with the bottom in place. Just set it beside the hive with the branches in front of its entrance. Open the entrance or replace the stick. *Do not try to put this box on the hive in the dark unless the weather is cold!* If you have never opened a hive in the dark, consider yourself wise or fortunate and don't. The bees are *very* defensive after dark and will attack and cling and crawl on you looking for a way to sting.

The next morning you can put the last box on top of the hive. Remove any equipment from the old site so they don't start clustering there.

Some field bees will return to the old location. If they paid attention and reoriented, they will then remember where they hive was and go back to that new location. If not, they will circle until they find the new location and then will be fine after that.

You can check in the evening before dark and see if any are clustering at the old location. If so, put a super there and they will move into it and you can move them after dark again. I have never had any clustered there by the next day and seldom had any at all.

# Treatments for Varroa not working

A lot of you use some treatment, and your mite drops don't change much and you assume you're not killing mites. So let's just look at some numbers.

Independent of *what* the treatment is, here is just a rough idea of what goes on. These are round numbers and probably underestimate the mites' reproduction and underestimate how many get groomed off by the bees.

Assuming treating every week and a treatment with 100% effectiveness on phoretic mites. If you assume that half the Varroa are in the cells and you have a total mite population of 32,000, and if we assume half the phoretic mites will go back in the cells and in one week, half of the mites in the cells will have one offspring each and emerge then the numbers look like this:

| 100% | | | | | | |
|---|---|---|---|---|---|---|
| Week | Phoretic | Capped | Killed | Reproduced | Emerged | Returned |
| 1 | 16,000 | 16,000 | 16,000 | 8,000 | 16,000* | 8,000 |
| 2 | 8,000 | 16,000 | 8,000 | 8,000 | 16,000 | 8,000 |
| 3 | 8,000 | 16,000 | 8,000 | 8,000 | 16,000 | 8,000 |
| 4 | 8,000 | 16,000 | 8,000 | 8,000 | 16,000 | 8,000 |

* half of the 16,000 plus 8,000 offspring
Capped is inside capped cells. Returned is the number that went back into cells and got capped.

Now let's assume treating every week and 50% effectiveness on phoretic mites with all the other assumptions the same:

| 50% | | | | | | |
|---|---|---|---|---|---|---|
| Week | Phoretic | Capped | Killed | Reproduced | Emerged | Returned |
| 1 | 16,000 | 16,000 | 8,000 | 8,000 | 16,000 | 12,000 |
| 2 | 12,000 | 20,000 | 6,000 | 10,000 | 20,000 | 13,000 |
| 3 | 13,000 | 23,000 | 6,500 | 11,500 | 23,000 | 14,750 |
| 4 | 14,750 | 26,250 | 7,375 | 13,125 | 26,250 | 16,813 |

Now let's assume treating once every week with 50% effectiveness with no brood in the hive:

| 50% | No | Brood | | | | |
|---|---|---|---|---|---|---|
| Week | Phoretic | Capped | Killed | Reproduced | Emerged | Returned |
| 1 | 32,000 | N/A | 16,000 | N/A | N/A | N/A |
| 2 | 16,000 | N/A | 8,000 | N/A | N/A | N/A |
| 3 | 8,000 | N/A | 4,000 | N/A | N/A | N/A |
| 4 | 4,000 | N/A | 2,000 | N/A | N/A | N/A |

Then of course there's 100% with no brood:

| 100% | No | Brood | | | | |
|---|---|---|---|---|---|---|
| Week | Phoretic | Capped | Killed | Reproduced | Emerged | Returned |
| 1 | 32,000 | N/A | 32,000 | N/A | N/A | N/A |
| 2 | N/A | N/A | N/A | N/A | N/A | N/A |
| 3 | N/A | N/A | N/A | N/A | N/A | N/A |
| 4 | N/A | N/A | N/A | N/A | N/A | N/A |

And no treatment would look like this:

| 0% | | | | | | |
|---|---|---|---|---|---|---|
| Week | Phoretic | Capped | Killed | Reproduced | Emerged | Returned |
| 1 | 16,000 | 16,000 | N/A | 8,000 | 16,000 | 16,000 |
| 2 | 16,000 | 24,000 | N/A | 12,000 | 24,000 | 20,000 |
| 3 | 20,000 | 32,000 | N/A | 16,000 | 32,000 | 26,000 |
| 4 | 26,000 | 42,000 | N/A | 21,000 | 42,000 | 34,000 |

A real mathematical model, of course, should take into account a lot of things including drifting, robbing, hygienic behavior (chewing out), grooming, time of year etc. I was just hoping to get the general principle across of what is happening when you treat.

# A Few Good Queens

### *Simple Queen Rearing for a Hobbyist*

I get this question a lot, so let's simplify this as much as possible while maximizing the quality of the queens as much as possible.

### *Labor and Resources*

The quality of a queen is directly related to how well she is fed which is related to the labor force available to feed the larvae (density of the bees) and available food.

### *Quality of Emergency Queens*

First let's talk about emergency queens and quality. There has been much speculation over the years on this matter and after reading the opinions of many very experienced queen breeders on this subject I'm convinced that the prevailing theory that bees start with too old of a larvae is not true. I think to get good quality queens from emergency cells one simply needs to insure they can tear down the cell walls and that they have resources of food and labor to properly care for the queen. This means a good density of bees (for labor), frames of pollen and honey (for resources), and nectar or syrup coming in (to convince them they have resources to spare).

So if one adds either new drawn wax comb or wax foundation without wires or even empty frames to the brood nest during a time of year they are anxious to raise queens (from about a month after the first blooms until the end of the main flow), they quickly draw this comb and lay it full of eggs. So four to five days after adding it, there should be frames of larvae on newly drawn wax with no cocoons to interfere with them tearing down the cell walls to build queen cells. If one were to do this in a strong hive and at this point remove the queen on a frame of brood and a frame of honey and put it aside in a nuc, the bees will start a lot of queen cells.

***The experts on emergency queens:***

**Jay Smith:**

> ***"It has been stated by a number of beekeepers who should know better (including myself) that the bees are in such a hurry to rear a queen that they choose larvae too old for best results. Later observation has shown the fallacy of this statement and has convinced me that bees do the very best that can be done under existing circumstances.***
>
> ***"The inferior queens caused by using the emergency method is because the bees cannot tear down the tough cells in the old combs lined with cocoons. The result is that the bees fill the worker cells with bee milk floating the larvae out the opening of the cells, then they build a little queen cell pointing downward. The larvae cannot eat the bee milk back in the bottom of the cells with the result that they***

> *are not well fed. However, if the colony is strong in bees, are well fed and have new combs, they can rear the best of queens. And please note— they will never make such a blunder as choosing larvae too old."— Better Queens. Jay Smith*

---

**C.C. Miller:**

> *"If it were true, as formerly believed, that queenless bees are in such haste to rear a queen that they will select a larva too old for the purpose, then it would hardly do to wait even nine days. A queen is matured in fifteen days from the time the egg is laid, and is fed throughout her larval lifetime on the same food that is given to a worker-larva during the first three days of its larval existence. So a worker-larva more than three days old, or more than six days from the laying of the egg would be too old for a good queen. If, now, the bees should select a larva more than three days old, the queen would emerge in less than nine days. I think no one has ever known this to occur. Bees do not prefer too old larvae. As a matter of fact bees do not use such poor judgment as to select larvae too old when larvae sufficiently young are present, as I*

***have proven by direct experiment and many observations."—Fifty Years Among the Bees, C.C. Miller***

***Equipment***

Second let's talk about equipment. One can set up mating nucs in standard boxes with dummy boards (or division boards) but only if you have the extra boxes or division boards. The advantage is that you can expand this as the hive grows if you don't use the queen. You can also build either two frame boxes or divide larger boxes into two frame boxes (commonly sold as queen castles). These need to be the same depth as your brood frames.

***Method:***

### Make sure they are well fed

Feed them for a few days before you start unless there is a strong flow on.

### Make them Queenless

So if we make a hive queenless (do what you like about having new comb or not) nine days after making them queenless these will be mostly mature and capped and be three days from emerging.

### Make up Mating Nucs

At this point unless you intend to use the cells to requeen your hives, we need to set up mating nucs. The "queen castles" or four way boxes that take your standard brood frames and make up four, two frame mating nucs in one box are very good for this, but dummy boards and regular boxes can work also. In my operation these are all medium depth two frame nucs. The queen we removed earlier goes well in one of these also. We now want a frame of brood and a frame of honey in each of the mating nucs.

## Transfer Queen Cells

The next day (ten days after making them queenless) we will cut out (with a sharp knife) the queen cells from the new wax combs we put in. If we used unwired foundation (or none) they should be easy to cut out without running into obstacles (as we would with wire and with plastic foundation) and can put each of the cells in a mating nuc. You can just press an indentation with your thumb and gently place the cell in the indentation. If you want you can also just put each frame that has cells on it in a mating nuc and sacrifice the extra cells (as the first queen out will destroy them). This is helpful if you have plastic foundation or you just don't want to mess with cutting out cells.

## Check for Eggs

Two weeks later we should see some eggs in the mating nucs. If not, then by three weeks we should. Let her lay up the nuc well before moving her to a hive or caging her and banking her for later.

Next round just make the mating nuc queenless again the day before adding cells.

Now that these nucs are well populated by the brood the queen has laid, we can make more queens by simply making a strong mating nuc queenless and they will raise more queens. Again, it's the density of bees and the supply of food that are the issues. We can also, if they are wax combs, cut cells out and make use of multiple cells in other mating nucs as well. In this case either set up those nucs the day before or remove the queen the day before.

And that is all there is to raising a few queens.

# Volume III Advanced

# Genetics

### *The Need for Genetic Diversity*

In any species that uses sexual reproduction, genetic diversity is essential for the overall success and health of the species. A lack of it leaves the population vulnerable to any new pest, disease or problem that comes along. A lot of it greatly improves the odds of having the necessary traits to survive such things. This need seems at odds with the concept of selective breeding, and to some extent it is. Selective breeding is just that—selective. Meaning you breed out traits you don't like. Of course this narrows the gene pool, hopefully in a positive way, but still it limits the variety as you keep selecting from fewer and fewer ancestors. Whether you believe in a Creator or evolution as the origin of nature, sexual reproduction has as its obvious goal, diversity. The queen mates, not just with one drone, but several, the hives make many drones to keep their genes out there, and even a hive doomed to die from queenlessness will put drones out there to try to preserve those genes in the pool. Every disease narrows the pool to only those that can survive that disease, and every pest narrows the pool to only those that can survive that pest. We beekeepers keep limiting that pool even more by selecting one queen and raising thousands of queens from her, something that never happens in nature, and by buying queens from only a few breeders, who do the same and who share stock with each other, we narrow it even more. The more we narrow the gene pool the less likely it is that the remaining genes will be sufficient to survive the next onslaught of diseases and pests. This is a scary prospect. And all of this is ignoring the built in control over this with the bees' method of gender control being sex alleles that limit the success of inbred bees. An inbred line of bees has many diploid (fertilized) droneeggs (because similar sex alleles line up) that will not be allowed by the bees to develop.

## Feral Bees Have Maintained This

The depth of the gene pool, for many years, has been maintained by the large pool of feral bees. In recent years, however this pool has shrunk significantly from the influx of diseases  not to mention loss of habitat, use of pesticides and fear of AHB.

## What can we do?

We cannot propagate bees with a limited gene pool and expect them to survive, let alone thrive. So what can we do to promote genetic diversity and still improve the breed of bees we raise? We can change our view from picking only the one best queen we have for the mother and the next best for the drone mother and start thinking in terms, instead of only breeding out the worst. In other words, if a queen has bad traits we don't want, such as bad tempered workers, then we cull those out. But if they have good traits we don't try to replace them with only the genetics of our best queen, but rather try to keep that line going by doing splits, or raising queens, or using the drones from those other lines. Don't use the same mother for every batch of queens. Don't requeen feral colonies that you remove or feral swarms that you catch. If a hive is hot but has other good traits, try raising a daughter and see if you can lose that trait instead of just wiping out that queen's line. Raise your own bees from the local survivors instead of buying queens. Raise your own bees even from the commercial queens you have so they will mate with the feral survivors. Support small local queen breeders so they can keep more genetic lines going. Do more splits and let them raise their own queens rather than buying queens, so that each colony can continue their line.

# Feral Bees

There is much talk that the feral bees died. In my observation there was a serious shift in what I found when catching feral bees. I used to find "leather" colored Italian looking bees. Now I'm finding more black bees with a little brown mixed in. I'm breeding these survivor bees for myself and for sale

Typically I'm asked how I know these are feral survivors instead of recent escapees. First, they act differently than any of the domestics. Just little things, mostly, but also they overwinter in very small clusters and are very frugal. They are also very variable in aspects that are usually bred for, like propolis or being runny. Also they are typically smaller when you find them, being from natural sized comb.

***Swarms***

...are the easiest way to get feral bees. But a lot of swarms are, and a lot of swarms aren't, feral bees. I'd take them either way, but if you're looking for feral survivor bees to raise queens then look for the smaller bees. Swarms with small bees are probably feral survivors. Swarms with larger bees are probably swarms from someone's hive. To get swarms, notify the local police and rescue people and the county agricultural extension office. If you want to do a lot of them run a yellow pages ad for swarm removal.

### ***Capturing a swarm***

Much has been written and each situation is both similar and unique. A swarm is a bunch of homeless bees with a queen. They may have already decided where they think they want to go, or they may still have scouts out looking. Swarms usually happen in the morning and they usually leave by early afternoon, but they may swarm in the afternoon and they may leave in a few minutes or a few days. If you chase swarms you will often get there too late and often get there in time. Both will happen. It's best to have all your equipment with you all the time. If you have to go get your equipment, you will probably be too late. Have a box with a screened bottom attached. This can be attached by nail little squares of plywood into both the box and the bottom or with the 2″ wide staples that are sold by bee suppliers for moving hives. You need a lid. I like a migratory cover because it's simple. Less moving parts. I like to have a #8 screen cut and bent to 90 degrees to block the door (but not attached yet). A stapler is nice for anchoring the screen to the door and the cover to the hive. The best are the ones labeled as light duty staplers instead of the heavy duty ones. They penetrate better and stay better. I don't know why. The ones that take the T50 staples are *not* the right ones, although if you already have one you can use it. The ones that take the J21 staples are easier to use. You need a veil minimum, but I like a jacket or a suit. Gloves and a brush are helpful. You can make or buy a rig with a 5 gallon bucket to knock them down with. The idea is that you add EMT (conduit) to it as a long handle and you slam it under the swarm to dislodge them into the bucket. Then you pull on the rope to put the lid on and lower the whole thing back down and dump them into a box. The main trick to swarms is to get the queen. If you can reach and see, try to find the queen. If you know you see her and can make sure she ends up in the box, close it up, brush off the stragglers and leave. If you're not sure, then let them settle in. It helps if the box smells like lemongrass essential oil. Either put some lemongrass essential oil in it (lasts longer) some swarm lure (costs more but works well) or actually spray some lemon pledge (cheap, easy to find, but doesn't last as long) in the box before you put the swarm in. If you pay attention when you buy a package or hive a swarm you'll notice it's what they smell like. Sometimes they will settle into the box. Sometimes you didn't get the queen, or she likes the branch she was on better, and they all start accumulating on the branch again. I just keep shaking them in until they stay. It usually works. In my observation, honey, brood etc. are no help in hiving a swarm although they may help anchor them once they have decided to move in. They are not looking for an occupied house, they are looking for an empty or abandoned house. Old empty comb sometimes helps. Some brood might help anchor them so they don't leave though. It's also well worth having some Queen Mandibular Pheromone. You can either keep your old retired queens in a jar of alcohol (queen juice), or buy Bee Boost (last I checked available from Mann Lake).

Always wear protective equipment. Swarms don't usually get mean, but can be unpredictable. Also be careful of power lines and falling off of ladders. It sounds redundant, but when a lot of bees are buzzing you, and especially if one gets in your bonnet, it's hard to stay calm, but it is a requirement if you are on top of a ladder.

My current favorite method for getting a swarm is skip ladders altogether. Take enough boxes to make a good size (one deep, two mediums) and preferable ones that have been lived in. Some old comb if you have it. Some QMP (a quarter of a stick of Bee Boost or the end of a Q-tip dipped in queen juice ) and some lemongrass essential oil. Dip the other end of the Q-tip in the lemongrass oil. Drop the Q-tip in the hive, put the lid on, put it near the swarm and come back after dark. They probably will have moved into the box. Staple screen over the entrance and take them home.

***Removal***

Sometimes called a "cut out". This is not the easiest way to get bees. It is exciting and fun, but sometimes requires some construction skills and lots of courage. The idea is to remove all of the bees and all of the combs from a tree, a house, or whatever they are living in. It often involves removing sections of walls and someone repairing them afterwards. It is not usually financially worth it unless you are being paid to remove them or you have a lot of free time.

Each removal is a separate situation. Sometimes they are in an old abandoned building and the owner doesn't care if you rip the wallboard off or tear the siding off. Usually it does matter and you can't go tearing it up, you have to put everything back when you are done or make it clear to the homeowner that they will need to hire a carpenter to do so. Ignoring, for the moment, the construction issues, if you get to the combs, whether they are in a house or a tree or whatever, you need to cut the brood to fit frames and tie around the frames to hold it in. This does not work well for honey, especially in new comb, because it's too heavy, so scrap the honey. Throw it in a five gallon bucket with a lid to keep out the bees trying to clean up the spill. Try to put the brood in an empty hive box and keep brushing or shaking the bees off into it. If you see the queen, then catch her with a hair clip queen catcher or put her in a cage and put her in the hive box. If you get some brood and the queen in the hive box the rest of the bees will eventually follow. If you don't see the queen, then just keep putting bees in the box and brood comb in frames in the box and honey in the bucket until the combs are all gone. Take the bucket and, if you can, leave for a few hours and let the bees figure out where the queen and the other bees are. The will all settle into the new box. At dark they should all be inside and you can close it up and take it home.

***Cone Method***

This method is used when it's impractical to tear into a hive and remove the comb or there are so many bees you don't want to face them all at once. This is a method where a screen wire cone is placed over the main entrance of the current home of the bees. All other entrances are blocked with screen wire stapled over them. Make the end of the cone so it has some frayed wires so that a bee can push the wires enough to get out (including drones and queens) but can't get back in. Aim it a bit up and it helps some on keeping them from finding the entrance. Now you put a hive that has just a frame of open brood, a couple of frames of emerging brood and some honey/pollen, right next to the hive. You may need to build a stand or something to get it close to where the returning foragers are clustered on the cone. Sometimes they will move into the box with the brood comb. Sometimes they just hang on the cone. The biggest problem I've had is that this causes many more bees to be looking for a way in and circling in the air and the homeowners often get antsy and spray the bees with insecticide because they are afraid of them. If you think this is likely, then *don't* put the box with the brood here, but rather at your bee-yard, hopefully at least 2 miles away, and you vacuum or brush the bees off into a box every night and take them and dump them in the box with the brood, you will eventually depopulate the hive. If you keep it up until no substantial number of bees are in it anymore, you can use some sulfur in a smoker to kill the bees (sulfur smoke is fatal but does not leave a poisonous residue) or some bee quick to drive the rest of them out of the tree (or house or whatever). And if you use the BeeQuick you may even get the queen to come out. If you do, catch her with a hair clip queen catcher and put her in a box and let the bees move into the box. Since the cone is still on the entrance they can't get back in the old hive. I'd leave it like this for a few days and then bring a strong hive and put it close to the old hive. Remove the cone and put some honey on the entrance to entice the bees to rob it. This is most effective during a dearth. Mid summer and late fall being likely dearths. Once they start robbing it, they will rob the entire hive out. This is especially important if removing them from a house, so that the wax doesn't melt and honey go everywhere or the honey attract mice and other . Now you can seal it up as best you can. The expanding polyurethane foam you buy in a can at the hardware store is not too bad for sealing the opening. It will go in and expand and make a fairly good barrier. Joe Waggle came up with this option, if you can keep a good eye on it is when they swarm, put the cone on and then the virgin queen will leave to mate and not be able to get back in. Then you can get a swarm with a queen from the cone.

***Bee Vacuum***

I will preface this that I don't like Bee vacuums. They kill a lot of bees make it hard to find the queen and likely to kill her. I hardly ever use them. They are nice for cleaning up the last stragglers at a colony, but I prefer to use a spray bottle of water to keep them from flying so much and a bee brush or shaking to get them off. I think a Bee vacuum is often a replacement for finesse and skill. Since they are occasionally useful, let's talk about them.

Brushy Mountain Bee Farm makes these, but you can modify a cheap shop vac to do it. The most important issues are these:

If you have too much vacuum it will kill too many bees. If you are converting a shop vac, cut a hole in the top or use a hole saw and drill a hole. You'll have to adjust this to fit the way the vac is designed, but if there is room you could just drill a three inch hole. If not you could drill and saw to make a longer hole. The idea is that we will take a piece of wood or plastic and make a damper by putting a screw through it on one corner and pivoting the damper to make a larger or smaller hole. This hole is covered on the inside by hardware cloth or screen wire. I just glue it with epoxy on the inside. Now when you adjust the damper to be more open there is less vacuum. When you close it more, there is more vacuum.

If the bees hit the bottom of the vacuum too hard they will die or be injured. The solution to that is put a piece of foam rubber on the bottom. Or wad up some newspaper and put it on the bottom—anything to soften their landing so they don't hit the hard plastic bottom.

Bees get torn up hitting the corrugations of the tube. If you get a smooth hose there will be less of this. If you get smaller corrugations there will be less of this.

If you run the vacuum too long the bees inside get hot, regurgitate their honey and die. If this happens you will notice they are a sticky mess. Don't run the vacuum any longer than you have to.

Adjust the vacuum carefully. You want just enough vacuum to pick the bees off the comb and no more. Too much and you'll have a canister full of squashed bees.

This tool can be used for bee removal. Getting bees off of the combs and not in the air is very helpful. Be careful. I have used them with good luck and I have also killed a lot of bees when I didn't mean to.

### *Transplanting Bees*

Moving bees from one "hive" to another (trees, old hives or other homes of bees).

People often have bees in an old rotting hive that is crumbling to pieces and is so cross-combed they can't manipulate it. Or they have a hive in a log gum, a box hive (no frames), a skep, a piece of a tree that fell down or some oddball equipment that they want to retire or even that they want to move them from all deeps to all mediums etc. If you want bees to abandon some current abode that can be taken home and manipulated here are some methods that I've used, and some variations that I have not used, but should work.

I have used this on box hives and log gums. You want the bees to abandon their old home, but you don't want to sacrifice all the brood. You want to get most of the bees and the queen out of the old hive into a box that is connected to the old hive. In other words there needs to be some connection between the two. A piece of plywood that is as large as the largest dimension of either one in both directions can then had a hole cut in the middle of it that is as large as the smaller of either on in both directions. By putting this between the new hive body and the old hive you have connected the two.

The next decision is whether you want to use Bee Go, Bee Quick (similar but smells nicer) or smoke and drumming or just patience.

It helps if the new hive has some drawn comb and, better yet, a frame of brood.

If you want to use the fumes (Bee Go and Bee Quick) then you put the old hive on top and the new hive body on the bottom. Have a queen excluder handy. Use a soaked rag for fumes and put it as near the top of the old hive as you can. This will drive the bees down into the box. When the box seems pretty full and the old hive seems pretty empty put the excluder between. If you can easily do it, put the old hive so that the combs are upside down from what they used to be. That way the bees will be more likely to abandon it eventually because honey runs out of the cells and the combs are the wrong way for brood.

If you want to smoke and drum, then you put the old hive on the bottom and the new one on the top. Smoke the old hive heavily and tap on the side with a pocketknife or a stick. You don't have to do it hard like a bass drum, just a tap tap tap. Lots of smoke helps. Again, when it looks like most of the bees are in the top put in the excluder. It doesn't matter what the orientation of the combs is for driving the bees out, but it helps if it is upside down now. The queen should be in the top and they will finish the brood in the bottom and then rework it for honey or abandon it.

If you want to use patience, just put the new hive on the top and wait for the bees to move up. This may or may not work for some time because the queen wants to stay in the brood chamber.

***Bait hives.***

Bait hives are empty boxes that are set out to try to entice a swarm to move in. They will not entice a hive to swarm, but they may offer a nice place for a hive that wants to swarm. I use Lemongrass oil and sometimes queen pheromone. You can buy QMP (Queen Mandibular Pheromone brand name Bee Boost). It is little tubular pieces of plastic that have the smell impregnated in them. When I use these for bait, I cut each of them into four equal pieces and use one piece and some lemongrass oil or some swarm lure. Swarm lure and QMP are available from bee supply places. You can get your own QMP by putting all your old queens when you requeen and any unused virgin queens in a jar of alcohol. Put a few drops of this in the bait hive. Old empty combs are nice too and using boxes that have had bees in them helps. I set out about seven of these last year and got one swarm. Not great odds, but I got some nice feral bees. There are things that have been researched to increase your odds such as the size of the box, the size of the opening and the height in the tree. There seem to be a lot of exceptions though. So far my best luck has been a box the size of a deep five frame nuc or a 8 frame medium with some kind of lure (homemade or otherwise), 12 feet or so up a tree, with about the equivalent of a 1" hole for an entrance. And foundationless frames (frames with a comb guide, see chapter *Foundationless Frames*). My problems have been wasps moving in, finches moving in and wax moths eating old combs and kids knocking them out of trees with rocks and destroying them. Try putting nails in the hole to make an "X" to make it hard for the finches or cover the hole with #4 hardware cloth. Paint them brown or "tree" colored to make them harder for the kids to see. Use starter strips or clean dry old comb so the wax moths don't move in or spray the old comb with Certan. Remember, this is like fishing. I would not count on it if you're trying to get started beekeeping. You might catch one the first year or you might not catch one for several years, or you might catch several. It's like fishing because you want fish for supper. You may be better off to buy some fish.

# Queen Rearing

For a live presentation by the author of this try a search for videos on the web for "Michael Bush Queen Rearing".

***Why rear your own queens?***

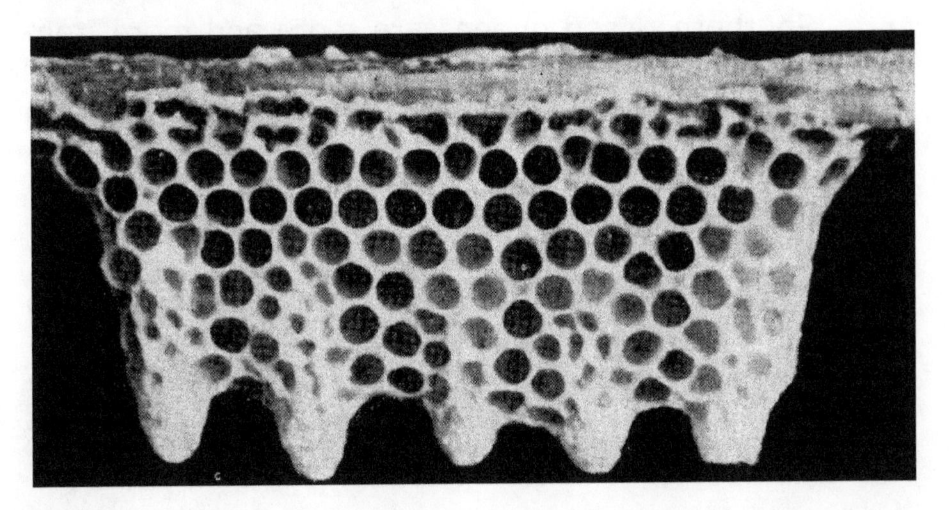

### Cost

A typical queen costs the beekeeper $20 and up counting shipping and may cost considerably more.

### Time

In an emergency you order a queen and it takes several days to make arrangements and get the queen. Often you need a queen yesterday. If you have some in mating nucs, on hand, then you already have a queen.

**Availability**

Often when you need a queen there are none available from suppliers. Again, if you have one on hand availability is not a problem.

**AHB**

Southern raised queens are more and more from Africanized honey bee areas. In order to keep AHB out of the North we should stop importing queens from those areas.

**Acclimatized bees**

It's unreasonable to expect bees bred in the deep South to winter well in the far North. Local feral stock is acclimatized to our local climate. Even breeding from commercial stock, you can breed from the ones that winter well in your locale.

**Mite and disease resistance**

Tracheal mite resistance is an easy trait to breed for. Just don't treat and you'll get resistant bees. Hygienic behavior, which is helpful to avoid AFB (American foulbrood) and other brood diseases as well as Varroa mite problems. And yet most queen breeders are treating their bees and not selecting, either on purpose or by default for these traits. The genetics of our queens if far too important to be left to people who don't have a stake in their success. People selling queens and bees actually make more money selling replacement queens and bees when the bees fail. Now I'm not saying they are purposely trying to raise queens that fail, but I am saying they have no financial incentive to produce queens that don't. This is not to say that some responsible queen breeders aren't doing the right thing here, but most are not. Basically to cash in on the benefits of not treating, you need to be rearing your own queens.

## Quality

Nothing is more important to success in beekeeping than the queen. The quality of your queens can often surpass that of a queen breeder. You have the time to spend to do things that a commercial breeder cannot afford to do. For instance, research has shown that a queen that is allowed to lay up until it is 21 days old will be a better queen with better developed ovarioles than one that is banked sooner. A longer wait will help even more, but that first 21 days is much more critical. A commercial queen producer typically looks for eggs at two weeks and if there are any it is banked and eventually shipped. You can let yours develop better by spending more time.

### *Concepts of Queen Rearing*

### *Reasons to rear queens*

Bees rear queens because of one of four conditions:

## Emergency

There is suddenly no queen so a new queen is made from some existing worker larvae.

## Supersedure

The bees think the queen is failing so they rear a new one.

## Reproductive swarming

The bees decide there are enough bees, and enough stores and enough of the season left to cast a swarm that has a good chance of building up enough to survive the winter without endangering the survival of the colony.

## Overcrowding swarm

The bees decide that there are too many bees and not enough room or not enough stores to continue under the current conditions, so they cast an overcrowding swarm as population control. This swarm doesn't have the best chance of survival but the colony believes it improves the colony's chances of survival.

We get the most cells and the best feeding for the queens if we simulate both Emergency and Overcrowding.

A beekeeper can easily get a queen simply by making a queenless split with the appropriate aged larvae. So why would we want to do queen rearing?

### *Most Queens with Least Resources*

The underlying concept of queen rearing is to get the most number of queens from the least resources from the genetics chosen for the traits you want.

To illustrate the resource issue let's examine the extremes. If we make a strong hive queenless. They could have, during that 24 days of having no laying queen, reared a full turnover of brood. The queen could have been laying several thousand eggs a day and a strong hive could easily rear those several thousand brood. Then we have lost the potential for about 30,000 or more workers by making this hive queenless and resulted in only one queen. And, actually, this hive made many queen cells, but they were all destroyed by the first queen out.

If we made a small nuc we would only have a couple of thousand queenless bees rearing several queen cells and those couple of thousand bees could only have reared a few hundred workers in that time. But again they made several queen cells and the results were only one queen.

In most queen rearing scenarios we are making the least number of bees queenless for the least amount of time and resulting in the most number of laying queens when we are done.

### ***Where queens come from***

A queen is made from a fertilized egg, exactly the same as a worker. It's the feeding that is different and that is only different from the fourth day on. So if you take a newly hatched worker egg, and put it in a queen cell (or in something that fools the bees into thinking it's a queen cell) in a hive that needs a queen (swarming or queenless) they will make those into queens.

### ***Methods of getting larvae into "queen cups"***

There are many methods. You can find the original books for many of these here:

http://bushfarms.com/beesoldbooks.htm

**Here are a few of them**:

### The Doolittle Method

Originally published by G.M. Doolittle, is to graft the appropriate aged larvae into some homemade wax cups. This requires a bit of dexterity and good eyesight, but is the most popular method used. Today plastic cups are often used in place of wax. The queen is sometimes confined to get the right aged larvae all in one place for easy selection. #5 hardware cloth works well for this as the workers can pass through it but the queen cannot. This is usually put on old dark brood comb to make the larvae easier to see and to make the cell bottom more sturdy for grafting. Once you have a good eye for the right age larvae this is less critical and one can do this by simply finding the right age larvae. On day 14 these are usually put in mating nucs.

### The Jenter method

Several variations of this are on the market under various names. The concept is that the queen lays the eggs in a confinement box that looks like worker cells. Every other cell bottom of every other row has a plug in the bottom. When the eggs hatch the plug is removed and placed in the top of a cup. This accomplished the same thing as the Doolittle method without the need for so much dexterity and eyesight. On day 14 these are usually put in mating nucs.

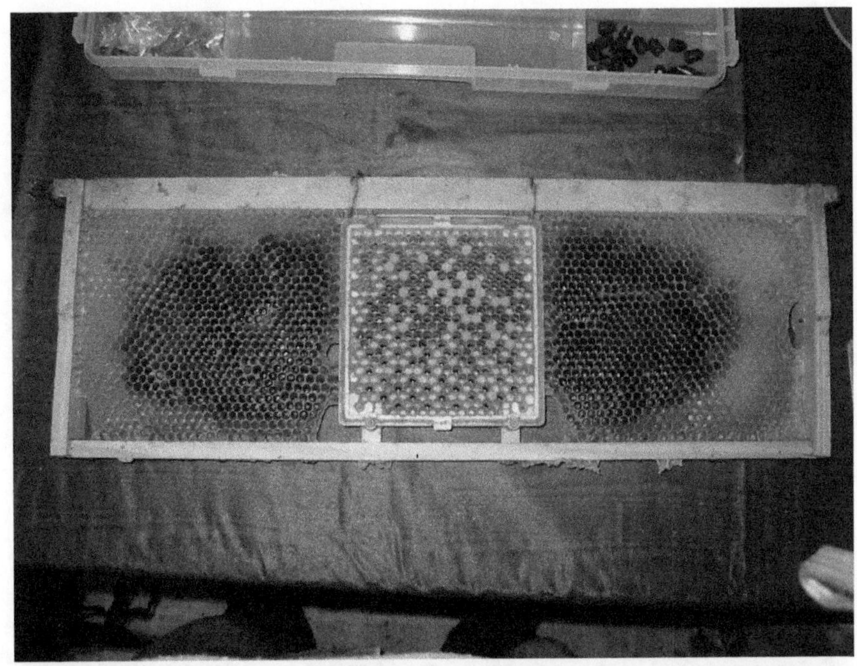

*Jenter Box Front*

*Jenter Box Back*

*Jenter Box Top*

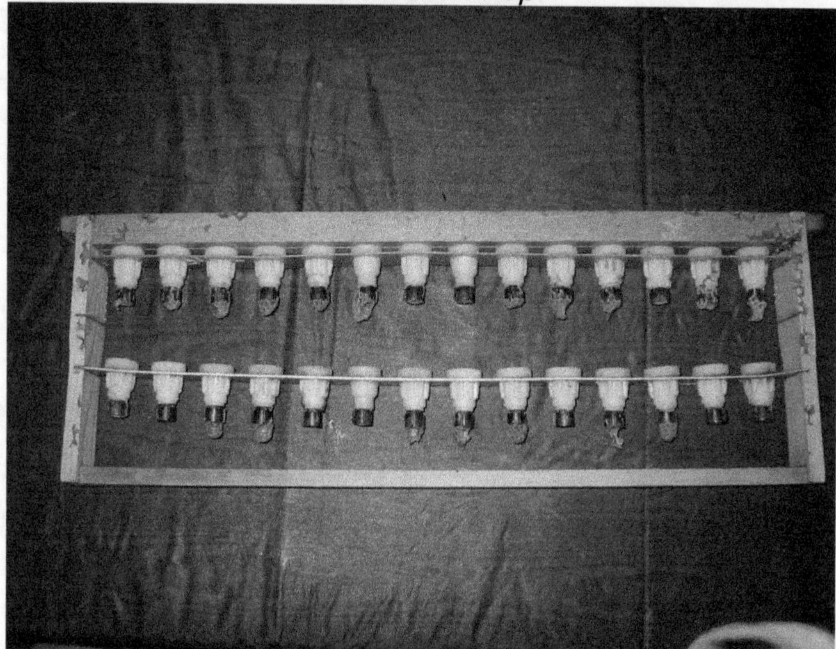

*Missed queen cell results in dead queens*

Jenter queen rearing system pictures. Front, back and top of the queen box and then a picture of a cell bar where I missed a queen cell the bees built in the cell builder. 17 queens dead.

**Advantages to Jenter**

- If you are a newbee you get to see exactly what the right age larvae looks like as you know when they were laid.
- If your eyesight isn't so good you don't have to be able to see the larvae (mine isn't the greatest)
- If you are not very coordinated (and I'm not) you don't have to be able to pick up something very tiny and down inside a cell without damaging it. You just move the plugs.

**Advantages to grafting**

- If the queen didn't lay in the Jenter cage and I'm on a schedule, I don't have any larvae the right age unless I go find some and graft (or do the Better Queens method).
- If I was too busy to confine the queen four days ago, I can just graft.
- If the queen mother is in an outyard, I don't have to make two trips, one to confine her, and another to transfer larvae.
- I don't have to buy a queen rearing kit.

**The Hopkins Method**

*#5 hardware cloth queen confinement cage*

In my variation, the queen is confined with #5 hardware cloth to get her to lay in the new comb and so we know the age of the larvae (as the Doolittle method but on new comb empty instead of old comb). This should be wax, preferably with no wires so you can cut the cells out without wires in the way, although Hopkins says you should used wired comb so it doesn't sag. If you use wired comb, be sure to work around the wires when leaving larvae so the wires won't interfere. Release the queen the next day. You can also just put the new comb in the middle of the brood nest and check every day to see if the queen has laid in it yet, to judge the age of the larvae.

On the fourth day (from when the queen was confined or she laid in the comb) the larvae will be hatched. In every other row of cells *all* the larvae are destroyed by poking them with a blunt nail, a kitchen match head, or similar instrument. Then the larvae in *every other cell* in the remaining rows is destroyed the same way (or two cells destroyed and one left) to leave larvae with space between them. This is then suspended flatways over a queenless hive. A simple spacer is an empty frame under the frame with the cells and a super over that. This will require angling the frames somewhat and laying a piece of cloth on top. The bees perceive these to be queen cells, because of the orientation, and build cells off of them. They should be spaced enough apart to allow cutting them out on day 14 and distributing them to either hives to be requeened (that would have been dequeened the day before) or to mating nucs.

*Hopkins shim to hold the frame over the box.*

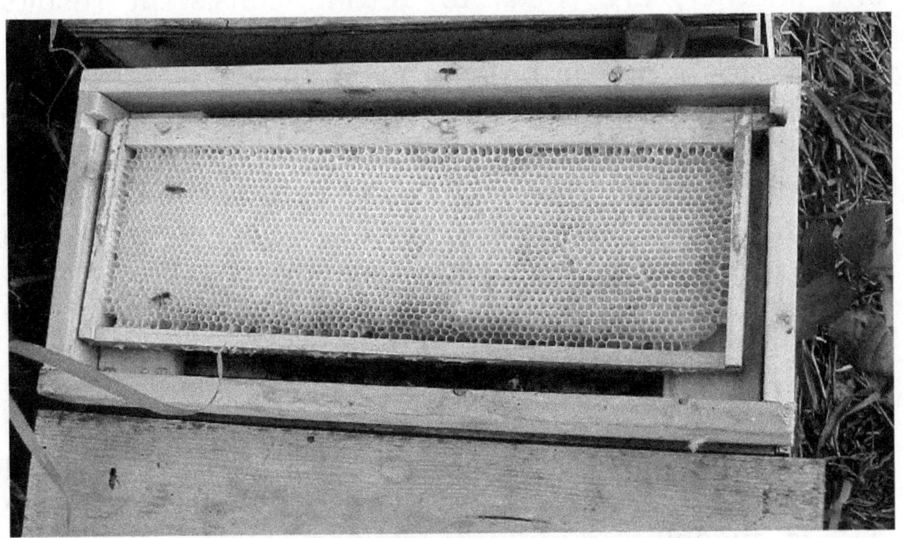

*Frame of larvae in the Hopkins shim.*

***Cell Starter***

For me the most difficult thing to get a grasp on and the most critical thing for queen rearing, other than the obvious issues of timing, was the cell starter. The most important thing about a cell starter is that it's overflowing with bees. Queenless is helpful too, but if I had to choose between queenless and overflowing with bees, I'd go for the bees. You want a very high density of bees. This can be in a small box or a large hive, it's the density that is the issue, not the total number. There are many different schemes to end up with queenless crowded bees that want to build cells, but don't ever expect a good amount of cells from a starter that is anything less than overflowing with bees.

The next most important issue with the starter is that it's well fed. If there is no flow you should feed to make sure they feed the larvae well.

Most of the rest of the complexity of the many queen rearing systems, which often seem at odds with one another, are tricks to getting consistent results under all circumstances. In other words, they are important to a queen breeder who needs a consistent supply of queens from early spring until fall regardless of flow and weather. For the amateur queen breeder, these are probably not so important as is the timing of your attempts. Rearing queens during prime swarm season just before or during the flow is quite simple. Rearing queens in a dearth or later or earlier than the prime swarm season will require more "tricks" and more work. For starters I would skip these "additions" and adopt them one at a time as you see the need.

A Cloake board (Floor Without a Floor) is a useful method. You can rearrange things so that part of the hive is queenless during the starter period and queenright as a finisher without a lot of disruption of the hive. But it's not necessary.

The simplest way I know of is to remove a queen from a strong colony the day before and cut it down to minimum space (remove all the empty frames so that you can remove some boxes and, if there are supers that are full remove those). This may even put them in a mood to swarm, but that will make a lot of queen cells. Make sure there aren't any queen cells when you start and if you use them for more than one batch be extra sure there are no extra queen cells in the hive as those will emerge and destroy your next batch of cells.

Another method is to shake a lot of bees into a swarm box aka a starter hive and give them a couple of frames of honey and a couple of frames of pollen and a frame of cells.

***Beekeeping Math***

| | Days | | | |
|---|---|---|---|---|
| Caste | Hatch | Cap | Emerge | |
| Queen | $3^1/_2$ | 8 +-1 | 16 +-1 | Laying 28 +-5 |

| | | | | |
|---|---|---|---|---|
| Worker | $3^1/_2$ | 9 +-1 | 20 +-1 | Foraging 42 +-7 |
| Drone | $3^1/_2$ | 10 +-1 | 24 +-1 | Flying to DCA 38 +-5 |

***Queen Rearing Calendar:***

Using the day the egg was laid as 0 (no time has elapsed)

Bold items require action by the beekeeper.

Day Action Concept

**-4 Put Jenter cage in hive Let the bees accept it, polish it and cover it with bee smell**

**0 Confine queen—So the queen will lay eggs of a known age in the Jenter box or the #5 wire cage**

**1 Release queen—So she doesn't lay too many eggs in each cell, she need to be released after 24 hours**

**3 Setup cell starter Make them queenless and make sure there is a *very* high density of bees.—This is so they will want queens and so they have a lot of bees to care for them. Also make sure they have plenty of pollen and nectar. Feed the starter for better acceptance.**

$3^1/_2$ Eggs hatch

**4 Transfer larvae and put queen cells in cell starter. Feed the starter for better acceptance.**

8 Queen cells capped

**13 Setup mating nucs Make up mating nucs, or hives to be requeened—So they will be queen-less and wanting a queen cell. Feed the mating nucs for better acceptance.**

**14 Transfer queen cells to mating nucs.—On day 14 the cells are at their toughest and in hot weather they may emerge on day 15 so we need them in the mating nucs or the hives to be re-queened if you prefer, so the first queen out doesn't kill the rest.**

15-17 Queens emerge (In hot weather, 15 is more likely. In cold weather, 17 is more likely. Typical-ly, 16 is most likely.)

17-21 Queens harden

21-24 Orientation flights

21-28 Mating flights

25-35 Queen starts laying

**28 If you intend to requeen your hives, look for laying queens in the mating nucs. If found, dequeen hive to be requeened.**

**29 Transfer laying queen to queenless hive to be requeened.**

***Mating Nucs***

*Two By Four Mating Nucs*

Splitting a ten frame box into four nucs with two frames each. Note the blue cloth sticking out. These are canvas inner covers so I can open one nuc at a time without them boiling over into the next nuc. Also note the Ready Date Nuc Calendars on the end.

**A note on mating nucs**

In my opinion it makes the most sense to use standard frames for your mating nucs. Here are a few beekeepers who agree with that:

> ***"Some queen-breeders use a very small hive with much smaller frames than their common ones for keeping their queens in till mated, but for several reasons I consider it best to have but the one frame in both the queen-rearing and the ordinary hives. In the first place, a nucleus colony can be formed in a few minutes from any hive by simply transferring two or three frames and the adhering bees from it to the nucleus hive. Then again, a nucleus colony can be built up at any time or united with another where the frames are all alike, with very little trouble. And lastly, we have only the one sized frames to make. I have always used a nucleus hive such as I have described, and would not care to use any other."—***

***Isaac Hopkins, The Australasian Bee Manual***

---

***"for the honey-producer there seems no great advantage in baby nuclei. He generally needs to make some increase, and it is more convenient for him to use 2 or 3-frame nuclei for queen-rearing, and then build them up into full colonies...I use a full hive for each nucleus, merely putting 3 or 4 frames in one side of the hive, with a dummy beside them. To be sure, it takes more bees than to have three nuclei in one hive, but it is a good bit more convenient to build up into a full colony a nucleus that has the whole hive to itself."—C.C. Miller, Fifty Years Among the Bees***

---

***"The small Baby Nucleus hive had a run for a while but is now generally considered a mere passing fad. It is so small that the bees are put into an unnatural condition, and they therefore perform in an unnatural manner...I strongly advise a nucleus hive that will take the regular brood-frame that is used in your hives. The one that I use is a twin***

***hive, each compartment large enough to hold two jumbo frames and a division-board."—Smith, Queen Rearing Simplified***

---

***"I was convinced that the best nucleus that I could possibly have, was one or two frames in an ordinary hive. In this way all work done by the nucleus was readily available for the use of any colony, after I was through with the nucleus...take a frame of brood and one of honey, together with all of the adhering bees, being careful not to get the old Queen, and put the frames into a hive where you wish the nucleus to stand...drawing up the division-board so as to adjust the hive to the size of the colony."—G. M. Doolittle, Scientific Queen-Rearing***

---

**Queen marking colors:**

Years Ending in:

- 1 or 6 – White
- 2 or 7 – Yellow
- 3 or 8 – Red
- 4 or 9 – Green
- 5 or 0 - Blue

***Queen Catching and marking***

Until you get the hang of it, there is always the risk of hurting the queen. But learning to do it is a worthwhile undertaking. I would buy a hair clip queen catcher and a marking tube and paint pens. Practice on a few drones with a color from a couple of years ago, or better yet the color for next year, so you don't confuse the drones with the queen. Use the current color for the queens.

My preferred method is to buy a "hair clip" queen catcher, a queen muff (Brushy Mountain) and a marking tube and a marking pen. Catch the queen gently with the hair clip. It is spaced so as not to easily harm the queen, but still be careful. If you put this and the marking tube and the paint pen (after it is shaken and started) in the queen muff then the queen can't fly off while you do this. Take the marking tube and slid out the plunger. If you move away from the hive you can lose some of the bees that are in and on the clip. Don't shake it while holding the clip portion or you may shake the queen out. If you take it in a bathroom with a window and turn off the lights you can be more assured she won't fly off. Or buy a queen muff from Brushy Mountain. Use a brush or a feather and brush off the workers as they come out and then try to guide the queen into the tube. She tends to go up and she tends to go for the light, so open the clip so she will run into the tube. If she doesn't and she runs onto your hand or glove, don't panic, just quickly drop the clip and gently but quickly put the tube over her. Cover the tube with your hand to block the light so she runs to the top of the tube. Put the plunger in. Be quick but don't hurry too much. Gently pin the queen to the top of the marking tube and touch a small dot of paint (start the paint pen on a piece of wood or paper first so there is paint in the tip already) on the middle of the back of her thorax right between her wings. If it doesn't look big enough just leave it. You need to keep her pinned for several more seconds while you blow on the paint to dry it. Don't let her go too soon or the paint will get smeared into the joint between her body sections and it may cripple or kill her. After the paint is dry (20 seconds or so) back the plunger up to halfway so the queen can move. Pull the plunger and aim the open end to the top bars and the queen will usually run right back down into the hive.

***Jay Smith***

Some quotes from Jay Smith (famous queen breeder and beekeeper who probably raised more queens than anyone who ever lived):

**Queen longevity:**

From "Better Queens" page 18:

> ***"In Indiana we had a queen we named Alice which lived to the ripe old age of eight years and two months and did excellent work in her seventh year. There can be no doubt about the authenticity of this statement. We sold her to John Chapel of Oakland City, Indiana, and she was the only queen in his yard with wings clipped. This, however is a rare exception. At the time I was experimenting with artificial combs with wooden cells in which the queen laid."—Jay Smith***

I would point out that Jay says: "This, however is a rare exception."

I think three years has always been pretty typical of the useful life of a queen.

**Emergency queens:**

> ***"It has been stated by a number of beekeepers who should know better (including myself) that the bees are in such a hurry to rear a queen that***

***they choose larvae too old for best results. later observation has shown the fallacy of this statement and has convinced me that bees do the very best that can be done under existing circumstances.***

***"The inferior queens caused by using the emergency method is because the bees cannot tear down the tough cells in the old combs lined with cocoons. The result is that the bees fill the worker cells with bee milk floating the larvae out the opening of the cells, then they build a little queen cell pointing downward. The larvae cannot eat the bee milk back in the bottom of the cells with the result that they are not well fed. However, if the colony is strong in bees, are well fed and have new combs, they can rear the best of queens. And please note— they will never make such a blunder as choosing larvae too old."—Jay Smith***

---

***C.C. Miller***

C.C. Miller's view of emergency queens

***"If it were true, as formerly believed, that queenless bees are in such haste to rear a queen that they will select a larva too old for the***

***purpose, then it would hardly do to wait even nine days. A queen is matured in fifteen days from the time the egg is laid, and is fed throughout her larval lifetime on the same food that is given to a worker-larva during the first three days of its larval existence. So a worker-larva more than three days old, or more than six days from the laying of the egg would be too old for a good queen. If, now, the bees should select a larva more than three days old, the queen would emerge in less than nine days. I think no one has ever known this to occur. Bees do not prefer too old larvae. As a matter of fact bees do not use such poor judgment as to select larvae too old when larvae sufficiently young are present, as I have proven by direct experiment and many observations."—Fifty Years Among the Bees, C.C. Miller***

---

***Queen Banks***

A beekeeper can keep a number of queens in one hive if you get bees that are in the mood to accept a queen (queenless overnight or a mixture of bees shaken from several hives) and the queens are in cages so they can't kill each other. I've done these with a $^{3}/_{4}$" shim on top of a nuc or a frame with plastic bars that hold the JZBZ cages. I put a frame of brood in periodically to keep them from developing laying workers or running out of young bees to feed the queens.

## ***FWOF***

(Floor With Out a Floor aka Cloake Board). Used to allow converting a top box on a queen rearing hive to change from a queenless cell starter to a queenright cell builder or finisher. This one is made with a $^3/_4$″ by $^3/_4$″ piece of wood with a $^3/_8$″ x $^3/_8$″ groove in it. Hang it out $^3/_4$″or more in front and put a piece across the front under the sides to make a landing board. Cut a piece of $^3/_{16}$″ or $^1/_4$″ luan to slide in for a removable bottom. Coat edges with Vaseline to keep the bees from gluing it in. From left to right: The frame on a hive with the floor out. Inserting the floor. The FWOF with the floor in.

# Nucs

### *Optimal Space*

I'm a big believer in giving bees just the room they need, up until the main honey flow. Raising brood and making wax require heat. Nuc boxes allow you to limit the space that a small number of bees and brood has to take care of while they get established or while they overwinter. Here are some pictures of my nucs and my overwinter setup.

### **Various Sized Nucs**

*Two Frame By Four Mating Nucs*

*Assorted Width Nucs*

On the left are *Two By Four* mating nucs. Four nucs with two frames each in one ten frame sized box. Note the blue cloth sticking out. There are canvas inner covers so I can open one nuc at a time without them boiling over into the next nuc. Also note the Ready Date Nuc Calendars on the end. On the right is assorted medium depth nucs. Number of frames from left to right 2, 3, 4, 5, 8, 10. I like the two frame nucs for mating nucs. The 8 frame medium boxes make a nice nuc as they are the same volume as a 5 frame deep.

***Overwintering Nucs***

According to research to survive cold temperatures, a group of at least 2,000 bees is required (Southwick 1984). I don't know *how* cold that small of a group is supposed to survive, but my nucs that size usually do fine until a long sub zero cold snap. But they don't usually survive subzero temps for very long. I shoot for an eight frame medium box that is fairly full of bees going into winter.

Here are some things I've tried to overwinter nucs the last couple of winters. There are 14 eight frame and 20 five frame nucs. The base is four by eight sheets of $^{3}/_{4}$" plywood with a sheet of Styrofoam and a sheet of $^{1}/_{4}$" luan on top of that. The nucs are in rows on that. The bottom is made of $^{1}/_{4}$" luan with a vent in the back. The top is also luan with a hole for a quart jar feeder (with #8 mesh under it) and another vent in the top. The entrance is about an inch wide by $^{3}/_{8}$ inches high on the five frame nucs and about $2^{1}/_{2}$ inches wide on the eight frame nucs. I had to reduce them all down with #8 hardware cloth to cut down on robbing so all of them are now about $^{3}/_{8}$ by $^{3}/_{8}$ inches. Two got robbed out and died already but the rest seem to be doing well. One has a queen bank in it and has a terrarium heater under that one. The top is big box made of one by eight and a sheet of Styrofoam (for each section) on top of that to close it off. There's a thermostatic electric space heater inside set to 70º F. The biggest problem I had was the feeders leaking and keeping the bees in the queen bank from clustering and leaving out the queens. A terrarium heater underneath helped with the queen bank. Feeding seem to cause the most problems. Syrup makes a lot of moisture and sometimes the jars leak on the bees.

HUSKER EXTRA
Osborne's

**Feeding dry sugar**

The first two pictures are feeding dry sugar, which is what I did for the nucs this year. The next picture is a frame feeder full of dry sugar. The next is feeding on the side without the frame feeder, just removing a couple of frames. The last two are the setup for wintering this year. There is a gap down the center with a small thermostatic space heater set at 60 F. Styrofoam covers three sides of the cluster of nucs. The doubles have an extra bottom on top to fill the space and the singles on top of each other each have their own bottom board. The bottoms are feeders so syrup could be put on the bottom in the spring or warm weather for feeding. This has worked well for me.

---

I recommend having at least a couple of nucs for a beginner. They are so useful for starting hives and rearing queens and keeping a spare queen. Since I've recommended mediums for everything, I'll point out that you can buy five frame medium nucs from Brushy Mt Bee Farm. You can also buy 8 frame boxes which are a nice intermediate nuc size that is the same size as a 5 frame deep nuc box. I think Miller Bee Supply has medium nucs as do Rossman's and possibly some others. A deep nuc could be cut down also. You can make your own if you're handy with wood. I find an attached bottom board and a migratory cover are adequate for a nuc. I have made them in two frame (mostly for setting aside a queen or for mating nucs) three frame, four frames and five frames. Since I'm running mediums, I suppose an eight frame box is the equivalent to a five frame deep nuc. I also use the eight frame boxes for nucs. I tend to use them to give a minimum size to a colony starting out. Any excess space is more work for a small colony.

***What Nucs are Good For:***

## Splits

You can put a frame of brood with eggs a frame of emerging brood a couple of frames of honey and pollen and put them in a nuc and shake another couple of frame of bees from some brood in and the bees will raise a queen and you will have a new hive. When they fill the nuc, move them to a standard box.

## Artificial swarm

If the bees are trying to swarm, do as above except add the old queen to the nuc and take out all but one or two of the swarm cells in the hive.

## Making queens from swarm cells

As above you can do a split to get them to make a queen, but also when they are trying to swarm you can as in the first (splits) and put a queen cell in each nuc with the brood and honey and bees and they will hatch the queen and you can use them for requeening or selling or whatever you like. Of course you can also do queen rearing to get the cells to put in. If you have multiple queen cells you can cut some off and put them in nucs.

## Keeping a backup queen

When you requeen take some of those old queens and put them in nucs with a frame of brood and honey and if the new queen gets rejected you still have a spare. Also, if you just keep a nuc with a queen in it for a spare, you can requeen a hive with that queen. To keep it weak, keep taking sealed brood out and giving to other hives.

### Foolproof requeening

If you do as in the first (splits) and put a caged queen in the nurse bees will quickly accept the queen. After she is laying you can kill the queen in the hive to be requeened and do a newspaper combine. Bees readily accept a laying queen.

### Queen bank

I built a shim that is the size of a nuc but $^{3}/_{4}$" thick and put queen cages with the wire down to keep them for several days or weeks before introducing them.

### Comb building

This is especially nice with regressed bees. Since the problem with 4.9mm foundation isn't getting the bees to use the cells, it's getting unnatural large bees to *build* the cells. If you start a nuc with small bees as in the first (splits) and after it's established, put frames with 4.9mm foundation in the 1,2,4 and 5 position. Feed it well and remove some drawn frames every day. If there are eggs, put it in another colony to let them emerge and then steal the frame. Keep 3 or 4 pounds of bees in the nuc.

## Swarm catching

Nucs are nice for hiving small swarms.

## Bait hives

Nucs are nice for bait hives for swarms. You could use a 10 frame box and that is a nice size too, but is harder to attach in a tree and for best results they need to be 10 feet or so up a tree.

## Shaken swarms

You can put a screen bottom on the nuc and shake bees from brood frames from several hives (being careful *not* to get a queen) and you have a bunch of homeless queenless bees. These can be put in hive with some brood so they can raise one or added to a nuc with a caged queen.

## Transporting honey

Nucs are nice and light even with five frames of honey, compared to a ten frame box. Nice for putting frames in as you brush off the bees to harvest and nice to carry around.

# Lighter Equipment

### *Mediums instead of deeps*

My first step in the direction of lighter beekeeping equipment was trying horizontal hives, which I like a lot. But I still had a lot of old equipment around, so I started cutting the deeps down to mediums and quit using deeps and shallows. Then I cut the ten frame boxes to eight frames. If you want to understand why, a ten frame deep full of honey weighs 90 pounds. A ten frame medium weighs 60 pounds. An eight frame medium weighs 48 pounds.

On the left is a "typical" beekeeping setup as recommended in the books. From bottom to top it is: a bottom board, two deep boxes for the brood, a queen excluder, two shallow supers an inner cover and a telescopic cover. A ten frame deep full of honey weighs 90 pounds. A medium full of honey weights 60 pounds. An eight frame medium full of honey weighs 48 pounds. The one on the right is one of my vertical hives. This one has four medium boxes for brood and honey (no excluder) and a migratory top with a shim on both sides to make a top entrance and no bottom entrance. Using all the same size frames greatly simplifies beekeeping management as any honey can be used for winter feed and any brood found in the supers can be moved back down since the frames are all interchangeable. Leaving out the excluder helps prevent a honey bound brood nest and doesn't restrict the bees working the supers. It also saves having to have a bottom entrance because the drones can get out the top (no excluder to stop them).

***Eight frame instead of ten frame***

I'm still tired of heavy beekeeping boxes, so I started buying eight frame boxes. But I still had a lot of tens. Here's a couple of tens for the bottom followed by eights on top. The board on the side covers the crack. The next picture is a ten frame hive between two eight frame hives. Last time I went through the hives I didn't lift a single box because all the clusters were at the top and couldn't figure out why my back hurt when I got done. Then I remembered the concrete blocks. I started making wire clips out of #10 wire to hold the lids on and get rid of the blocks. (see chapter *Miscellaneous Equipment*) But those 60 mph winds tend to blow the lids off without them and blow the hives over sometimes in spite of them.

*Eight Frame Super on Ten Frame Brood Nest*

*Eight Frame Hive Next to Ten Frame Hive*

I cut down all my deep beekeeping boxes and frames. The left picture is what I did with the solid bottom bars. The picture on the right is what I did with the broken bottom bars and split bottom bars. I made a new bottom bar from the corner of a one by.

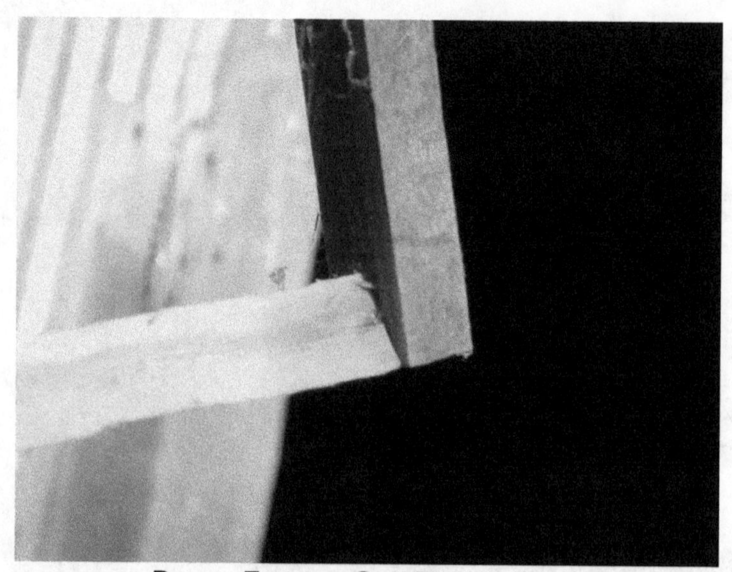

*Deep Frame Cut To Medium*

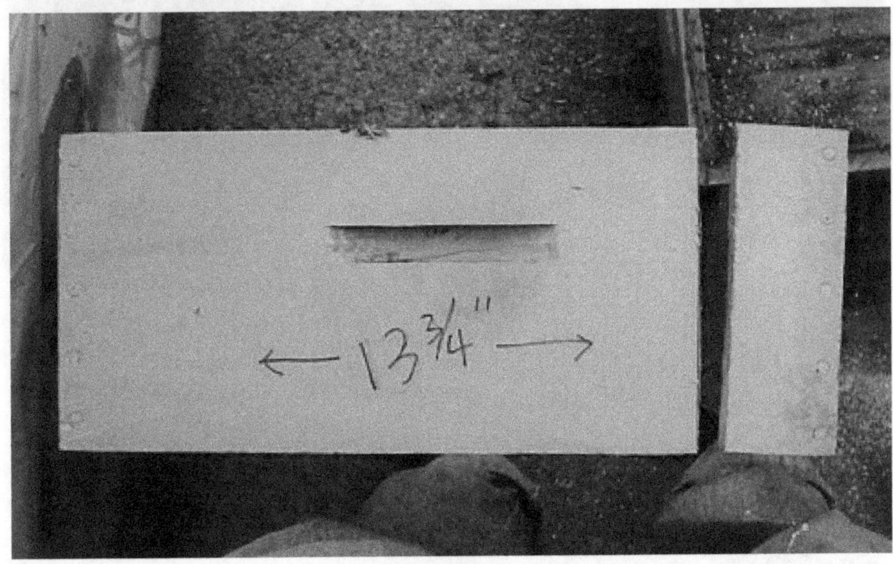
← 13 3/4" →

SAW.

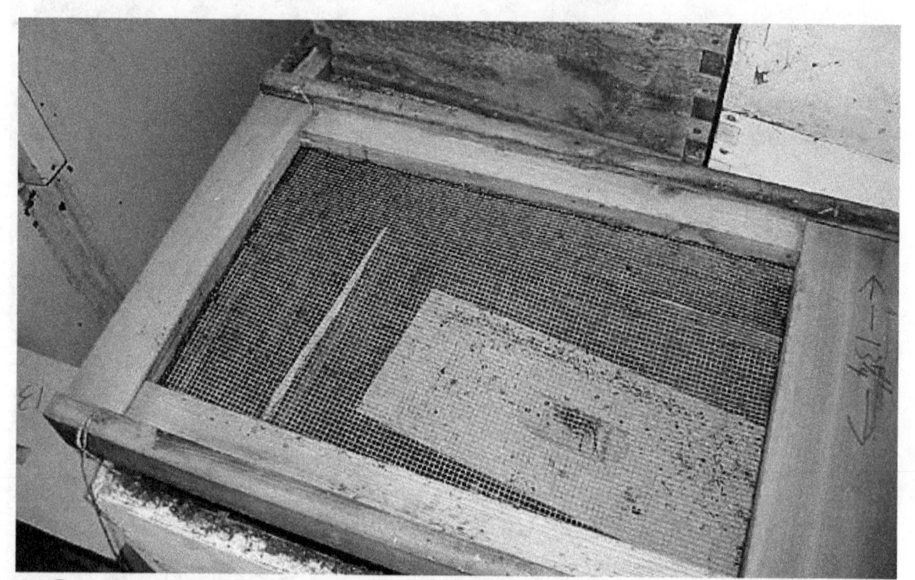

*Cutting ten frame boxes and bottom boards down to eight frame*

I am now cutting down all my 10 frame medium beekeeping boxes and bottom boards. Here is the sequence of events to make a 10 frame box and Brushy Mountain screened bottom board into an 8 frame. The handsaw cut is to finish the skill saw cut square because of the curve of the blade to make the small ears on the ends.

# Wax Dipping Equipment

I was expanding my beekeeping and bought a lot of new equipment so I decided to try dipping in wax and gum rosin to preserve the equipment. I got the tank from a friend who had it custom made. It would have been nice if it was taller, but it works ok and I didn't have the time or money to get a better one made. The standard method is 2 parts paraffin and 1 part gum rosin. I went with 2 parts beeswax and 1 part gum rosin. The gum rosin is from Mann Lake. The wax/gum rosin mixture was melted and heated to between 230° and 250° F (110° and 121° C). At 250° the boxes cook nicely (like deep fat frying them) in about six to eight minutes. At 230, they take more like 10 to 12 minutes. You can't leave this unattended or unmonitored (and you need a thermometer) as the fire hazard is huge if you do. Keep a fire extinguisher handy. I use a timer so I don't lose track of time. This isn't like burning your beans. If this catches you have a couple hundred pounds of hydrocarbons for fuel!

*Bottoms in the tank*

*Simmering Some Boxes.*
*The extras on top are to hold them down because they float.*

*Boxes and bottoms after dipping. The beekeeping equipment looks and smells wonderful and the water just beads up on them.*

*The bees seem to think the rosin and wax is propolis. Here's one gathering it off my gloves.*

# Colony Decisions

I've been thinking about this for some time, but a presentation by Tom Seeley on swarms finding a home at a Kansas Honey Producers Association meeting and two days (and late into the night) of talking to Walt Wright has crystallized some of those thoughts.

In my observation, one of the causes of a slow down with bees is when the colony needs to make a decision. This could be as simple as which way the winter cluster wants to go to find some stores or whether to start drawing on some plastic foundation or move through an excluder or move into comb honey sections. In many situations opposite strategies on the part of the beekeeper can have the same results because the proper decision was clear, where something more moderate can have poor results because of indecision.

Take something that most people have seen, like trying to get bees through an excluder. If the bees have room in the bottom they don't seem to want to cross it. But if you crowd them they have no real choice. Once they make up their mind, the cross it without any thought.

I saw Dr. Thomas Seeley do a presentation on how bees decide where to go when they swarm. It's pretty much a matter of coming to a consensus and that takes time.

Another example is deeps, Dadant deeps and mediums. With mediums they never seem to hesitate to move up or down a box if they need the room. With deeps they often get stuck in one box and don't want to move up or down. With Dadant deeps they have enough room they don't *need* to move up or down. I find I have better results with either the Dadant deep, where they don't need to decide, or the medium where the decision is pretty much required.

I think this is the cause of the enthusiasm (and speed) with which they draw their own comb compared to drawing foundation of any type and especially plastic. They know what they want to build but they have to come to terms with making a decision as to what to do with this sheet of foundation.

I think this is often why people doing opposite things have similar results. Once the bees have made up their mind they do things quickly. If they have to come to a consensus, it takes time. A cluster in a long medium hive has only one way to go, sideways. A cluster in an eight frame vertical hive has only one way to go if they are at the bottom, up. If they are at the top, down.

I think we beekeepers often give the bees too many decisions to make. How many have seen a cluster in the midst of stores with a gap all around them that didn't move to stores? I think they just couldn't decide.

Indecision requires a lot of energy and wasted time for the bees. Sometimes this just sets them back and sometimes it even gets them killed. As beekeepers we need to be aware of this and use it to our advantage and avoid it working to the bees' disadvantage.

# Two Queen Hives

I will preface this with the fact that I've done this and think it is *usually* easier to just run two one queen hives. The biggest problem for me is that you have a super hive with supers stacked up to the clouds and bees everywhere and to do anything with the queens requires moving and disturbing every box. All those bees can be very intimidating, especially to a beginner. I think to be practical it requires a system that does not require moving any boxes to get to either queen.

That said, the concept is that two queens will lay twice as many eggs and build up twice as fast in the spring. More workers, more honey.

There are a few different tactics you can use to accomplish this. One would be the low equipment, low labor, less reliable method of just raising queen cells and putting them in the top box to emerge. This often, but not always results in a two queen hive with minimal effort. You can increase the odds by putting a queen excluder somewhere in the middle of the boxes. Of course both have to have a way for the drones and virgin queen to get out. This often works but in the worst case they get requeened and best case they end up with two laying queens. I've done this accidently when queen rearing on several occasions. For details on how to mate a queen in the top of a hive see Doolittle's information on it in *Scientific Queen Rearing*.

A type of Demaree also works fairly well to end up with one. Just build a double screen board (or two single screen boards) and put one box of brood over the screen board. The bees rear a new queen in the queen-less part (whichever that may be) and when you approach the main flow, you can do a newspaper combine with or without a queen excluder.

If you want to be more reliable, here is my design for a manageable two queen hive. I would set up a horizontal hive that is three boxes long. ($48^3/_4$") with the entrances on the long side. Make it so you can open or close an entrance on any third of the box on any of the two long sides.

The box needs two grooves into which a piece of a queen excluder fits to divide it into thirds. This allows a queen on each end and supers in the middle.

You can use any of several methods to get the hive to accept two queens, but they are separated enough to not fight and you have two brood nests and one stack of supers in the middle. You can purchase queens, leave the hive queenless for 24 hours and split the brood nest into the two brood boxes with a caged queen in each and try for simultaneous introduction.

If you raise your own queens, you could put a virgin on each end and hope they fly back to the right hive when they are done mating.

The best time to get two queens laying is early in the spring. The earlier the better. During the honey flow you might be better off to split the hive and put all of the open brood in one of them and most of the bees in the other to up the production in that hive because lots of brood rearing *during* a honey flow does not help production.

Snelgrove had a plan for using one hive to stock the other that was quite ingenious by manipulating entrances above and below a double screen board and perhaps some way could be figured out to do that in a more horizontal configuration.

The whole point of a two queen hive is to get a "super hive" with a huge population of bees. Another way to accomplish this is the "cutdown split/combine". See the chapter on "Splits" for more information.

# Top Bar Hives

### *Kenya Top Bar Hive*

*Kenya style Top Bar Hive being constructed. The sides are one by twelves $46^1/_2$" long. The bottom is a one by six $46^1/_2$" long.*

*The ends are one by twelves 15" long. None of the boards is ripped or beveled. They are just cut for length and nailed together.*

*The sides are spread to where they fit the ends and the ends are nailed and then screwed with deck screws. I ended up using deck screws on the end because when I pried the bars over I would pry the end off of the hive.*

*With bees. The top bars are ripped from one bys with a beveled comb guide glued and nailed on. You can see a bar on top of the hive on the right end. The brood nest is $1^1/_4$" wide bars and the honey is $1^1/_2$" wide bars These bars are 15" long.*

*Comb from the KTBH. Can you spot the queen?*

*A close-up of the queen on the KTBH comb.*

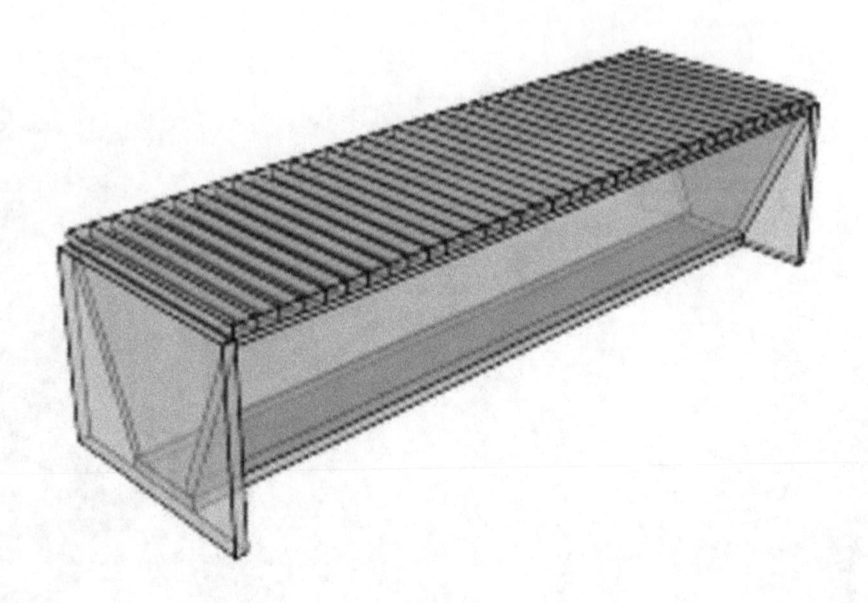

*See through drawing (thanks to Chris Somerlot).*

The object of a Top Bar Hive (TBH) is to be easy and cheap to construct, easy to work and having natural sized cells. A Kenya style (sloped sides) is so that the combs are more naturally strong and less likely to break and collapse when they are full of honey. This hive worked very well with no comb collapses. The small combs are easy to handle and not nearly as fragile as large free hanging combs. The pictures are, from left to right:

The entrance to the KTBH is just the front bar back from the front at least $^3/_8$" The top sets on top of a $^3/_4$" top bar so the entrance is $^3/_4$" high and $^3/_8$" wide and is really just the gap in front of the first bar.

**Parts List:**

- 2- one by twelves $46^1/_2$"
- 2- one by twelves 15"

- 1- one by six $46^1/_2$"
- Any kind of lid 15" by 48"
- 16- bars 15" by $1^1/_4$" by $^3/_4$"
- 18- bars 15" by $1^1/_2$" by $^3/_4$"
- 34- triangular comb guides cut from chamfer molding or the corner of a one by $^3/_4$" by $^3/_4$" by 1" by 13"
- 2- four by fours 16" long cedar or treated for stand.

All cuts are square cuts unless you cut your own chamfer from a one by.

One of the difficult issues seems to be communicating the entrance design. I think it's because you don't have to build an entrance to have one. You simply leave the front bar back (as you always have left over space anyway) and the bars raise the cover by the thickness of the bars this leaves an entrance.

*Entrance*
*(Photo by Theresa Cassidy)*

*Entrance with top cover pushed back*
*(Photo by Theresa Cassidy)*

Tanzanian Top Bar Hive

*Tanzanian Top Bar Hive*

*TTBH Open*

*TTBH Comb*

Here is a long medium depth hive. This one has top bars in it instead of frames. The entrance is just a propped up migratory cover and the front bar back $^{3}/_{8}$" from the front. The advantage to this one is that standard medium frames fit in it so if it needs resources from one of my other hives I can get a frame of brood that fits. Also, I can start one with some frames of brood from one of my other hives (which are all mediums). I haven't seen any more attachment with this hive than the sloped sides.

**Parts List:**

- 2- one by eights $46^{1}/_{2}$″ with $^{3}/_{8}$″ by $^{3}/_{4}$″ rabbet for frame rest.
- 2- one by eights $19^{7}/_{8}$″
- 1-bottom (plywood, coroplast or other) 48″ x $19^{7}/_{8}$″
- Any kind of lid $19^{7}/_{8}$″‟ by 48″ (plywood, coroplast or roofing tin) or three migratory covers.
- 16- bars 19″ by $1^{1}/_{4}$″ by $^{3}/_{8}$″
- 18- bars 19″ by $1^{1}/_{2}$″ by $^{3}/_{8}$″
- 34-triangular comb guides cut from chamfer molding or the corner of a one by $^{3}/_{4}$″ by $^{3}/_{4}$″ by 1″ by $17^{1}/_{2}$″
- 2- four by fours 16″ long cedar or treated for stand.

## Comb Measurements

*4.7mm Comb Measurement*

Just to show some cell size measurements. Here is a brood comb from my Kenya Top Bar Hive. To measure, start at the 10mm mark and count over 10 cells. Looks like 4.7cm for ten cells to me. That's 4.7mm. Notice I started at 10cm because it's hard to say precisely where zero is.

***FAQs***

## Wintering

**Q:** Some people say that TBH's don't winter well in cold climates. Do they?

**A:** I have them in Nebraska and others have them places as cold as Casper Wyoming. I have rarely heard reports from anyone keeping bees in top bar hives that they don't overwinter well in cold climates. I have usually heard it from people who have not attempted it. It is a good plan to get the cluster to one end at the beginning of winter so they can work their way to the other end over winter. If they are in the middle they may work their way to one end and starve with stores at the other end. The bigger problems are having top bar hives in very *hot* climates and yet people seem to do that as well. I have the most problems on the over a hundred degree F days when I have comb collapses.

**Tropical?**

**Q:** Top Bar Hives were developed in Africa right? So it's a tropical hive?

**A:** Actually they were developed in Greece thousands of years ago, and then used in many other places. But the real concern seems to be that there is a belief that bees won't move horizontally. Obviously this is not true. I've seen hives in hollow horizontal branches, I've seen them in floors, and I've overwintered them in Horizontal hives, both TBHs and Langstroth frame hives. Bees do tend to only move in one direction when clustered and have trouble changing direction in a cluster in the cold. But they don't seem to care if that direction is horizontal or vertical. Trough hives (chest hives, or whatever else you wish to call a horizontal hive) have been kept in Scandinavian countries for centuries. According to Eva Crane most of the hives in the world today and throughout history have been horizontal hives in every area from the far north to the tropics.

**Excluder?**

**Q:** Without a queen excluder how do you keep the queen out of the honey?

**A:** I don't use a queen excluder on regular hives either. The queen is not looking to lay all over the place. When you end up with brood in honey supers in a Langstroth hive it's because one of two things has happened. Either the queen was looking for a place to lay some drone brood, which you didn't allow in the brood nest because of either culling it or using only worker foundation; or the queen needed to expand the brood nest or swarm. Would you rather they swarm? The bees want a consolidated brood nest. They don't want brood everywhere. Some people try to have some capped honey as their "queen excluder". I do the opposite. I try to get them to expand the brood nest as much as possible to keep them from swarming and to get a bigger force to gather the honey. So I add empty bars in the brood nest during prime swarm season.

### Harvest

**Q:** How do you harvest the honey from a top bar hive?

**A:** You can either do crush and strain; or you can cut it for comb honey. If you really want to, Swienty has an extractor that will work with top bar hives. But if you only have a few hives an extractor is seldom worth the expense.

### Top Entrance?

**Q:** Some people say a top entrance lets the heat out. How do you do your entrances?

**A:** In any hive (top bar or otherwise) I think a top entrance in the winter is always a good plan. It lets out the moisture and cuts down on condensation. Heat is seldom the problem, condensation is the problem in winter. A top entrance will let it out. Mine are all *just* top entrances. The reason I went with them was the skunks. My first TBH had a bottom entrance and the skunks were a serious problem. After going to the top entrances they have ceased being a problem. My entrances are simply the gap at the front of the hive between the first bar and the front wall. No holes to drill.

### Sloped Sides?

**Q:** Does a KTBH have less attachments than a TTBH?

**A:** In my experience no. I only know of one TBH beekeeper who actually seems to think so. Most have had the same experience as I have, which is that they do little attachment either way.

### Varroa?

**Q:** How do you treat for Varroa in a top bar hive?

**A:** I don't. I depend on the smaller natural cell size. But you could put a hole in and use oxalic acid vapor or you could drizzle oxalic acid or you could use powdered sugar.

### Feeding?

**Q:** How do you feed a top bar hive?

**A:** Since I usually only feed for emergencies, dry sugar on the bottom (if it's not screened) works fine. Spray it with a little water to get them interested in eating it and to get it clumped so the house bees don't carry it out. You could use a baggie feeder on the bottom or, if you build it to take Langstroth frames you could put a frame feeder in or, if not, you could build one to fit. The long mediums I can use most anything that could be used on a regular hive. In the long medium I've usually used frame feeders with floats in them.

### Management?

**Q:** What is different about the management of a top bar hive or long hive?

**A:**

- The most important thing to grasp is that bees build parallel combs. Therefore one good comb leads to another in the same way that one bad comb leads to another. You cannot afford to not be paying attention to how they start off. The most common cause of a mess of comb is leaving the queen cage in as they always start the first comb from that and then the mess begins. I can't believe how many people want to "play it safe" and hang the queen cage. They obviously can't grasp that it is almost a guarantee of failure to get the first comb started right, which without intervention is guaranteed to mean every comb in the hive will be messed up. Once you have a mess the most important thing is to make sure the *last* comb is straight as this is always the guide for the *next* comb. You can't take a "hopeful" view that the bees will get back on track. They will not. You have to put them back on track. This has nothing to do with wires or no wires. Nothing to do with frames or no frames. It has to do with the last comb being straight.
- The need for frequent harvesting to keep space in the honey area open.

- The need for empty bars in the brood nest during prime "reproductive" swarm season to expand the brood nest more and prevent swarming.
- The need to have the cluster at one end of the hive at the beginning of winter (at least in Northern climates) so they don't work their way to one end and subsequently starve while leaving stores at the opposite end because of indecision. This is easily done by simply moving the bars containing the cluster to one end and putting the bars they replaced at the other. Since the brood nest is usually by the entrance, having the entrance on the end avoids this problem. Having it in the center causes it.
- The need to handle combs more carefully. You need to be aware of the angle of the comb with the earth. Anytime you get flatways with a comb that is very heavy it's likely to break. Keep the combs "hanging" in tune with gravity. You can flip them over but you have to rotate them with the flat of the comb vertical and not horizontal. You also need to check for attachments to walls, floor and other combs before you pull a comb out. Cut these attachments first if they are there.

## Production?

**Q:** Which makes more honey? A top bar hive or a Langstroth hive?

**A:** It comes down to management differences. If you have the TBH where you can get to it easily and you check it weekly during a heavy flow and manage their space by harvesting frequently, I think it's about even. If the TBH is in an outyard and you don't get there often or even if it's in your backyard and you don't get there often, the Langstroth will probably make more honey.

While a TBH takes more *frequent* manipulation it does not take more labor as you don't have to lift and move boxes around when doing inspections.

### SBB?

**Q:** Can I put a screened bottom board on my TBH?

**A:** You can. But I wouldn't leave the whole thing open as this will be too much ventilation. In my experience it makes little difference on Varroa.

**Q:** How can you have too much ventilation? Isn't ventilation a good thing?

**A:** Of course in the winter, too much ventilation means too much heat loss. But even in the summer the bees are cooling the hive by evaporation, so on a hot day the inside of the hive may be cooler than the outside air. So too much ventilation could result in the bees being unable to maintain a cooler temperature inside. When wax heats up past the normal operating temperatures of a hive (> 93 F) it gets very weak and combs can collapse. According to Huber's experiments on ventilation, more vents actually resulted in less ventilation.

### Cross Ventilation

**Q:** On Langstroth hives you often have a top and bottom vent to get sufficient ventilation. Should I provide cross ventilation in my TBH?

**A:** Bees seem to have more trouble ventilating a vertical hive with no vent at the top. They have to force dry air (which wants to go down) up to the top and hot moist air at the top (which wants to go up), back down and out the bottom. It's sort of like walking 20 miles to school, uphill both ways. So a top vent or top entrance in a vertical hive seems to be very helpful as it allows the hot moist air out the top which sucks the dry air in the bottom. With a horizontal hive, this is not an issue. They just move the air in a circular fashion in one side and back out the other side and out the door. Sort of like a nice level walk with no hills. This seems to work well. With cross ventilation (such as a front and back vent or entrance) the wind may blow through the hive and that may be a bad thing.

### Landing board?

**Q:** Don't I need a landing board on the entrance?

**A:** No. Have you ever seen a bee tree with a landing board? Landing boards just give mice a place to jump on to get in the hive. It's not needed at all for the bees and is, in my opinion, counterproductive because of mice.

### Length?

**Q:** What's the optimum length for a TBH?

**A:** In my experience, something around four feet seems to be good. Less is difficult to keep them from swarming. More is hard to get the bees to occupy the whole length. Brother Adam's research on bees and hives shows the maximum long hive he encountered was five feet long. I would save five feet is the maximum useful length.

### Bar Width

**Q:** Why can't I make all the bars the same width?

**A:** You can. But regardless of what you do, the bees won't build all the combs the same thickness, so it's difficult to keep them on the bars. If you want to build them all the same width, I'd make them all $1^1/_4$" wide and make a lot of $^1/_4$" spacers to put in between when the bees decide to make fatter combs to get them back in the center of the bars.

### Comb Guide

**Q:** What's the best comb guide?

**A:** There's nothing wrong with most of commonly used guides except perhaps the wax in a groove method. Which is barely a suggestion and not at all a good guide. You need something that protrudes significantly. $^1/_4$" is good. $^1/_2$" won't hurt. Anything from a wax starter strip to a triangular guide works, but there are advantages and disadvantages. In my opinion the one with the most advantages and least disadvantages is the triangular wooden guide. The bees follow it the most reliably and attach it the most solidly. I like a wax starter strip the least as it's fragile and hot weather can cause them to fall off. I think the least reliable would be dribbling a bead across a plain bar. Not that this can't work, but the reliability of this method is at the bottom of the list.

**Waxing Guides**

**Q:** Do I have to put wax on the wooden guide?

**A:** No. I not only don't put beeswax on the wood comb guides, I don't recommend it. The wax you put on the guide will not be attached as well as what the bees will attach the comb. So it actually weakens the connection to dip the edge of the guide in beeswax. In my experience, the bees will not follow the guide any better or worse with or without the wax.

**Slatted Rack**

**Q:** Can I build a slatted rack into my TBH (or any other fancier piece of equipment)?

**A:** Of course. But to me the most attractive thing about a top bar hive, aside from not having to lift boxes, is its simplicity. I prefer to keep it as simple as practical.

# Horizontal Hives

*Long medium depth hive.*

One of the first things that occurred to me when I wanted to stop lifting so much in my beekeeping, was a long hive. I first built one back in about 1975 for a friend but I never really used them myself. My next one was in about 2002. The concept is simply to have the hive running horizontally so you don't have to lift. These are popular in many parts of the world. Another variation of this is a top bar hive (see previous chapter for parts list and info on top bar hives) where it not only runs horizontally but has no frames for the combs. I have, currently in use, two 12 frame deeps hives, one 22 frame deep hive, and five 33 frame medium hives. I hope to make several more every year. My entrances are just propped up migratory covers. The advantage is, not only that I don't have to drill holes or worry about skunks but that the entrance moves with the supers so the bees tend to work the supers better as I add them.

*Long hive from the front. This one has medium frames. Mostly PermaComb*

***Management***

Management issues and questions are similar to top bar hive management issues so see that chapter for details.

*Long hive with supers. This one is mostly foundationless frames.*

# Observation Hives

***Why an observation hive?***

I love my observation hives. I have learned much more from them in a year than many years of keeping bees in a hive. Having one, in addition to your hives, gives you an idea what is happening outside in the other hives. You can see if pollen is coming in, if nectar is coming in, if robbing is happening etc. You can watch them raise a queen. Watch how it acts while she is mating, watch them swarm. You can count days or hours on capping times, post capping times etc. You will get to see waggle dances, "get it off me" dances etc. You get to hear what the bees sound like when they are queenless, when they are being robbed, when the queen is emerging etc. I started building one a couple of times, but never got it done. Now I don't know how I did without it.

***Pictures of Different Kinds of Observation Hives***

*Langstroth Deep Observation Hive Bees On Top Bars*
*10 frame Langstroth style observation hive.*

This works very well with foundationless frames. The view is from the face of the combs, not from the end bars. It's not that useful with frames of full sheets of foundation. On the right is a picture of bees in the Langstroth size deep observation box. These are on top bars instead of frames. These were moved into a double wide deep box (standard deep depth and $32^1/_2$ " long) that was kept in the shade. The deep top bar combs eventually all collapsed like a row of dominoes, so I went to medium depth for Langstroth sized top bar hives instead. The observation hive is still nice. I have a board that fits in the inset portion and blocks the sun so it's not a solar wax melter.

*Glass frame feeder for indoor observation hive I built this to fit the odd space left when I reworked the hive to hold four medium frames instead of two deeps and two shallows.*

*The privacy curtain*

*The crack in the glass is an insert I put in to correct the beespace. The outside glass is safety glass. The insert is inside, and is regular glass cut to fit. Unfortunately I bumped it with a hive tool when cleaning and put a nick in it. Over time it turned into a crack that slowly went across the entire pane.*

*The tube going out the window through a one by four insert.*

*Burr On Glass wrong sloped cells*

Bees build most cells sloped so that from the bottom of the cell to the mouth is uphill about 15 degrees. But sometimes they build upside down comb on their own, or the beekeeper puts comb in upside down to get the bees to abandon it. I have had the bees refill these upside down cells with honey. But the queen does seem to not like laying in them much. For anyone wanting to see upside down sloped cells you can see them on the bottoms of the smaller burrs on the right hand picture. You can see how the honey does not follow gravity but rather the workings of the bees in the burr in the left picture. See how the honey does not lay flat in the cell and is often straight up and down. If you look at the cells in the picture on the left they are often either completely horizontal or even a bit down sloped.

*Brood In PermaComb*

***Getting an Observation Hive***

## You Can Build One or Buy One

I will preface this with a disclaimer. *All* of the observation hives I have actually seen or measured or used have been wrong on their beespace. Some are too small. Some are too large. All but the Brushy Mountain ones that were available a few years ago are not well planned from the point of view of having an observation hive and managing it. This may encourage you to build your own. You may find that is best. You may also find that buying one and then reworking it is easier for you. But here's what I want in an observation hive.

I like one big enough I can keep it all year round one frame thick.

That way I can always find the queen, eggs and brood, so let's assume that is the goal.

Also, availability is changing all the time so some of this will be outdated by the time it's published.

## Glass or Plexiglas

I like them both. If you are buying one, safety glass is pretty durable. That's what my Draper hive is and the grandsons have hit it a few times with toys and it's still in one piece. Plexiglas is less breakable and lighter weight and easier to work with when building your own. Glass is easier to clean. To clean the glass just use a razor blade scraper and scrape it clean. Follow-up with some window cleaner. To clean the Plexiglas you need WD40 or maybe FGMO (Food Grade Mineral Oil). You can get the FGMO at the drugstore as Mineral Oil Laxative. Both solvents have to soak to soften the wax and propolis.

## Other Nice Features

In spite of the excess space on my Draper hive, I love it. It has a swivel base so I can flip the hive around to see either side. I finally put a extra piece of glass inside to fix the beespace problem.

## Exit

You need an exit for the hive. I use tubing made for a sump pump. It's about $1^{1}/_{4}$″. I cut some one by fours to fit the width of my window and storm window and used a hole saw to make $1^{1}/_{4}$″ holes in both that line up. Then I worked the hose through and put duct tape on the outside so when the grandsons pull on the hose it won't come back in the house. This is clamped onto the outlet from the hive with an automotive hose clamp. The Brushy Mountain hive required a small block to fill the square hole on the end and I drilled a $1^{1}/_{8}$″ hole in that and screwed a 1″ (inside diameter) pipe into that for the outlet to clamp the hose to. It helps to have the hive by a window that won't get direct sun (either because it's shaded by trees or whatever) so it won't turn into a solar wax melter.

## Privacy

I have the best luck by just buying black cotton broadcloth and folding it double and laying it over the observation hive double again. This can be cut to fit exactly and you now have a curtain that is easy to remove, easy to put on and easy to make. Bees will prefer darkness most of the time.

***Observation Hive Issues***

## Frame Size

Brushy Mountain seems to be the only one who understands that in order to maintain an observation hive, it should be one size frame and that size should match the brood chambers of your other hives. They have stopped offering any but the "Ulster" hive now. They used to offer one that is all deeps (Huber hive) and one that is all mediums (Von Frisch). I reworked the Draper hive to take four mediums and a homemade glass sided feeder to fill in the difference at the top.

## Overall Size

I have never had much luck raising bees with the small Tew hive (which it really wasn't designed to do anyway), even though I reworked it extensively (and will talk more about that later). The bees have never thrived in it. It's just too small. I think the minimum size for a sustainable observation hive is three mediums or two deeps, but four mediums or three deeps is better. Since you have to carry it outside to work it (at least if you keep it in your living room as I do) you want it light enough you can move it. I find the four medium frame ones are about as large as I can easily manage. So I would say that is the ideal size. Four mediums or three deeps (depending on what you use for brood in your hives). You can rework them by changing the rests to take different size frames you can make up the odd left over amounts by making feeders or just putting in a top bar to fill the gap with a beespace above and below.

## Space Between the Glass

For reasons unknown to me, no one seems to get this right. The Draper has about $2^1/_4$″ between the glass and the bees burr the glass up a lot. The Brushy Mountain hives have $1^1/_2$″ between the glass and when I put in frames of brood from a hive it was too tight a fit and the brood could not emerge and the bees absconded. I reworked the Brushy Mountain hives by adding a screen molding (available at the hardware store) which is $^1/_4$″ thick. I put it behind the hinges on the hinge side and behind the door as a stop on the opposite side and added one next to the door just to match the other side. This has worked perfectly and it is my most thriving hive now. $1^3/_4$″ is just the right amount of space between the glass for an observation hive. $1^7/_8$″ is ok.

## Feeder

An observation hive is in the house (usually) and therefore you need to be able to feed it without taking it outside. The Brushy Mountain Van Frisch had a screened in feeder station on it where you put a quart jar with holes in the lid to feed it. It works well. The Draper had no feeder so I made a frame feeder with glass sides and put it on top with a hole to fill it on top covered with #7 hardware cloth. I can also dump in some pollen if I want since it will go through the #7 just fine. But I had problems when I dumped it into the syrup, because it would cause the syrup to ferment. I put another hole further to one side so it would miss the hole in the feeder and I can feed pollen there, again with #7 hardware cloth to cover it.

## Ventilation

Ventilation seems to be more difficult to get just right for both you and the bees. The long tube going out the window makes it difficult for them to ventilate the hive through the entrance. I reworked the Tew hive several times before I *reduced* the ventilation enough that they could raise any brood at all. I had to increase the ventilation in the Draper hive so the condensation on the glass would go away and the chalk brood would clear up. You need to pay attention to the bees needs. If there is condensation on the glass there is not enough ventilation. If there is chalk brood in the hive, there is not enough. If they are having a lot of trouble raising any brood, there is probably too much.

## Robbing

An observation hive is by definition a small hive and is prone to robbing by the stronger hives in the yard. Again the Von Frisch has a piece of Plexiglas that drops into the part where the tube going outside is that reduces the entrance. You flip it over and drop it in and it blocks the exit altogether. The Draper does not and that has been a problem from time to time.

## Disconnecting

I've tried a variety of fancy gadgets to disconnect the hive to take it outside and block the incoming bees and the outgoing bees. None have worked that well. What I end up doing is taking three pieces of cloth large enough to cover the tube and three rubber band hair ties and disconnecting the tube and quickly cover the ends with cloth and hair ties. I do just separate them enough to slip in the cloth first. If someone is available to help I have them hold the cloth on one end while I rubber band the other. After the tube going out is blocked and the hookup for the tube on the hive is blocked I go outside and do the tube out there so there won't be a traffic jam inside the tube when I'm trying to connect it back up. Then I haul the hive outside, do my manipulations and bring it back in.

## Working the Hive

It seems as soon as you open the observation hive the bees start overflowing out onto the hive. You will need a smoker and a brush to get the door closed again. Try to smoke them back into the hive and then brush as many as you can out of the way of closing the door. Another advantage to the Von Frisch *after* I put in the extra spacer is that the bees don't get crushed so much in the hinge or the door side because there is a $^{1}/_{4}$" gap all the way around. I brush them off once, move the hive a ways, and do it again. Then I take the hive back in the house and put the two tubes against each other and remove the cloth as quickly as I can and reconnect things. If I do this with a minimum amount of time of the tube being open, I almost never have a bee get into the house. If they do they will just try to go out the window and you can catch them with a glass and a piece of paper. Put the glass over the bee and slide the piece of paper under the glass. You now have a bee in the glass. Take it outside and let it go.

Whenever I need to rework the hive or do a thorough cleanup, I just put the frames into a nuc with the entrance at the same place as the tube with the tube still closed. In my case the nuc is on top of an empty deep box to get it the right height. If the entrance to the nuc is the same place, they quickly find the nuc. This gives me several days, if I want it, to clean up the burr, the propolis, rework whatever things were frustrating me, like making a feeder, putting in something to maintain the spacing, a hole to feed pollen, more or less ventilation etc. Then when I'm done, I just put the frames back in the observation hive, remove the nuc and connect everything back up.

# Box Jig

I was expanding my beekeeping and bought a lot of new equipment so I decided to build a jig to assemble the boxes. Here are pictures.

*Box jig without the follower boards*

*Follower boards being put in*

*Ends being put in the jig*

*Sides being put on*

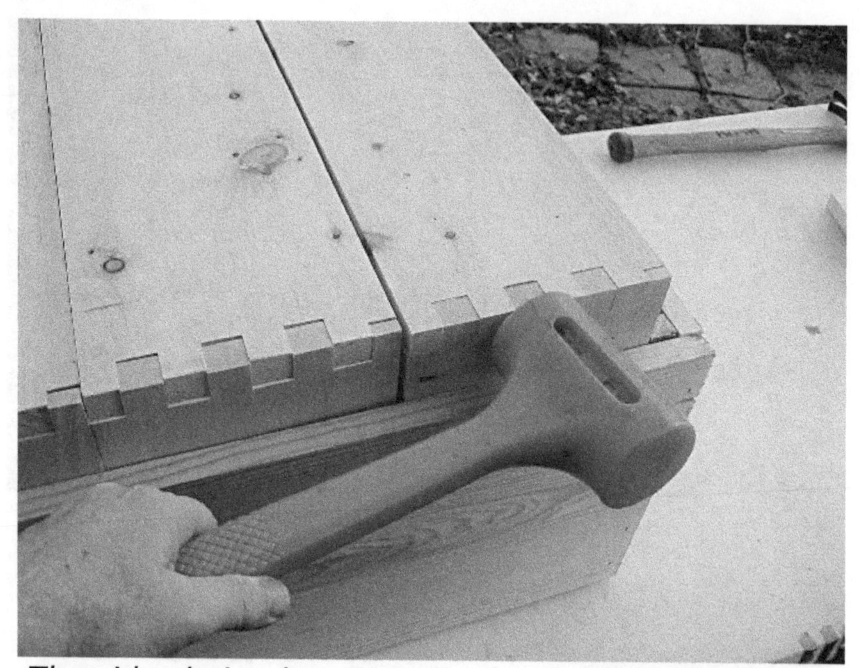

*The sides being hammered into place with a mallet*

*The sides being nailed*

*Jig being flipped to do the other side*

*Jig being removed after nailing the other side*

*Follower boards being removed from the middle of the boxes*

# Miscellaneous Equipment

Here are some odds and ends of equipment that I have modified one way or another and some other miscellaneous pictures.

***Top Clip***

*Clip to hold the top on*

This is a clip to hold the lid on. I saw one of these on a video and decided to make some to save lifting bricks. The clip catches in the hand holds. It's made of #9 galvanized steel wire.

***Hive Stand***

*Hive Stands*

zintent is to have a stand I can easily level just once for 14 hives, and be able to push them all together for the winter for warmth. The long runners are 16" apart with the front set so if the backs are in the center against each other the front edge of the hive is at the front edge of the two by four. And the back one is so that if the front is even with the front of the ends then the back is still on the two by four in the back.

***Plantain***

*Plantain*

This isn't exactly equipment, but if you get a sting it's the best thing I've found to treat it. Just take a leaf and bite it to crush it and put it on the sting as a poultice (after you scrape out the stinger of course).

If you can't find Plantain, here are my favorite sting remedies in order of preference:

1) plantain poultice
2) crushed wet aspirin poultice
3) tobacco poultice
4) baking soda poultice
5) MSG (mono sodium glutamate) poultice
6) Epsom salt poultice
7) NaCl (Salt) poultice

***Bucket Float***

*Bucket Feeder Float*

For using 5 gallon buckets for open feeders. Made from $^{1}/_{4}$" exterior glue Luan Plywood. Bees still seem to drown in feeders no matter what I do. If you do this be sure to have enough buckets that they don't pile up in the bottom trying to feed. I lose a lot less bees with more buckets than with less buckets. If there are other apiaries nearby open feeding may not be practical.

***Smoker Insert***

*Smoker Insert Smoker Insert*

This provides a constant source of oxygen for the smoker so it doesn't go out. Cut and fold out some legs on the bottom to hold it up.

***Wiring Tools***

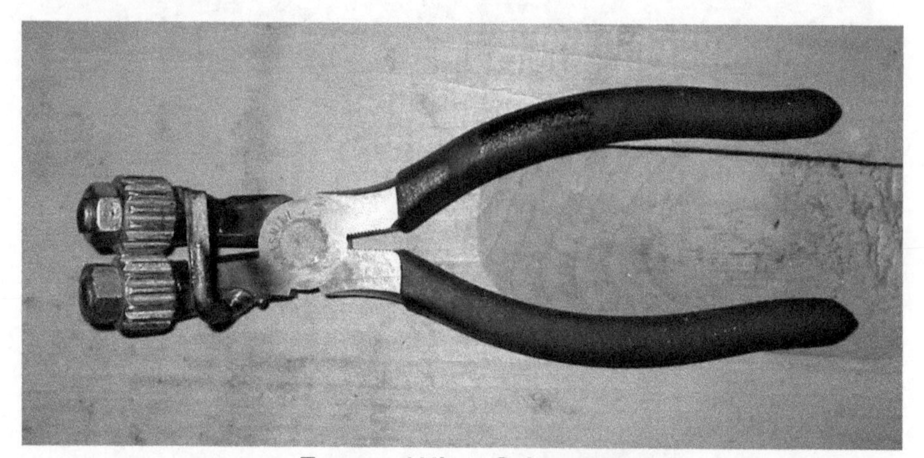

*Frame Wire Crimpers*

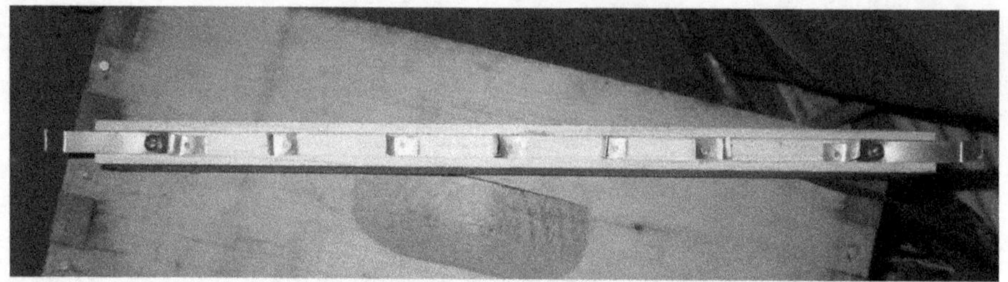

*Wire Embedder*

I bought an embedder from Walter T. Kelley but it wasn't getting the ends embedded at all and often missed spots in the center. I added all the silver metal pieces between their brass ones and now it works perfectly.

Dee Lusby convinced me to try wiring. I got frustrated with the cheap plastic crimpers. In order to squeeze tight enough to get them to work, my hands were getting bruised. So based on ones that I've seen made before, I got the local welder to weld these up. He cut the end of the lineman's pliers at a 45 degree angle and welded on two bolts for the shafts and a piece of welding rod for a stop for the wire. He just punched the threads so the nuts would stay in position. Works like a charm. I had to get used to not squeezing so hard because I now have leverage.

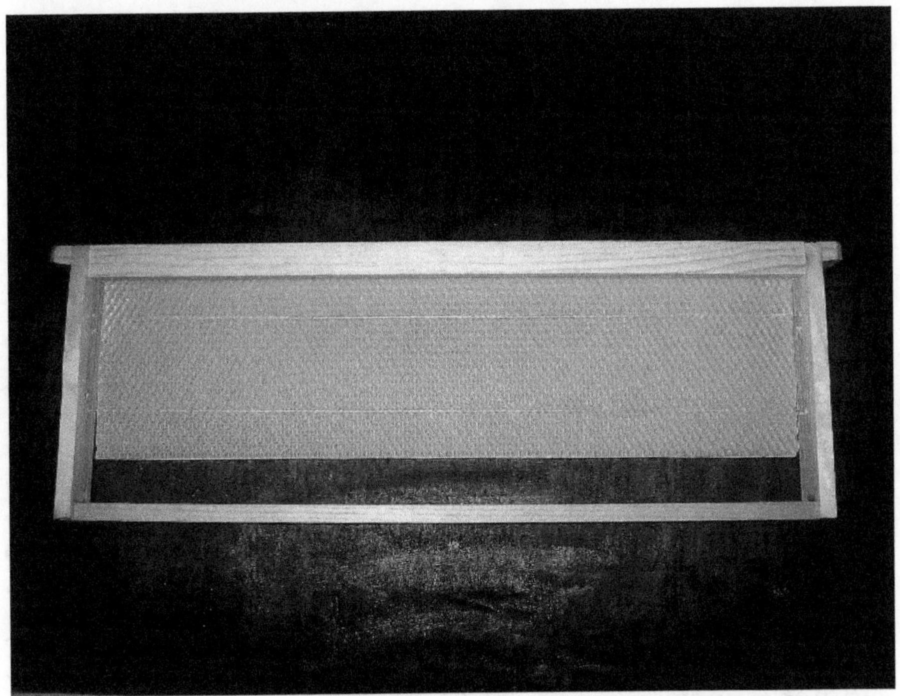

*Deep 4.9mm Foundation cut in half in medium frame*

I have used a little bit of 4.9mm foundation. Since I run all medium boxes and since it used to only come in deep I cut the foundation in half and put half in one medium frame and leave the gap at the bottom. The bees need somewhere to build what they want anyway, so I leave them a place to do it. This one has two horizontal wires and the end bars cut down to $1^1/_4$"

# Things I did *not* invent

***"Christopher Columbus, as everyone knows, is honoured by posterity because he was the last to discover America"—James Joyce***

***"The thing that has been, it is that which shall be; and that which is done is that which shall be done: and there is no new thing under the sun. Is there any thing whereof it may be said, See, this is new? it has been already of old time, which was before us."—Ecclesiastes 1:9,10***

This will be a recap of some of the things we have covered but also from time to time someone accuses me of trying to take credit for some idea or another. So just to clarify, I am not trying to take credit for inventing anything and here is a list of a few of the things that that some have accused me of taking credit for which I did *not* invent:

***Beespace***

Yes, I've actually been accused of claiming this. Not only did I not invent this (obviously the bees did) and I did not discover this (obviously it has been used for a long time), we probably don't know who did. The Greeks figured out how to space the combs to get it between the combs. Huber measured it with quite a bit of accuracy. Langstroth didn't even invent the idea of using it around frames. Jan Dzierzon did that well before Langstroth. So probably you could say the Langstroth hive was invented by Jan Dzierzon.

***Using All Mediums***

I am not sure who first tried to convince others to try it but Steve at Brushy Mountain has been suggesting this for a long time. So have many others. I'm actually a recent convert (started converting about 2003 or so after 31 years of beekeeping) I just think it's a good idea.

### ***Using 8 frame boxes***

They were invented more than 100 years ago. Probably about 150 years ago. Kim Flottum has been a proponent for a very long time. C.C. Miller, and Carl Killion also. I just think they are a good idea.

### ***Top Bar Hives***

The Greeks invented them several thousand years ago. They also invented the idea of a comb guide on the bars. I built one based on the Greek basket hive out of wood back in the 70's before I'd seen a modern one. But the idea was from the Greeks. Mine was not a long hive (I hadn't thought of that yet) so it wasn't very useful and when I saw an article in American Bee Journal in the early 80's with a picture of a Kenya Top Bar Hive I realized they had already perfected what I had tried to copy from the Greeks.

*Top Bar Hive*

***Foundationless Frames***

These have been in use for a very long time. Jan Dzierzon, Huber, Langstroth and many others had foundationless frames. All of them really based on the Greek basket hive's top bars. Something close to what I now make is in Langstroth's book and his patents and Kings books. A.I. Root and other early beekeeping supply houses manufactured them for years. More recently the late Charles Martin Simon had tried to repopularize them. I do think they are a great idea.

*Narrow Frames*

***Narrow Frames***

These have also been in use for a very long time. I can't find exact measurements on the Greek basket hives, but Huber used $1^1/_4$″ frames in the late 1700s. Many proponents over the years have used them and suggested them. Koover, more recently was a proponent. The Russians did studies on them and concluded that they had less Nosema, and more brood rearing with the narrower frames. I just think they are a good way to get small cell more quickly and, also, to get 9 frames of nice straight brood comb in my eight frame brood boxes.

***Long Hives***

I did come up with the idea when I hadn't seen one, but it was just an attempt to solve the problems of lifting full deeps for an old lady who loved bees and had a bad back. But others invented it long before I thought of it. It's an obvious idea if you're trying to solve the problem of lifting boxes. It has been around for centuries. It is still the most popular arrangement for a hive in the world, even today, and is popular from Northern Europe to the Middle East to Africa and beyond.

***Smoker Insert***

The soupcan insert that I make is just a copy, except made from a free tin can, of the one in the Rauchboy smoker. I certainly did not invent it, but I like it and simply wanted to convert all my smokers. So I made them from an old tin can. Probably someone did it before Rauchboy the same way.

***Not Painting Hives***

This was not my idea. It is, of course, an obvious step for any lazy beekeeper, but C.C. Miller, G.M. Doolittle and Richard Taylor published the concept long before I did.

> ***"Following the teachings of G. M. Doolittle, in whose ideas I have great confidence, I think there is better chance for the moisture to dry out of unpainted hives than out of painted ones. I have seen a painted hive in my cellar damp and moldy when all the unpainted ones***

***were in much better condition."—***
***C.C. Miller***

---

### *Small Cell Beekeeping*

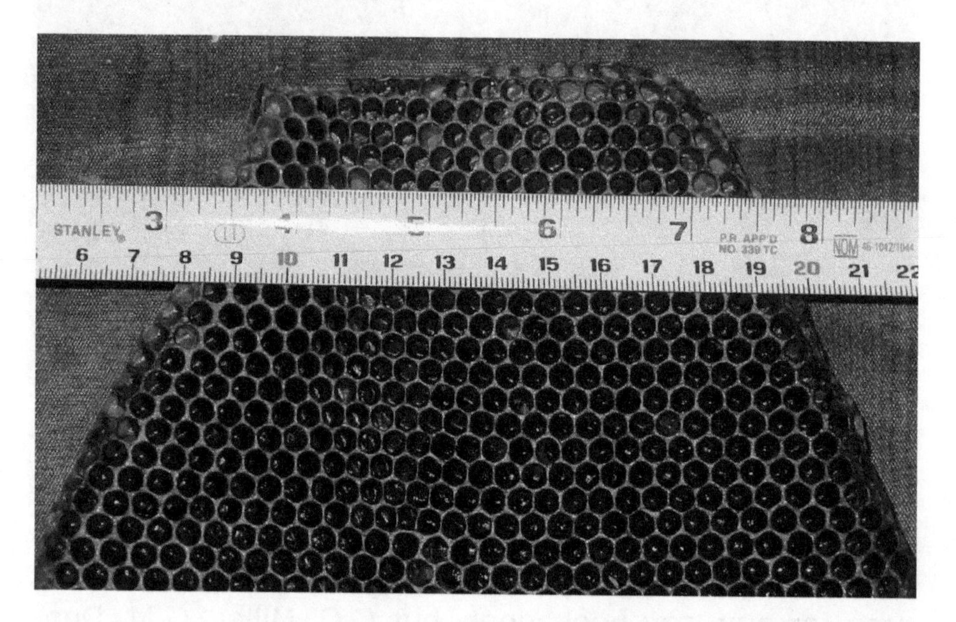


Of course the bees invented natural cell size. Lusbys, as far as I can tell, were the first to associate it with disease prevention and bee health. I'm a late player in the small cell game. Lusbys started in 1984. I started in late 2001 based on reading and lurking on www.beesource.com.

### *Top Entrances*

I'm not sure who all has tried this over the years or who to give credit to. Someone was quoting some Eastern European beekeeper who credits top entrances with all sorts of benefits that I have not observed, but I have found it a simple way to keep bees while resolving several problems I had with  and ventilation. Lloyd Spears was certainly doing it and being a proponent of it long before I came along and he is where I got the idea for using shingle shims to hold up the lid.

***Opening the Brood Nest***

I'm not sure who first tried opening the brood nest for swarm prevention. It's another mystery to me. I've been doing it for years because I read it somewhere. At first I thought I was just helping the bees keep the broodnest open because they somehow accidentally fill it with nectar, commonly called "honeybound" in the old bee books, which causes them to swarm. Eventually I began to realize it was their intention to fill it in order to swarm. But regardless of the reason. Keeping it open avoids them swarming. Various people over the years have used, encouraged, and named this various things and done variations of the implementation. The end result is still the same. An expanded brood nest that heads off swarming.

# Beekeeping Math

All of the numbers about the life cycle of bees may seem irrelevant, so let's put them in a chart here and talk about what they are useful for.

| Caste | Hatch | Cap | Emerge | | |
|---|---|---|---|---|---|
| Queen | $3^1/_2$ days | 8 days +-1 | 16 days +-1 | Laying | 28 days +-5 |
| Worker | $3^1/_2$ days | 9 days +-1 | 20 days +-1 | Foraging | 42 days +-7 |
| Drone | $3^1/_2$ days | 10 days +-1 | 24 days +-1 | Flying to DCA | 38 days +-5 |

If you find eggs, and no queen how long ago do you *know* there was a queen? At least there was one three days ago and possibly is one now. If you find just hatched larvae and open brood but no eggs when was there a queen? Four days.

If you put an excluder between two boxes and come back in four days and find eggs in one and not the other, what do you know? That the queen is in the one with eggs.

If you find a capped queen cell, how long before it should have emerged for sure? Nine days, but probably eight.

If you find a capped queen cell, how long before you should see eggs from that queen? 20-27 days.

If you killed or lost a queen, how long before you'll have a laying queen again? 24-31 days because the bees will start from a just hatched larvae.

If you start from larvae and graft, how long before you need to transfer the larvae to a mating nuc? 10 days. (day 14)

If you confine the queen to get the larvae how long before you graft? Four days because some won't have hatched at the beginning for day 3.

If you confined the queen to get the larvae how long before we have a laying queen? 28-35 days.

If a queen is killed and the bees raise a new one how much brood will be left in the hive just before the new queen starts to lay? None. It will take 24-31 days for the new queen (raised from a four day old) to be laying and in 21 days all the workers will have emerged and in 24 days all the drones will have emerged.

If the queens starts laying today how long before that brood will be foraging for honey? About 42 days.

You can see how knowing how long things take helps you predict where things are going or where things have been.

Sometimes you just have to figure best and worst case. For instance, an uncapped queen cell with a larvae in it is between four and eight days old (from the egg). A capped queen cell is between eight and sixteen days old. By looking at the tip of the cell you can tell one that is just capped (soft and white) from one that is about to emerge (brown and papery and often cleaned down to the cocoon by the workers). A soft white queen cell is between eight and twelve days old. A papery one is between thirteen and sixteen days old. The queen will emerge at sixteen (fifteen if it's hot out). She'll be laying by twenty eight days usually.

If you're unsure of them having a queen or not, see the chapter "BLUF" in Volume I.

# Unnatural Things in Beekeeping

Certainly in some ways beekeeping is always natural because, in the end, the bees tend to do what they want. But in some ways it's never natural because, in the end, we keep the bees in situations that aren't what occurs in nature.

Things that we change from nature by the way we raise bees:

Genetics:
- We breed less:
  - Defensive.
  - Swarming.
  - Propolis.
  - Burr comb.
  - Nervousness on the comb.
  - Drone rearing.
- We breed more:
  - Hoarding.
  - Spring build up and fall let down.
- We are now breeding:
  - AFB resistance.
  - More "hygienic" (meaning they tear out cells that are infested with mites or other problems)
  - Suppressed Mite Reproduction (I don't think we really know what this is except there are less mites)

Disturbances:
- Smoking.
- Opening the hive.
- Rearranging the frames.
- Confining the queen with an excluder.
- Forcing the bees through an excluder.
- Forcing the bees through a pollen trap.

Robbing honey.

Food:

Pollen substitute instead of pollen.

Sugar syrup instead of honey.

Poisons and chemicals in the hive:

Essential oils.

Organic acids (formic oxalic etc.)

Acaracides (Apistan and CheckMite)

Pesticides (from crop spraying and mosquito spraying)

Antibiotics (TM and Fumidil).

Because of embossed wax foundation:

Organization of the hive:

Cell size.

Amount of drone cells.

Orientation of cells.

Distribution of cell sizes.

Population of the hive:

We try to get less drones.

We do get less subcastes of different sizes.

Accumulated contaminates that are wax soluble.

Because of frames or bars:

Spacing between combs.

Thickness of combs.

Distribution of thickness of combs.

Accumulation of chemicals and possibly spores in the wax of the foundation.

Ventilation around the combs. Frames have gaps on the top. Natural combs are attached at the top.

Because of supers, expanding and contracting volume of the hive to prevent swarming and to overwinter.

Natural hives vary in many ways anyway, but because of hives:

Ventilation

Size

Communication inside the hive because of gaps between boxes and gaps at the top.

Condensation and absorption and distribution of condensation.

Beespaces above and on the ends where in a natural hive it is usually solid at the top with no communication there and only passages here and there at the whim of the bees elsewhere based on either convenience of movement or ventilation.

Entrance location.

Detritus at the bottom (wax scales, dead bees, wax moths etc.)

Miscellaneous:

Some clip the queen, which keeps her from making any kind of flights after she is clipped (and hopefully mated). Some of us have observed queens outside of the hive on occasion. For what reason I can only imagine, but what if it's important?

We mark the queen with some paint.

We replace the queen more often than nature does.

We often interfere with nature replacing the queen by not allowing swarming or supersedure to complete.

I'm not saying that all of these things we change are bad, nor am I saying all of these things we change are good, but if we want to create a natural sustainable way to keep bees, we do need to understand the natural sustainable way the bees keep themselves. I would like to see research on the effects, both good and bad, that all of these changes we have made have on natural balance of the colony of bees and their parasites.

## Scientific Studies

***Quotes***

> ***"The bulk of the world's knowledge is an imaginary construction."— Helen Keller***
>
> ***"One does not divine the ways of nature, it lays out methods that confound our science, and it is only by studying it carefully that we may succeed in unveiling some of its mysteries."-- Huber, New Observations on Bees Volume II***
>
> ***"It will be readily appreciated that in the course of many years and daily contact with bees, the professional bee-keeper will of necessity gain a knowledge and insight into the mysterious ways of the honeybee, usually denied to the scientist in the laboratory and the amateur in possession of a few colonies. Indeed, a limited practical experience will inevitably lead to views and conclusions, which are often completely at variance to the findings of a wide practical nature. The professional bee-keeper is at all times compelled to assess things realistically and to keep an open mind in regard to every problem he may be confronted with. He is also***

***forced to base his methods of management on concrete results and must sharply differentiate between essentials and inessentials."—Beekeeping at Buckfast Abbey, Brother Adam***

***"Use only that which works, and take it from any place you can find it."—Bruce Lee***

***"I never learned from a man who agreed with me."— Robert A. Heinlein***

---

I love scientific studies. I have read many of them on many subjects from cover to cover. There is much to be learned by them. I often disagree with the conclusions drawn by the researchers though.

*Post hoc ergo proptor hoc* (After this therefore because of this) is the primary error in logic and is a trap fallen into by humans and animals alike. The big temptation of this error is that "Post hoc ergo proptor hoc" is a good basis for a theory. The error isn't using it for a theory it's using it as proof.

Let's examine the error of this, first. Every morning at my house, the roosters crow. Every morning after the roosters crow, the sun comes up. Does this mean that the roosters cause the sun to come up? Because we can't see any mechanism to connect them other than the sequence of events, most of us would assume that the roosters are not the cause.

Every culture I know of has folk tales and or jokes to make fun of this error. One in our culture is "pull my finger". Because you pull the finger and immediately afterwards something happens, your brain makes a connection and for a second you fall prey to this error. Then after a second or two your brain catches up with its processing and the absurdity of that connection hits you and you laugh. The Africans often tell the "roosters causing the sun to come up" story and the Lakota tell it as the horses whinnying. Foolish anthropologists often record these stories as if the people telling them believe this connection, but my experience with primitive cultures is that they tell these stories to teach the error of that way of thinking. Of course they watch to see if the anthropologists believe the foolish conclusion and after watching them diligently write it down without so much as a comment, or a chuckle the natives shake their heads at the foolishness.

I have done things while driving that were immediately followed by some noise. My first conclusion is that I caused the noise and I'm wondering what it is I've caused. After trying a couple of more times and the noise does not follow it, I find out it was one of my children making the noise. It was mere coincidence that they happened simultaneously.

Any "statistical proof" really constitutes no proof. As I collect a larger and larger sample it becomes more and more likely that what I'm seeing statistically is an actual connection and not a coincidence, but it never constitutes analytical proof. Unless I have a mechanism and can prove that mechanism is the cause, by some means other than simple statistics, then I only have an increasing likelihood.

I can prove this to anyone who understands basic probability. What are the odds that if I flip this quarter it will land on heads? 50/50. So I flip it and it comes up heads. What are the odds if I flip this quarter again that it will come up heads again? 50/50 same as before. So I flip it and it comes up heads. I personally have flipped a quarter 27 times in a row and got heads every time.

Does this prove that the odds are not 50/50? No it proves my sample was too small to be statistically valid. How many times do I have to flip it before my results are an absolute fact? No matter how many times I do it, I only get closer and closer to the actual answer. It is not a matter of absolute proof but a matter of accumulating a large enough sample. The larger the sample the closer I get to the answer, but it's like the old math problem of going half way and half the remaining way and half of that and so on. When will I get to the end? Never. I can only get closer and closer.

This was just trying to prove that flipping a quarter has odds of 50/50. The life cycle of any organism is infinitely more complex than flipping a quarter and affected by more things than we can know. If I do a certain thing and get a certain result how many times will it take to prove absolutely that what I did contributed to that result? If I have a very large sample and I have a very large success rate compared to a very large control group with a very small success rate, it is very likely that my theory is correct. The smaller the sample, the smaller the difference in success rate and the more other variables that could contribute to success or failure, or even worse, the more skewed those variables are in favor of either group, the less valid my results are.

> ***"The least movement is of importance to all nature. The entire ocean is affected by a pebble." — Blaise Pascal***

This is all assuming a lack of prejudice on the part of the researcher. As one of my teachers (he was a carpenter with a lot of wisdom, not a professor) once said, "everyone thinks their idea is better because they thought of it". This seems intuitively obvious, but it is important. I have a natural prejudice to my ideas because they fit my way of thinking. If they didn't, I wouldn't have thought of them! This is why in the scientific community it is important to be able to reproduce the results. Reproducibility is a good test, especially if someone else is doing the second or third study than did the first. It may eliminate some of the prejudice and also it may change some of the other unmeasured and unaccounted for variables.

The second problem with research is the motivation for doing it. The motivation for doing research is almost (but not always) personal gain. A few actual altruistic people have a love of some fellow creature, or some fellow humans and are actually involved because they want to reduce suffering or solve someone's problems. Unfortunately these people are not well funded and their research is usually not well received. I'm not saying every researcher is consciously prejudiced, but even a college professor with no other stake in the outcome needs to get published now and then.

A lot of research is funded by and prejudiced by some entity that has an agenda to prove their solution and that solution has to be something they can market and sell, preferable with a patent or copyright or some other protection to provide them with a monopoly. There is no profit in, and therefore no money for, research into simple common solutions to problems.

I'm sure some will disagree with me, but I think some entities, such as the USDA, have their own agenda that has been revealed by observing them over time. The big agenda of any government agency is to get more money, more power and try to appear that they are serving the purpose they were put there for. In the case of the USDA, it's obvious they have favored chemicals over natural solutions. They favor anything that appears to help the economy of agribusiness. This doesn't mean just the small farmer/beekeeper etc. but the whole of agribusiness. They seem to like to see money changing hands because it helps the economy.

Just because research was done on a subject and the researchers came to some conclusion, does not make that conclusion the truth.

Now, while we are talking about facts, let's talk about one of the reasons some people do not like science and prefer their own opinions. I covered one above, which is that we always like our own ideas because they fit our way of thinking, but the other is that people are fond of saying that something has not been proven scientifically as if that means it is *not* true because it has *not* been proven. Anything we have not proven is simply something that has not been proven. Because I have not proven it true does not make it false.

In 1847 Dr. Ignaz Philipp Semmelwis instituted the practice of hand washing before delivering babies. He came to this conclusion simply by the statistical evidence that mothers and babies who were attended by doctors who washed had less mortality than ones attended by doctors who did not wash. This was "Post hoc ergo proptor hoc"—the doctors washed and less mothers and babies died. This is not scientific proof and therefore his colleagues did not consider it scientific proof. Why? Because he could not provide a mechanism to explain it nor an experiment to prove that mechanism. Because he was a proponent of something he could not prove absolutely, he was driven out of the medical community as a quack. This is an example of something that had not been proven scientifically.

In the 1850's when Louis Pasteur and Robert Koch created the science of microbiology and the "germ theory" of disease Dr Semmelwis's theory finally was proven scientifically. Now there was a mechanism and they were able to create experiments to prove that mechanism. My point is, that it was true before they proved it and it was true after they proved it. The truth did not change because they proved it. There was, previous to this proof, evidence that would lead to the practice of hand washing, but not proof.

We live our lives and make decisions all the time based on our view of the world. This view is not truth, but it is based on our experience and our learning. Sometimes something comes along to change that view and we accept it because the evidence is strong enough. To ignore evidence that fits the pattern of what we see around us because it has not been proven is foolish. To ignorantly hang on to things that are proven to not be true is equally foolish. But just because the majority believe something to be proven does not mean has been. Just because the majority of people believe something is true does not make it true.

I would say, read research with a grain of salt. Look at their methods. Think about the contributing issues that they have overlooked. Pay attention to anything that would skew the population they are studying or the population of the control group. Look into whether or not the study has been duplicated and were the results similar or contrary. What was the size of the population? What was the difference in success? If there is only a small difference it may not be statistically important. Even if there is a large difference, was it duplicated at that large a difference? Also what might be the prejudices of the people doing the research?

***Not Proven Scientifically.***

Back to this. I often hear this quoted as if it proves something is not true: "it has not been proven scientifically" or some variation. This is often quoted as if lack of proof of something proves it wrong. Apparently they have not been paying much attention to history. What is "known" today and what is "not proven" today changes on a day by day basis. A "known fact" today is tomorrows "folly". A "folly" today is tomorrow's "known fact". I find it more useful to make my own observations and draw my own conclusions. But let's try one little glimpse of history and "waiting for scientific proof":

1604 "A Counterblaste to Tobacco" is written by King James I of England and he complains about passive smoking and warns of dangers to the lungs. There is, of course, no scientific basis for his beliefs.

1623-1640 Murad IV, sultan of the Ottoman Empire attempts to ban smoking by claiming it was a threat to public health. There is, of course, no scientific evidence. Just his observation.

1798 Physician (and Declaration of Independence signatory) Benjamin Rush claims tobacco use negatively impacts one's health, including causing cancer based merely on his personal observation and, of course, no scientific studies to support it.

1929 Fritz Lickint of Dresden, Germany, published a formal document showing statistical evidence of a lung cancer-tobacco link but this, of course, is merely a statistical correlation and not considered scientific proof as it's merely "post hoc ergo proptor hoc".

1948 British physiologist Richard Doll published the first major studies that "proved" that smoking could cause serious health damage. Of course the tobacco industry insists that it is not proof by the "scientific method" because there is no mechanism presented as to how it could cause it.

1950 Journal of the American Medical Association publishes its first major study definitively linking smoking to lung cancer. It is, of course, still only a statistical link but it is a statistically significant number.

1953 Dr. Ernst L. Wynder uncovers the first definitive biological link between smoking and cancer.

1957 Surgeon General Leroy E. Burney issues "Joint Report of Study Group on Smoking and Health," the first official statement on smoking by the Public Health Service.

1965 Congress passes the Federal Cigarette Labeling and Advertising Act requiring the surgeon general's warnings on cigarette packages.

**At what point would you quit smoking?**

***Differences in observations in general and as an example, differences in cell size observations.***

> ***"Contradiction is not a sign of falsity, nor the lack of contradiction a sign of truth." —Blaise Pascal***
>
> ***"People are usually more convinced by reasons they discovered themselves than by those found by others."—Blaise Pascal***

I've always been a bit amazed and amused that everyone always seems to think that on any issue one person is wrong and the other is right. Especially when that difference is based on each person's observations, and most especially when it relates to something as complex as bees. I'd be far more surprised if everyone's observations always agreed.

Bees are complex animals and what they do depends not only on the bees themselves but the stage of development the bee themselves are in and the stage of development the hive is in and the stage of development that the seasons are in and the stages of development that the surrounding vegetation is in. In other words, in almost anything related to beekeeping the results of almost any measurement or any manipulation will depend on everything else. There may be some generalizations you can make but it's amazing how often when you think you have one that's a sure thing it doesn't apply in circumstances that differ. What happens in a spring build up, a flow, a fall wind down, a dearth, a hive with brood, without brood, with a laying queen, a virgin queen, no queen etc. varies greatly. I'm not saying I can explain any difference in observation myself, but I have no doubt that the people involved have no motivation to lie to me on the matter.

Of course if we want to compare observations we need to try to equalize some of these things as well as making sure we are measuring the same thing. For instance, if we are measuring cell size are we averaging in anything smaller than a drone cell? Or are we averaging in anything that actually has brood in it? Or are we just measuring the core of the brood nest? Are we trying to establish a range? Or a mean? Are we measuring in the same manner, i.e. are we measuring across the flats or across the points? But still we have differences in observations.

In the case of cell size of natural drawn comb we have Dee Lusby's observation that the worker comb is very uniform in size, and Dennis Murrel's observation that they follow a pattern of small in the center and larger on the edges, with the largest along the top. We have mine, which is similar, but not identical to Dennis's. We have Tom Seeley who says:

> ***"The basic nest organization is honey storage above, brood nest below, and pollen storage in between. Associated with this arrangement are differences in comb structure. Compared to combs used for honey storage, combs of the brood nest are generally darker and more uniform in width and in cell form.*** Drone ***comb is located on the brood nest's periphery." (T. D. Seeley and R. A. Morse, 1976)***

Which sounds very similar to Dennis's and my observations, that there are honey storage cells and they are not the same as the brood cells.

**Langstroth said:**

> ***"The size of the cells in which the workers are reared never varies"***

Does this mean that Dee is mistaken? Dishonest? I think not. I've gone to Arizona and looked at the comb from cutouts she's done with the bees still on the comb and the comb in "swarm ketching frames" and the sizes are very uniform. So why are hers different? I have no idea. But my point is that she is reporting accurately what she sees. Dennis has had, in the past, the pictures and maps of measurements and cells sizes on his web site, so either he's quite a wiz at manufacturing pictures or he's honestly sharing what he's seen. Since it is more similar to what I see, and since I know him to be a straightforward guy, I believe it's just what he's seeing. I ask people doing cutouts, all the time, to report what they find as far as cell size and we see a lot of it in the area of 5.2mm and a lot of it in the area of 4.9mm. Is one of them wrong and one of them right? I don't think so. I think they are reporting what they find.

**As far as varying cell size:**

> ***"...a continuous range of behaviors and cell size measurements was noted between colonies considered "strongly European" and "strongly Africanized". "***
>
> ***"Due to the high degree of variation within and among feral and managed populations of Africanized bees, it is emphasized that the most effective solution to the Africanized "problem", in areas where Africanized bees have established permanent populations, is to consistently select for the most gentle and productive colonies among the existing honey bee population"—Marla Spivak — Identification and relative success of Africanized and European honey bees in Costa Rica. Spivak, M—Do measurements of worker cell size reliably distinguish Africanized from European honey bees (Apis mellifera L.)?. Spivak, M; Erickson, E.H., Jr.***

---

***Discounting scientific studies***

> ***"'Tis with our judgments as our watches, none go just alike, yet each believes his own." —Alexander Pope***
>
> ***"When we wish to correct with advantage and to show another that he errs, we must notice from what side he views the matter, for on that side it is usually true, and admit that truth to him, but reveal to him the side on which it is false. He is satisfied with that, for he sees that he was not mistaken and that he only failed to see all sides. Now, no one is offended at not seeing everything; but one does not like to be mistaken, and that perhaps arises from the fact that man naturally cannot see everything, and that naturally he cannot err in the side he looks at, since the perceptions of our senses are always true." —Blaise Pascal***
>
> ***"There is something fascinating about science. One gets such wholesale returns of conjecture out of such trifling investment of fact."—Mark Twain***

---

Seems like there are many who accuse people of simply trying to discount a study because they don't agree with it. Maybe for someone who has done nothing in the realm of trying to measure the thing that was in the study, this might be a valid accusation. However, I find that *everyone* does this in matters where the study disagrees with their personal experiences. *As they should!*

Even the "Scientifically minded" among us seem to discount more studies than they will accept in any given argument. Either they think the conclusion was unwarranted, the numbers were insignificant or the experiment just poorly designed, most will discount any study when its results are contrary to their own experience. The fact is your own experience was in a context of your actual application (*i.e.* your climate, your beeyard, your race of bees, your system of beekeeping) where the study was an attempt to control everything possible and probably was done either in a climate different from yours or some other circumstance different that yours. So your honest, and sincere response to this is to try to find that difference and point it out in order to explain the differences in outcome.

If anyone has paid any attention to scientific studies over the last few years, let alone the last few decades, let alone the last few centuries, you'll see that the results often vacillate between two opposite conclusions every other year or so. How many medications have been proven safe in a scientific study only to be pulled off the market after less than a year of use in the field? How many times has caffeine been proven good for you, bad for you and good for you again? Or chocolate? Anyone remember when doctors almost uniformly advised against eating it? Now it's an antioxidant that, according to a scientific study in Holland, will halve the chances of an over 50 male dying.

Only the foolish follow the results of scientific studies without question. The prudent hold them up against personal experience and common sense.

## Worldview

Since World View has a lot to do with this, I'll share a little more about my view of the world.

I think the world is too complex for anyone to ever grasp. It's why we create our own "view of the world". It gives us a basic framework within which to make decisions and solve problems. None of us can comprehend the whole thing, so all of us have, at best a very incomplete world view and at worse a very erroneous worldview.

## Empirical Vs Statistical

I am much in favor of the "scientific method". Especially if it is actually followed. There was a time in the "scientific world" that anything less than empirical truth was ignored. But, partly because of the previously mentioned faux paux where doctors ran off a brilliant doctor for proposing something based on statistical evidence (washing hands before delivering babies or performing surgery), the current trend in science and medicine is to actually give some credence to statistical evidence. Sometimes to a degree that is not entirely reasonable.

As I mentioned in the "flipping a quarter" illustration, sometimes the statistics we have gathered are skewed by simple random chance. Sometimes the results are skewed by other factors also. It is one of the reasons that scientists in the past discounted statistical evidence and insisted on empirical evidence.

In the case of some statistical issues, the sample is large (sometimes an entire country or continent) the other factors are well averaged out and the differences in the results are large. For instance, women who smoke are twelve times more likely to die of lung cancer than women who don't smoke. This is not an insignificant number. If it were twice as many it would be pretty significant, but twelve times as many is very significant. When these numbers are from a very large sampling it becomes even more significant.

On the other hand this is not empirical evidence. If all we did was collect the statistics then we only have a *"post hoc ergo proptor hoc"* situation. Still it's too big to ignore. But then there are studies as to how the constituents of tobacco smoke cause cellular changes and eventually cancer. This study has more empirical evidence by the fact that we can expose cells to the substances in tobacco and see the changes. And we have studied it to the point of knowing how some of those chemicals cause some of those changes.

There is not time in my lifetime to do as extensive of experimentation as the cancer studies on every aspect of everything I'm involved in. In fact there probably isn't even time to read every study that's already been done. What I (and everyone else) have done as I process my experiences I have, is look for patterns. The patterns are the trail that leads us down paths of experimentation. They are how a scientist comes up with a theory. We see a pattern that this is the general way most things work and come up with a theory based on the pattern continuing into the realm we are studying. Sometimes the difference between one course of action and another are insignificant enough not to warrant too much work and investigation. Sometimes, especially when difficulties arise, it is worth trying to discover the cause of the difficulties. This is the time to study something and apply scientific methods to discovering a solution.

Let's try this from a simple personal view. If I touch some glowing hot metal and my finger hurts and gets a blister, is that empirical evidence that touching glowing hot metal burns my finger? If all I know is "I touched that metal and my finger hurt" then no, it does not. But I have some other things to consider. One is that I know a bit about the metal. I know that it had been heated and know that I could feel heat coming off of it. Also I know that when I apply heat to other things they combust or they melt or they are damaged in other ways. Therefore, it is reasonable for me to believe that the metal caused the burn because I not only have a chronological connection (one followed the other) but a mechanism. I have observed other things burning when they are hot, so it's reasonable to assume it is the heat (not the metal) that caused my pain. It would be reasonable for me not to touch the metal again when it is hot. On the other hand, if I'm not paying attention to the details and I come to the erroneous conclusion that touching metal burns my finger and don't take into account the mechanism (the heat in the metal) I might go through my life never touching metal again. This may seem silly, but other situations are often much more complex than the metal and finger situation and a significant aspect of this other situation goes unnoticed and we go through life with an erroneous belief.

Often there is not time to really be scientific. When your bees are dying, for instance, you may, out of desperation, try several things at the same time and they may get well. If you do, you will never know for sure what, if any of those several things made any difference. Even if you try only one thing, you won't really know if it made a difference or they would have recovered anyway.

A woman I know is fond of saying "the method of potty training you tried just before your child succeeds is the one you'll swear by". Her point is they would have gotten potty trained with or without your help, but you will be certain your method was the cause *("post hoc")*.

When you go to the doctor and get medicine and then you get well, you'll probably think it was the medicine. Statistically there was, with or without the medicine, a 99% chance you would get well, but you will credit what you did just before as the cause of your recovery. Conversely if you take the medicine and get worse you will blame the medicine. Statistically this is more likely. According to a recent study from the National Academy Institute of Medicine, each year more people die from medical errors than from motor vehicle accidents (43,458), breast cancer (42,297), or AIDS (16,516). So odds are it *was* the medicine. But it is not a known fact unless we do far more research. These kinds of simple conclusions, not based on enough evidence to be scientific, are often what we live by because we never have the time, the energy or the opportunity to do a large enough sample to come to any significant conclusions. These conclusions are not scientific, and are sometimes wrong, but they are quite often correct conclusions also.

## Natural Things

I admit to being prejudiced toward things that are natural. This is not just some fanatical belief with no basis, it is based on my experience and observation. It is one of the patterns I have observed. Over time I have seen many nonnatural solutions to problems fail miserably. Sometimes with catastrophic consequences.

When I was young, science was going to solve all of our problems. Cure all of the diseases, give us vaccinations for everything. They were going to eradicate (does this word sound familiar?) flies, mosquitoes, mice, rats and prairie dogs. Humans had been pretty successful at eradicating things like bears and wolves (of course it wasn't science it was 14 year old kids collecting bounties for the ears). The result of this thinking was DDT being sprayed everywhere, rat poison spread extensively and the near annihilation of every raptor on the continent, not to mention all of the predators of the prairie dogs. Of course there wasn't even a significant dent in the mosquitoes, rats, mice or flies. This is but one in a series of many "scientific" fiascoes.

I have found that not only are doctors and scientists often mistaken they are often doing the opposite of what should be done. I realize this will open another can of worms, but I am a Lakota Sundancer. Going for four days and nights with no food and no water dancing from sunup to sundown in weather that is often well over 100 degrees Fahrenheit, I have seen many cases of heat exhaustion, and have had a severe case of it on two occasions myself. These are people with hot dry skin, nauseated, vomiting, and confused. There is only one cure that I've seen work and I've never seen it fail. This is on people who still don't get anything to drink and turn around and dance for two more days. These are people who quit sweating at least a day ago because there wasn't anything left to sweat. If I took any of these people to a medical doctor they would immediately try to cool them down. When you have heat stroke your body gets confused and can't decide what to do. The body starts heating you up because it's not sure which way to go. The intuitively obvious thing to do is cool them down. This fails quite often. When doctors use the "cooling down" treatment people often die. Literally hundreds of people die in one large city in one heat wave and these people have access to water, access to medical care and their bodies have enough moisture to sweat. The first time I had heat exhaustion I sat in the Niobrara River for some time with no relief at all.

The treatment that I have never seen fail, is to put the person in a very hot, very wet, very short sweat. This means you take them in a small hut with red hot rocks, close it up and pour the water on the rocks, making lots of steam, until the place is so hot you can't stand it. The effects on the body are immediate. First the body immediately realizes that it is hot. How could it be confused when the air is approaching the boiling point? The second thing that happens is the skin is covered with condensation. When they get out, the body is now convinced to accept the cooling and the water is there to help do the job. I do not think I will ever hear of a scientific study as to the efficacy of this treatment, because it goes against their view of the world.

Doctors have the view that whatever the body is doing that they don't want, they will try to force it to stop. I have the view that whatever my body is trying to do I will help it do it until it decides to stop. When I have a fever I either get in as hot a tub of water as I can stand or a sweat or a sauna. If the body wants a fever I help it have one. I do not take aspirin or anything else unless the fever persists after the sweat or sauna, which, in my case, it has not done.

Following nature and working with it is my view of the world. It is based on my experiences. It's true that sometimes our experiences lead us in the wrong direction and lead us to erroneous conclusions, but more often they help us learn about the patterns of what is around us.

**Paradigms.**

> ***"All models are wrong, but some are useful" —George E.P. Box***

Part of the problem with all this is that any model we have is incomplete. A new word has crept into our language. It has probably been there for awhile, but now it is moving into the mainstream. We computer programmers use it a lot. It is "paradigm" (pronounced para dime usually and sometimes para dim). To put it simply, a paradigm is a point of view, a model, a simplified way of looking at a particular problem that allows us to solve it.

An example would be Newtonian physics. Newtonian physics is a set of mathematical rules that allows us to predict things like the path of a bullet, the amount of energy in a car wreck or the motion of the planets. In short, it solves most problems to do with motion and energy at speeds well below the speed of light. It is a useful paradigm. It is still used daily and taught in High School and College, because of its usefulness.

The problem with it is that it isn't true. For years it was accepted as indisputable truth, until some evidence turned up, to contradict it. The evidence was usually at the atomic level, and at close to light speed, but it was hard to refute. These atomic level and light speed problems remained insolvable until Einstein, a mathematician (who flunked math in school), with no degree in physics, threw out the Newtonian paradigm and proposed the Relativity paradigm. This then stood as truth (in spite of the fact that most problems were still much easier to solve by the Newtonian paradigm and are still being solved that way) until other contradictions forced another shift and a new paradigm, Quantum physics.

Einstein took a lot of flack for throwing out Newtonian physics. It was accepted as absolute truth and he questioned it. But no one could solve these light speed problems until they threw out the old paradigm and found a new one that worked.

***"Always listen to experts. They'll tell you what can't be done, and why. Then do it."— Robert A. Heinlein***

***"What we need to discover is often effectively blocked by what we know already."—Paul Mace, author of "Mace Utilities"***

---

This method of problem solving is called a paradigm shift. The biggest block to the next paradigm is holding on, too tightly, to the last.

This is the purpose of the paradigm shift. To throw out (at least temporarily) what we know already so it won't block us off from what we need to discover.

The classic paradigm for our relationship to the sun is that the sun rises in the east and sets in the west. This paradigm is quite useful for figuring out what direction I'm walking and what direction to face my barn, house, beehives or tipi. In fact most anything that is terrestrial it works fine. However it fails miserably when trying to explain what is happening in our solar system.

For that we tend to rely instead on Galileo's paradigm, Copernicanism, which says that the sun is the center of the solar system and that it is fixed and we circle around it and spin. It's our spinning that causes the illusion that the sun comes up in the east and goes down in the west. Of course it doesn't really, and yet we will often state it as an absolute fact that it does come up in the east. You see from our point of view, here on the earth, it does.

So is the classic model that the sun comes up in the east true? No. Is it useful? Yes. Is Galileo's model true? No. The sun isn't fixed, it's actually hurtling through space, but from our solar system's point of view it appears to be true and when dealing with things only within our solar system it's a pretty useful model.

Our view of the world is a series of paradigms that we have adopted. We often confuse this worldview and these paradigms with truth. But in order to be true it would have to be the universe itself. The whole point of the paradigm is to make a simple, abstract model. To isolate the essential elements to make a solution possible to grasp. So by its nature a paradigm will never be the whole truth, because the whole truth is infinite, and we would be overwhelmed.

The danger of paradigms is that we confuse them with truth. They aren't. When the paradigm we have doesn't work it's time for a paradigm shift. Borrow another worldview. Make one up from scratch, but be willing to put aside the one that doesn't work.

One paradigm (made up of many smaller ones) is philosophy. It's great for the "Big Questions" like "Why am I here?" "Where am I going?", but it's lousy for fixing your car.

Another paradigm is the "Scientific Method." Great for fixing your car, worthless for building relationships.

***Scientific numerics in complex systems***

## It's not that simple

I realize everyone would like to think what they are measuring is scientific. Things like weight, temperature, volume are simple to quantify and therefore seem very scientific when trying to prove something one way or the other. The problem is that even fairly simple systems are more complicated than just a simple measurement. We often express these more complex things with vague statements such as "it's not heavy, it's just awkward". This is a way of expressing that although we know (from a scientific point of view) that if we put this item on a scale it will not say that it weighs much more than objects that we can easily lift, this object is very difficult to lift. We feel that weight should translate into how difficult it is to lift, but we also know that the reality is that it doesn't.

***Weight as an example***

Weight is only one aspect of how difficult something is to lift. Any object where we end up with a lot of weight a long ways from our body is "awkward". The leverage of the weight is against us in such a way as to put far more stress on our backs than the weight of the object would seem to indicate. That's because how difficult something is to lift or move, is not just about weight. It's about leverage and mechanical advantage and disadvantage. It's also about how quickly we can set the object down or how gently we have to set the object down.

Moving fifty pound bags of grain where I can drop them or throw them into a pile, is much easier than fifty pound boxes of bees and honey that need to be set down gently. It's also about how far we have to bend over to get to it and how far we have to bend over to set it down. Weight is only one small aspect of the whole issue.

An eight frame box is much easier to handle than its weight would indicate. True it weighs less than a ten frame box of otherwise equal circumstances (full of honey, same depth etc.), but the weight you eliminated was the two frames furthest from your body, meaning that the mechanical disadvantage of those two frames was much greater than the rest of them. So looking at it from one simple measurement (weight) is misleading.

We need to take into account many other things. These are things that probably can be quantified, but doing so is much more complex. Trying to figure out the "mechanical weight" (meaning the weight times the mechanical advantage or disadvantage) is much more complicated than just putting it on a scale and weighing it.

***Overwintering as another example***

I bring this up, not just to talk about boxes, but about things in general and about other things like the thermodynamics of a wintering hive. I am not attempting here to explain the answer to the thermodynamics of a hive, but merely to try to outline the question and show that the metrics are more complicated than they first appear. Let's see how many significant aspects of the thermodynamics of a wintering hive we can list:

• **Temperature**. This is the simple one. It's easy to measure temperature by putting a thermometer where you want to measure it. Measure the temperature of the distant points in the hive and in the cluster and on the edge of the cluster and outside the hive. These are the "facts" usually used to try to explain the thermodynamics of a winter hive. These facts are one very small piece of the whole picture.

• **Heat production.** The cluster is producing heat. You can argue all day that they don't heat the hive, and obviously that is not their intent, but they do produce heat in the hive and that heat dissipates into the hive and, depending on other factors, into the outside, at some rate. This is a "thermostatically" controlled source of heat in that the bees will produce more heat as the temperatures decline to make up for heat loss, or less as it warms up. The temperature in your house is the same with the back door open or closed, but that doesn't mean that leaving it open doesn't matter. A thermostatically controlled environment can be misleading when we try to measure it in temperature and don't take into account heat loss.

• **Respiration.** There is a change in humidity in the hive caused by the metabolic processes of the bees. This water is put into the air by respiration. It is warm and moist air. This changes the humidity and the humidity changes other aspects.

• **Humidity.** The moisture in the air changes many other aspects of the thermodynamics as it causes more heat transfer by convection, more heat that is stored by the air, more condensation and less evaporation. We express this difference when referring to the weather in things like "it was hot but it was a dry heat" or "it wasn't the cold, it was the dampness".

• **Condensation.** Condensation of water gives off heat. There is water condensing on the cold sides and lid of the hive all through the winter and this affects the temperature. Condensation is caused by a temperature difference between a surface and the air contacting that surface. It occurs when the humidity of the air is high enough that when the air is cooled on the surface, the air (now cooler) can no longer hold that amount of humidity.

• **Evaporation.** Water that has condensed and run down the sides to the bottom or dripped on the bees, evaporates. This absorbs heat as it evaporates. Wet bees have to burn up a huge amount of energy to evaporate water that has dripped on them. Puddles of water on the bottom continue to absorb heat until they evaporate.

• **Thermal Mass.** The mass of all of the honey in the hive holds heat and dissipates heat over time. It changes the time period over which changes in temperatures occur. It holds a lot of the heat that is in the hive. A lot of cold honey can keep a hive cold even when it's warm out. A lot of warm honey can keep a hive warmer even when it's cold out. It moderates the effects of temperature changes and it holds and gives off heat. This is more related to the amount of heat in the system than the temperature. A large mass of moderate temperature may actually hold more heat than a small mass of higher temperature.

- **Air Exchange.** I am splitting this out from convection, although convection is involved, because I am differentiating an exchange of air with the outside as opposed to convection taking place within the hive. Outside air coming into the hive is essential to the bees having enough oxygen for aerobic metabolism , but the more of it there is the more it affects the temperatures in the hive. If this is minimized during winter, the temperature in the hive will exceed the temperature outside the hive. If it is too minimized the bees will suffocate. If it is too maximized the bees will have to work much harder to maintain the heat of the cluster. Even if you were to increase this gradually to the point of the inside and outside temperatures being indistinguishable, more air exchange from that point would not change the temperatures, inside, outside or of the cluster but *will* cause more heat loss to the cluster thereby causing them to make more heat to compensate. If you rely only on measuring temperature you will not see this difference.

- **Convection** within the hive. Convection is how an object with some thermal mass and therefore some kinetic heat, loses its heat to the air. The air on the surface either picks up or gives off heat (depending on the direction of the heat difference) and if the air heats up it rises bringing more cool air into its place. If it cools it sinks bringing more warm air into its place. Things that block air or divide it into layers will add to warmth. That's how things like blankets and quilts work. They create dead space where the air can't move so easily. A vacuum thermos works on the principle that if there is no air, it can't carry away the heat by convection. The more open space there is in the hive, the more convection can take place. The more you limit things to layers the less convection takes place. We sometimes refer to an excess of convection in our houses as "it was 70 degrees in the house but it was drafty".

• **Conduction.** Conduction is how the heat moves through an object. Take the outside wall of a hive. At night if it's colder outside, it absorbs heat from the inside that comes from convection (warmer air against its surface) and heat from radiation (heat radiating from the cluster) and that heat warms the wood. The rate at which that heat moves through the wood to the outside is its conductivity. The heat is conducted to the outside where convection carries off the heat from the surface. On a sunny day on the South side, the sun will heat the wall, the heat will move by conduction through the wall to the inside where convection will transfer the heat to the air. Insulation or Styrofoam hives will slow down conduction.

• **Radiation.** Radiation is the process in which energy is emitted by one body, transmitted through an intervening medium or space without significantly affecting the temperature of the medium, and absorbed by another body. A heat lamp or heat from a fire are tangible examples of this. In the case of a wintering hive the two main sources of radiant heat are the cluster and the sun. During a sunny day the radiant heat of the sun hits the side of the hive and turns into kinetic heat and is transferred by conduction to the inside of the hive. The radiant heat from the cluster hits the surrounding combs of honey and walls, cover and bottom. Some is absorbed by the honey and walls, and some is reflected back. The amount is dependent on how close the cluster is and how reflective the surface is. Real life experience of radiant heat would be being in the sun on an otherwise cool day or putting a thermometer in the sun and getting a dramatically different reading than one in the shade.

- **Temperature differences.** The amount of the difference in temperatures between the cluster and the outside is a significant factor. If your outside temperatures in winter average say 32° F and your lows are rarely 0° F the significance of some of these things may be minimal. On the other hand if your winters often have subzero temperatures of -20° to -40° F for long periods then these issues are much more significant.

The real question is, "How do all of these interact in a wintering hive?"

One clue to understand some of it is by watching the bees. They adjust based on what they are experiencing as far as heat loss, rather than what it says on the thermometer. The cluster is drawn to the place where they lose less heat. This should be a clue to us on where and how they are losing heat.

My point is, if you look at most things they are much more complicated than a simple measurement and yet we have a tendency to try to reduce them to that.

# Requeening a Hot Hive

A really vicious hive is in great need of requeening, but is also the most difficult to find a queen in. Between the distraction of a hundred thousand bees trying to kill you and the bees running all over the combs, the vicious queen is also usually quite mobile and hard to find. Also, though, keep in mind that a queenless hive can get vicious, so try to make sure you have eggs or signs of a queen before you spend a lot of time trying to find her. Also check for signs of queenlessness like a dissonant roar when the hive isn't even being opened. When I need to requeen, here is what I have done under those circumstances.

First, Be prepared to be stung. Be prepared to walk away for a while. Be prepared to run away for a while. I find running through some brush is a good way to get rid of clinging and following bees.

***Divide and conquer.***

The object of this is to split the hive up into manageable parts. One part will be an empty box at the old location to draw off the field bees, who are usually the hardest to deal with and we will know there is no queen there. If you have a dolly and some help, you may be able to move the hive in one piece 10 yards away or so and put an empty box at the old location to get these field bees out before dealing with the hive at all. I never have that much help, so I just do a box at a time from the start. We want all the rest of the boxes of the hive on their own bottom with their own top. Each will need a queen, so if you intend to order queens, order one more queen than the number of boxes on the hive. Now set as many bottom boards, ten steps away from the original hive, as there are boxes in the original hive. Make sure you have a full bee suit, have rubber bands on your ankles to keep them out of your pants, have a zip on veil and leather gauntlet gloves. Put as many lids as you have boxes next to the hive and one extra bottom. Get the smoker going really well and smoke the hive until smoke is coming out the top. You just want to make sure every bee is smelling smoke instead of pheromones. Don't blow flames in until they are angry, just smoke. Wait at least 60 seconds. Now pry the top box loose leaving on the lid. Set it on the bottom and set one of the lids on the top of the main hive. Carry the removed box to one of the bottom boards. Take note of any that seem to have the most bees and least weight (most likely to be brood or have a queen) and mark them with a rock or some other sign. Repeat this until there are *no* boxes left on the original bottom. If you didn't move the whole hive, now put an empty box with frames on the bottom board and a cover on that. This is to catch the field bees coming back. Now walk away and come back in an hour or a day.

When you come back start with the most populated boxes that are most likely to have a queen. Set another bottom board and an empty box (no frames) on that bottom board. Smoke lightly this time. You don't want to run the queen around too much. Wait a minute. Open the box and look for the frame with the most bees and pull it looking for the queen. If you find her, kill her. If not put that frame in the empty box and keep going through all the frames. If you can't handle them at this strength then split the 10 frames into two five frame nucs. Let the nucs settle down and then look through them. Find the queen and killed her. Leave as often as you want to let them calm down, but stay at it until you are done. Look for clues. The box with the most bees is probably the one with the queen. After the queen is dead any box that has been queenless at least 24 hours is ready to be requeened. Introduce a caged queen. Don't open up the candy, just put the queen in with the screen down so the bees can feed her. Some vicious bees will not accept a new queen. Don't worry about it for now. Whatever ones do accept the queen can be combined with whatever ones don't. After three or four days I take out the cork and poke a hole in the candy or, if the bees seem eager to get her out and are not biting and posturing at the screen wire, I might just pop open the screen and let her out.

Four or five weak vicious hives are much less aggressive than one big vicious hive so immediately they should be somewhat calmer. In six weeks or so they will be much calmer. In 12 weeks or so they should be back to normal.

If you want to save even looking for the queen you can wait overnight after you do the break up, and put a queen in a candy cage in each box. Come back the next day after that and see if there is a dead queen or one where they are biting the cage. The one where they are biting the cage or have killed the queen is probably the one with the queen. Look there. If you have to put half of the frames in another box and let them calm down again and search even less bees. Afterwards you can pull the cork on the candy end and let the bees release the queens in each box. If the new queen for the box with the queen is dead, you can combine it back with one of the boxes with a queen cage. You can also requeen the field bees, but they will be more difficult. You can also do a newspaper combine with them after you get the queen accepted in one of the splits.

# CCD

This subject comes up a lot and I've been misquoted a lot. Here is the only thing I've actually said on the subject.

After several years of CCD (Colony Collapse Disorder) still being out there and a lot of study on microbes in bees and the hive, I have come up with a theory. It is, of course, only a theory and I'm not privy to all the scientists are working on. But it seems to me that they reason they can't find a microbe as the cause or they keep changing their mind as to which microbe is the cause, is because it's not there. And neither are the ones that should be. There are over 8,000 microbes that have been isolated that live in a healthy bee hive and the healthy gut of the bee. Many we know are necessary for the fermentation of the bee bread (pollen, nectar, several bacteria, some yeasts and other fungi). If pollen is not fermented it is not digestible to the bees. Also the bacteria living in the bees' gut displaces many pathogens. Also keep in mind that this ecology of 8,000 or more microbes live in a balance. Even the pathogens are preventing other pathogens. We know that chalkbrood fungus prevents EFB and stonebrood fungus prevents Nosema. There are many such balances in a healthy hive.

So let's introduce Terramycin in the mix. Beekeepers started using it several decades ago and those microbes have had many years to develop resistance. And while I'm sure Terramycin does disrupt this balance, a new balance was struck.

Now we introduce Tylosin (which is only supposed to be used for TM resistant AFB but is now in widespread use and is more powerful more broad spectrum and longer lived) and we move from Apistan and coumaphos, which are causing no harm to the microbes but cause major problems for the bees and kill off other insects and mites that are part of the ecology, and we start using oxalic and formic acid which does a drastic shift in the pH of the hive and changes what microbes live and what microbes die as well as shocking and killing most microbes off the bat. So now between the Tylosin and the organic acids we have wiped out and restructured the entire ecosystem of microbes and other creatures in the hive. What would you expect as a result? Among other things, I'd expect to find signs of malnutrition because the pollen is now undigestible, in the midst of an abundance of food. I'd expect a serious collapse of the infrastructure of the hive.

So that's my theory.

# About the Author

***"His writing is like his talks, with more content, detail, and depth than one would think possible with such few words...his website and PowerPoint presentations are the gold standard for diverse and common sense beekeeping practices."—Dean Stiglitz***

Michael Bush is one of the leading proponents of treatment free beekeeping. He has had an eclectic set of careers from printing and graphic arts, to construction to computer programming and a few more in between. Currently he is working in computers. He has been keeping bees since the mid 70's, usually from two to seven hives up until the year 2000. Varroa forced more experimentation which required more hives and the number has grown steadily over the years from then. By 2008 it was about 200 hives. He is active on many of the Beekeeping forums with last count at about 50,000 posts between all of them. He has a web site on beekeeping at:

www.bushfarms.com/bees.htm

# Index to *The Practical Beekeeper*